PHILIP HENSHER's novels include *Kitchen Venom*, which won the Somerset Maugham Award, *Other Lulus* and *The Mulberry Empire*, which was longlisted for the Man Booker Prize, shortlisted for the WH Smith 'People's Choice' Award and highlighted by no fewer than twelve reviewers as their 'book of the year'. Chosen by Granta to appear on their prestigious, once-a-decade list of the twenty best young British novelists, Philip Hensher is also a columnist for the *Independent* and chief book reviewer for the *Spectator*. He lives in south London.

From the reviews for *Pleasured*:

'A sublimely structured and sophisticated novel set in 1988 Berlin in which Hensher conflates the drug culture of the Summer of Love and the imminent demise of Checkpoint Charlie. Ian McEwan with a sense of humour – yikes, there's no stopping this man.'

ROGER CLARKE, *Independent on Sunday*

'A novel whose ambitious scale is matched only by the steely elegance of its author's control . . . *Pleasured* ends with a last image as haunting as it is ambiguous – at which point one can let out one's breath, which one has been holding ever since realising what Hensher was attempting.'

Daily Telegraph

'An engrossing read . . . Perhaps the greatest achievement of this highly original and accomplished novel is the skill with which the themes of evasion and loss – and the prospect of recovery – are related to the looming presence of the Wall.' BARRY UNSWORTH, *Daily Telegraph*

By the same author

OTHER LULUS
KITCHEN VENOM
THE BEDROOM OF THE MISTER'S WIFE
THE MULBERRY EMPIRE
THE FIT

PLEASURED

Philip Hensher

HARPER PERENNIAL

Harper Perennial
An imprint of HarperCollins*Publishers*
77–85 Fulham Palace Road
Hammersmith
London W6 8JB

www.harpercollins.co.uk/harperperennial

First published in Great Britain by Chatto & Windus in 1998

This edition published by Harper Perennial 2004

1

A catalogue record for this book is
available from the British Library

This novel is entirely a work of fiction. The names,
characters and incidents portrayed in it are the work of the
author's imagination. Any resemblance to actual persons,
living or dead, events or localities is entirely coincidental.

ISBN 0-00-718020-9

Typeset in Stempel Garamond and Diotima by
Palimpsest Book Production Limited, Polmont, Stirlingshire

Printed and bound in Great Britain by
Clays Ltd, St Ives plc

For Christian Tagger

WAS BEDEUTET DIE BEWEGUNG
BRINGT DER OST MIR FROHE KUNDE
SEINER SCHWINGEN FRISCHE REGUNG
KÜHLT DES HERZENS TIEFE WUNDE

Goethe

(What vast uproar is this? Is it the East, bringing
fresh news to me? The rushing breeze soothes
the heart's sore wounds.)

— CONTENTS —

ONE: KAPUTT

TWO: GENUG

THREE: REICHSKRISTALLNACHT

ONE

KAPUTT

AND THE COLOURED GIRLS SING

A T THE END of the story, when the city and the world had changed a little, there were more people in Friedrich's life. More people to think about; to worry about; to argue with and be civil to, to grow bored with; to sleep with; whose names had to be remembered, whose stories had to be listened to. It started with a bit of rubber bursting. A small thing, serving only to keep two different sorts of air apart. It was a puncture. It stopped a car; it started something else.

They were still thirty kilometres from Berlin when the tyre blew. The worst place in the world for a tyre to blow, at the worst time. There was an unfamiliar single noise, somehow inside the car. It was exactly like a noise from childhood, Friedrich found himself thinking; the noise a paper bag filled with water made, hitting the pavement. The car hit something sharp, and a second later, in his mind, Friedrich was ten again, and engaged in his favourite occupation, of filling a paper bag with water to drop it from the third floor apartment, dropping it to hit the pavement just in front of some old lady, ducking his head inside so as not to be seen. That was the noise, and it was strange to be reminded of it here; strange to think of ducking your head inside the window so as not to be seen; to remember that it was always enough to hear the wet plosive slap of the bursting paper bladder and the outraged shout – never a feminine shriek, always a hoarse shout of complaint – from the unknown old lady fifteen metres below. Strange to think of it, here, as he gripped the side of his seat as the car thuddingly, too fast, limped to the hard shoulder, like a vertiginous downhill cripple, to be reminded of a forgotten moment of delirious pleasure twenty years before. And just for the moment, not to feel concern or worry at where he was, but just to think of a remaindered instance of pleasure.

The car drew to a standstill. The moment of fear and memory and excitement was gone. He was stuck in the middle of a vast and terrifyingly foreign country, on an East German transit road between the borders of West Germany and West Berlin, with two strangers, on New Year's Eve. The worst place, the worst time, the worst people. Friedrich and the driver looked in front of them, looking at the snow which was just beginning to settle.

There was a huge rumpus from the back seat as the girl – Daphne, Friedrich remembered – surfaced from the nest of blankets she had built around herself.

'What is it?' she said. 'Why have we stopped?'

'We've had a puncture,' the man said. He was tight-lipped, as weary as if he had already explained the fact a dozen times.

'Oh,' she said. 'Where are we?'

'On the transit road,' Friedrich said. 'Still on the corridor. About thirty kilometres from Berlin, I suppose.'

She seemed to digest this.

'I promised Mario I'd be in Berlin by nine,' she said. 'What time is it?'

'Half-past seven,' Friedrich said. She was one of those people, he had noted, who referred to her friends by their first names, as if people so well known to her could hardly be unknown to anyone she happened to be talking to. My egotism, Friedrich thought irrelevantly, shows itself in different ways.

'An hour and a half,' she said. 'Will we make it?'

'I don't know,' the driver said, with the same ostentatious patience as before. 'It might not be impossible. Does it matter?'

'We'll be fine,' Friedrich said. 'We just need to change a wheel and we'll be on our way.'

'How long, do you think,' Daphne said, politely, 'it would take the three of us to change it?'

'I don't know,' the man said. 'I don't have a spare wheel. I'm sorry. It never occurred to me. We'll have to try to flag someone down, and buy their spare wheel off them.'

They looked out at the East German snow falling on the quiet East German barricaded transit motorway. The brutally constructed road, one slab of raw concrete laid next to another, was empty; it seemed, all at once, surrounded by a vast and listening silence. The car was alone on the road; the only help they could get was help none of them wanted. A small car burbled past, somehow nervously. They watched it approach, its thirty-watt headlights lighting its uncertain path, and silently watched it pass them and continue into the obscure brightness of the falling snow. They sat, and soon the road was quiet again.

Friedrich had only once before used the Mitfahrzentrale. He had never needed to; he was not someone who travelled from town to town. He lived in Berlin and that was that. In the ten years in which he had lived in Berlin, he had left the city no more than a dozen times. He never thought there was much point to it. But even Friedrich, once or twice, had had to go and visit his mother in Cologne, where she still lived – where he had lived until he moved to Berlin. He had gone to see her, and to get to Cologne, had used the Mitfahrzentrale.

The first time he had had to go back to Cologne had been four years before. His mother had been ill. Over the telephone, talking to his sisters and to her, it was impossible to discover whether it was anything serious or whether their tone, alternately stoic and whingeing, meant only that they thought a son ought to visit his mother before he was obliged to. In the end, he agreed to go and see her.

He was broke; completely, hopelessly broke; too short to think of getting there by train. The only way was using the Mitfahrzentrale. It was a sort of organized hitchhiking. They arranged a lift with someone who happened to be going in the right direction; you spoke to the driver, and negotiated some kind of contribution towards the petrol. You didn't know whether you were going to end up with someone you wouldn't mind spending time with, or whether the system would turn up a bore. But at least – unlike out-and-out hitching – you weren't going to get a real psychopath, because the office knew who you were and who the driver was. Theoretically, at least.

He had called up the office of the Mitfahrzentrale, telling them he wanted to go to Cologne at some point in the next week. They fixed him up with a jolly middle-aged lady from Charlottenburg, driving off for a week in the north of France. She was, she said, refusing Friedrich's offer of contribution to the petrol, far more in need of entertaining company than any money. Friedrich enjoyed the few hours they spent together, managing to hoot even at the absurdity of the sealed-off grimness of the transit road between Berlin and the West German border. Apart from the convenience and the cheapness of the trip, he liked the sealed-off relationship he had with the cheerful, hearty woman. She hinted excitingly at unhappy romances and adventures on holiday; he let her have the pleasure of elaborating, and, with a kindness which surprised him in himself, interrupted her with invented stories of his own entanglements and disappointments. Privately, he thought that what she so thrillingly hinted at was the ordinary truth that she was a Lesbian. It was a nice few hours, one which he could think of with pleasure even four years later. There was no question of her inviting him to continue with her to France, nor any question, if the offer had been made, of his accepting, or declining other than gracefully, with thanks.

The enjoyable trip had put him in a good mood to deal with his female relations in Cologne. His mother had a bad cough she couldn't get rid of, that was all. But he didn't mind. His mood lasted all week and all through the journey back with one of his sisters, who had expressed a desire to come to Berlin and see how he lived. It didn't last through the following week, when his sister stayed with him in his flat in Kreuzberg; he spent most of it listening to her exclamations over the state of his lavatory, his kitchen, his lack of anything resembling a sense of domesticity, and going to bed at a time when he might normally have been thinking of getting dressed and going out. He still sent the woman who had driven him to Cologne occasional postcards – he sometimes saw something which made him think, unaccountably, 'That's one for that respectable Lesbian' – and always enjoyed bumping into her in the street. His general sense was that, if he ever had to go to Cologne again, the Mitfahrzentrale wasn't such a bad way of doing it. Although he had to remember that you didn't always get a lift with the same woman.

Four years passed; he didn't go home at all. In early December, 1988, he was in a very late bar in Kreuzberg with his best friend, a boy called Martin. Their relationship was a long-term thing, based on them both coming from the same bit of the country, the Ruhrgebiet; a matter of periodic violent assaults and silent recriminations, lapsing into night-long drinking sessions. Friedrich occasionally wondered why Martin was his best friend; he had long ago come to the conclusion that it was because he spent so much time with him, and not the other way round. 'I'd do anything for you, Martin,' Friedrich sometimes said, although not often before five o'clock in the morning, and it was true; there are almost no limits to a friendship which still exists after one partner has kicked the other – it hardly matters who kicked who – in the head.

'What are you doing for Christmas?' Friedrich said.

'Got to go back,' Martin said. 'Christ knows why. I loathe it. They loathe me going back. We all have a miserable time, I can't wait to get back here, they can't wait for me to leave, and every year, about the middle of September, they start phoning me up and saying' – dowager's falsetto – 'When are you coming home for Christmas, Martin dear? I'd rather disembowel goats with my teeth, I really would. Don't you just hate it?'

'Yes,' Friedrich said. 'So I don't go back.'

'You don't at all?' Martin said. 'What, never? Cool. I wish I could get out of it. I've tried everything. I didn't want to leave my fictitious girlfriend. I didn't want to leave my fictitious pet cat. I was worried about burglars, like, right. I'd developed a worrying crush on my seven-year-old cousin Monika and my psychoanalyst thought it would be best if I didn't see her for the time being. Nothing works, though they sent poor old cousin Monika off skiing to Austria to keep her from my rampant advances. Every year, twice a year, Christmas and my parents' birthday – they have the same birthday, so it's a big deal. Five days completely wasted, and it always takes me about two weeks to get over it. Do you never go and see your parents, never at all?'

'No,' Friedrich said. 'Just my mother and my sisters. And aunts and stuff. No, not for years, not at all. We talk on the phone, of course. Maybe I should. I don't know. Four years, it's been now.'

'Christ,' Martin said. 'I wish I could only do it every four years. Why do we come here?'

'No idea,' Friedrich said. 'Is there anywhere else?'

They both looked round at the strip-lit bar. Two knackered drag queens were lying back in the corner, stilettos off. A girl, asleep over a table, was submitting to being periodically woken with a long stick by the thuggish, neckless barman.

'There's only two weeks left and I've got to go again. Can't wait.'

An idea – a five a.m. strip-lit idea – hit Friedrich hard.

'How do you get there?'

'I drive,' he said. 'Got to know you can escape, if you have to. And you always have to.'

'You know,' Friedrich said. 'I know this sounds weird, but I might not mind going home for Christmas this year. It's not that bad if you don't do it every year, or start to feel what they want you to feel, that it's an obligation. Would you give me a lift home?'

Martin lit a cigarette. He had a virtuoso method, which involved placing a filter between his lips, and then constructing a rolled-up cigarette around it, without looking at what he was doing. Martin claimed that girls found it irresistible; to Friedrich it seemed like a lot of effort to go to, just to make yourself irresistible.

'I could, I suppose,' he said. 'But I want you to think carefully about this first. You're talking about something pretty serious here. It's not a picnic. You're talking about spending Christmas with your mum. You have to understand the sort of stuff you're getting into. You shouldn't say these things if you don't mean them. You shouldn't talk about this stuff lightly.'

'I know,' Friedrich said. 'It's just that it's been kind of a long time. And they're pretty bad, but they're not as bad as yours. And even if they are, maybe you need to remind yourself from time to time just how terrible they are.'

'You know,' Martin said. 'You know I can say this to you. You know, you ought to get used to the idea that you might never hear anything about your dad ever again.'

Friedrich lit his own cigarette. He would not roll his own; that was part of his idea of his own dignity.

'Maybe I've already got used to the idea,' he said. 'Maybe it's none of your fucking business.'

'I don't give a fuck, you understand,' Martin said. 'I just think you ought to think about this stuff.'

'I'm better off not thinking about it,' Friedrich said. 'I just felt like going home for Christmas. Don't try to psychoanalyse me.'

'I could understand you going home if you were really fucked up,' Martin said. 'I just can't understand you going home because you want to go home. Well, if you don't mind putting yourself through it, you're old enough to know your own mind. I can't stop you. Of course I'll give you a lift.'

Friedrich's mother sounded surprised, but not altogether displeased, that he'd be coming home for Christmas. He left with Martin on the day before Christmas Eve. Martin had a cold coming on and was uncharacteristically uncommunicative. Or perhaps it was characteristic; Friedrich had hardly ever seen him in daylight. At eleven, before lunch, going to see his horrible enormous Catholic family, he was different, edgy, pained. His personality had screwed up its eyes against the unfamiliar harshness of daylight. Friedrich sat meekly in the passenger seat, glancing sometimes at Martin, hunched and sneezing, his nose reddened. Friedrich was supposed to guide them, and he sat with a map on his lap; it proved unnecessary, since the road signs indicated their destination with a painful inevitability. The nervous irritation which always took over the car on the barrier-lined transit road continued for the whole journey. Friedrich listened, in a detached and twitching way, to their conversation, going round in circles. He thought a couple of times of suggesting that they play a car game, just to keep things going.

He didn't know quite what he expected from his mother's Christmas; in a way, he found exactly what he knew he would find, and yet he was disappointed by the usual events of the eve, the day, and the grim day after. He watched the cycle, the rise and fall of his emotions, and registered his disgust, occurring with the same regularity, at the same moments of the festival, as predictably as the traditional events of the invented, pathetically sustained family holiday.

The day after Christmas Day, he called Martin's family number to find out when he was going back to Berlin.

'He's already gone,' his father said. There was a terrible shrieking close to the telephone, like an animal being slaughtered. '*Quiet*. Grandfather's on the telephone.'

'I'm sorry?' Friedrich said.

'I said – I'm sorry, a madhouse here with the children – I said he's gone.'

'Gone?'

'Yes, yes, first thing this morning, off he went, no word, not a word to his mother or me.'

'Has he perhaps gone back to Berlin?' Friedrich said. He had no real understanding of what the man was saying to him. He had the awful sensation, which he could not escape from with any rational application of purpose, that he was trapped with his sisters and his aunts indefinitely.

'We don't know,' the father said. 'No idea at all. He just went this morning, without a word. We don't worry. We're sure he'll be all right.'

'I'm sure,' Friedrich said. 'I'll catch up with him later. Thanks a lot.'

'Tell him from us,' Martin's father said ironically, 'that maybe he ought to call us some time. No. No. Not now. That is,' he went on, having shooed away some child or other, 'if he's not too busy with his *Berlin* friends.'

'I will,' Friedrich said, quite equal to this. 'Thanks, anyway. I'm sorry he went off like that.'

He put the telephone down and contemplated the sheer miserable tinsel of his mother's traditional Westphalian Christmas.

Back to the Mitfahrzentrale.

The man the Mitfahrzentrale came up with to give him a lift back to Berlin wasn't going until New Year's Eve. That was three days longer than Friedrich had meant to stay in Cologne, but the delay just had to be put up with. The office let him know he was lucky to find anyone at all at this time of year at such short notice. In the end, being in Cologne with your family was tolerable, Friedrich thought, as long as there was a definite end to it. At least now, although he'd missed the usual wreckage of the Kreuzberg Christmas bar-crawl, he'd be back for the usual wreckage of the Kreuzberg New Year's Eve, which, the year before, had extended without sleep until lunchtime on the third of January, when Friedrich had woken in the bed of a girl he'd never seen before, wearing shirt, trousers and boots which belonged neither to him, nor the girl, nor the girl's boyfriend, whose blitzing snores into Friedrich's ear were what had woken him up in the first place, and with the certain hungover hope that no sexual act had taken place between any of them. Well, he would be back for that, or for something resembling it in every single detail.

He telephoned the number the Mitfahrzentrale had given him.

'You'll need to be here,' the precise and foreign voice at the other end said, 'around three on the thirty-first. I can't leave before that, I'm afraid. I'll give you the address. Please don't be late or I shall have to go without you. There is a girl coming as well. Is she with you? Do you know her?'

'No,' Friedrich said. 'I don't know anything about that.'

The man gave him an address in Cologne. 'Know it?'

'I don't,' Friedrich said. 'I haven't lived here for years though. I'm sure I can find it.'

'Come to the corner of the street. I will meet you there. There is another person, a girl, coming with us. My name is Herr Picker,' the man said.

'Yes,' Friedrich said. 'They told me.'

The man gave the name of the district his flat was in. Friedrich knew the name, but no more; he resolved to look it up on a map rather than take detailed instructions from Herr Picker. He thought all this fairly unfriendly of the man; the only other time he had used the Mitfahrzentrale, the driver had quite cheerfully come, wouldn't hear of anything else, all the way to Kreuzberg, though he imagined it hadn't been on the tweedy spinster's usual round.

He told his mother he'd agreed with Martin to stay a day or two longer in Cologne than he had originally planned. Small lies came easily, when he spoke to her, and he did not always wonder what made him lie to her. He was slightly disappointed that she didn't seem to be more pleased that he wasn't going when he said, was staying longer; it never occurred to him that his visits were anything but a trial to him, a pleasure to her. There was so much they did not talk about. He wouldn't, though, give her any additional cause for worry by telling her that his lift came from the Mitfahrzentrale.

The district was so white, regimented and unremarkable it was not surprising that it had called no associations to Friedrich's mind; it was difficult to imagine even its inhabitants feeling any kind of fondness for its empty streets. When he reached the street corner, there was no one there except a girl, shivering next to a suitcase. This was clearly the girl who was coming with them. She was quite pretty; her jaw too big for her thin face, her hair, white as if it had been bleached, cut crudely and close to the head. He came up to her, smiling, and held out his hand. She almost succeeded in blanking him.

'Are we waiting for the same lift?' he said.

'I don't know,' the girl said.

'We must be,' he said. He introduced himself; there was the familiar slightly puzzled wrinkling of the brow as he said his name. He was used to this; he was used even to the way the girl stared at him for a second, before giving up trying to work out what was odd or recognizable about the name *Friedrich Kaiser*, and replying with her name.

'Daphne,' the girl said, and just as she introduced herself, with an air of relief, of accepting Friedrich, more like a hostess whose last, overstaying guest has announced his departure than someone greeting a stranger, he was struck by an unexpected and incongruous scent on her; a scent of money, of femininity, of purchased favourite perfume, odd and erotic on this scrub-haired girl in a rusty black coat and black boots, an old-fashioned air, here on this cold Cologne street, and for a second he had an unfamiliar feeling, the feeling that she could be lovely. She dropped her eyes; there must have been some oddity in his gaze.

'Here he is,' she said, as a big blue English car drew up. The engine stopped and a man got out. His face was unfriendly, blankly frowning in the way someone overtaken by worry can appear to frown. He was fat; his face pale to the point that it seemed like white jelly laid on a blue cloth; his black hair both sparse and long, stuck to his head by his pale sweat. Friedrich noted, not for the first time, that very fat men often do not buy trousers which fit them; they usually buy trousers which would fit much thinner men, and fasten them to their anatomies where they can. In Picker's case, as in the case of most very fat men, he had fastened them virtually on his groin, allowing the vast ballooning bulk of the stomach to be held in as best it could by the straining shirt.

'I am Herr Picker,' the man said.

'Friedrich,' Friedrich said.

'Daphne,' the girl said. Friedrich could not quite dislike her, and wondered, in a way, why not; he always disliked these names girls took on. They awoke in him the same dislike he always felt, in reading a novel written by a woman, when he came across a heroine with an improbably romantic name (Miranda, Alessandra, Renée) and divined from a character's name the chubby authoress of the novel, the weak suburban ambitions her readers might share, would never admit to sharing. But he did not dislike this girl. He wondered, in his way, why not.

'Let's go,' Picker said.

'Are we ready?' Friedrich said.

'Of course,' Picker said. 'Let's go. I hate driving in the dark.'

'It'll soon be dark,' Friedrich said.

'I don't want to drive in the dark more than necessary,' Picker said. He spoke to them like someone issuing instructions to a class. He wheezed slightly, as if heavily out of breath. Friedrich noted that, although it was a cold day, and Picker was standing three metres from him, he could smell his sweat. Daphne smiled, and picked her suitcase up; in her busy hands you could see the nervousness of a well-brought-up middle-class girl who disliked hearing the near-arguments of others.

They were on the road for twenty minutes before anyone spoke.

'It just takes so long to get out of Cologne,' Daphne said. 'I always get lost. I wasn't born here, though.'

'Nor was I,' Picker said. 'I don't know if I get lost or not. I just follow the road signs to where I have to get to.'

'I don't think we did get lost,' Daphne said. 'I've gone round and round in circles before now.'

'It's not so difficult to get out of,' Friedrich said. 'The difficulty is knowing when you're out of Cologne and into some other town. They just meld into each other round here. That was really pretty quick. Maybe you know the best route, Herr Picker.'

'No,' Picker said. 'I don't know the roads at all well round here. I just followed my nose, and the road signs.'

'Maybe we were just lucky,' Daphne said. 'Or maybe your idea of following the road signs is the best one.'

Picker nodded. 'It works in Germany. It's always the best way, if you don't know a city well. They're always good, the road signs in Germany. The road signs in Germany always tell you where you want to go, and they never disappear when you're half-way along the route.'

'Do you often come to Cologne?' Friedrich said.

'Sometimes,' Picker said. 'Sometimes I drive, but not always.'

They sat for a while in the car.

'So, are you visiting Berlin?' Friedrich said.

'No,' Daphne said. 'I live there. I've been away for Christmas. I don't come from there, though. I come from Cologne. I mean, that's where my parents live. I wasn't born there. I come from – I mean I was born in – a place called Cloppenburg. I've lived in Berlin for a couple of years. Sometimes I think no one comes from Berlin. Everyone I know there grew up somewhere else and moved to Berlin. It's kind of nice, when you think of it.'

She faltered a little. Friedrich left an indifferent pause. The wind was strong, with a bass rattle round the car.

'No, actually I meant Herr Picker,' he said.

'What are you saying?' Picker said.

Friedrich thought of dropping it.

'I just asked if you were visiting Berlin,' Friedrich said.

'No,' Picker said. 'I live there. I was born in England, but I live in Berlin now. For the moment anyway.'

'I thought you had an odd accent. I couldn't place it. What do you do in Berlin?' Friedrich said.

Picker was silent for a moment. Friedrich imagined

that this was the way the rest of the journey could be, waiting for an answer to a question which, perhaps, Picker hadn't heard, hadn't understood, or, more probably, just wouldn't answer. How long would it be before they could start to talk about something else without seeming to interrupt Picker; how long it would be was, somehow, dictated by the comfortable English car they found themselves in. In a room, in a house, Friedrich could have quickly turned to Daphne, to talk about something else. Here, it was as if the mapless driver inevitably directed the conversation.

'This and that,' Picker said eventually; his manner was so final it was hardly possible to respond. Daphne, however, broke in quite innocently; and Friedrich would have been prepared to bet that she hadn't been called Daphne for more than eighteen months, so marked was the difference between her polite smile, her polite willingness to keep a conversation going, the pungent perfume of some not-long-abandoned Monika or Ulrike and the scruffy black-clad and booted lecture-room existentialist who might call herself Daphne.

'Do you work in Berlin?' she said. 'Sorry, I can't hear what you're saying back here. Did he just ask that? What do you do?'

'I live near Charlottenburg,' Picker said. 'I like it there.'

'In Charlottenburg?' Daphne said. 'So do I. Nice. Where do you live?'

'Near Charlottenburg,' Picker said. 'I've been there a couple of years now. No, I think I must have lived there for nearly four years. A long time. It's easy. I like living in safe places. Charlottenburg's really safe.'

'Near Charlottenburg,' Friedrich said.

'As I said,' Picker said.

'Everywhere's safe in Berlin,' Friedrich said. 'Who do you work for?'

'I don't agree,' Picker said. 'I don't think Berlin's safe at all. I've heard stories about people being attacked.'

'It seems pretty safe,' Daphne said. 'I've never worried about going out at night. I leave that to my aunt.'

'Your aunt?' Friedrich said.

'I live with my aunt,' Daphne said, as if reminding him of something he already knew. 'She's always saying when will you be back, and don't go out without your whistle. It drives me mental.'

'She's quite right,' Picker said. 'There are places in Berlin I wouldn't go out in after dark.'

'Where?' Friedrich said.

'Well, Kreuzberg, for instance,' Picker said.

'I live in Kreuzberg,' Friedrich said. 'Have you ever been there?'

'I said, I wouldn't go to Kreuzberg,' Picker said.

'So how do you know you wouldn't go?' Friedrich said.

'I know I wouldn't go because I don't go,' Picker said.

'You ought to try it out,' Daphne said. 'It's not dangerous. It's fun. You can have a lot of fun there.'

'So people are always saying to me,' Picker said. 'I don't know. As a foreigner, one always reads in guide books, or people are always saying to you, you must go to such and such a part of town, because it's where the really lively and enjoyable bars are where really lively and enjoyable young people go to enjoy themselves. But when you go, it's always to a bar where everybody knows each other, and you sit in a corner and watch other people having fun, and look at drunk people just sitting around. I don't like to drink alcohol or smoke, so for me it isn't fun at all.'

'There's something in what you say,' Friedrich said.

They looked ahead of them. Picker seemed, however, to have a sense that he was proving difficult in conversation, and said, in relation to nothing at all, 'Do you know England, Herr Kaiser?'

'No,' Friedrich said. 'I've never been.'

'Do you speak English at all?'

'No,' Friedrich said. He had learnt it at school, and completely forgotten every single word. Then he felt, feebly, that, wishing to be abrupt and rude, he had only made himself look stupid. So he added, 'But I speak very good French. Very good indeed.' This was not true; he knew even less French than English, but a confrontational tone to the conversation had made him want to produce a trump card.

'Oh, how nice to speak French well,' Picker said. 'I don't speak it well at all. Have you spent time in France?'

'Yes,' Friedrich said. 'But –' he let his word hang in the air. He did not want enthusiastic inquiries about his summers in St-Remy, the jobs he had taken as a waiter in Lyons.

'Shall we stop here?' Daphne said. They were just coming up to a café, brightly lit in the gloomy midwinter late afternoon.

'No,' Picker said. 'Look at those clouds. It's going to start snowing soon. Let's press on. What do you do, Herr Kaiser?'

Friedrich closed his eyes, leaving, in his turn, this question unanswered. When against his eyelids he thought about himself, and his life, what came to Friedrich's mind was not the looming snow, but rain; a heavy winter rain which, driven by wind, formed unpredictably into eddies and sudden thicknesses, like the folds of a veil, like shot silk, falling hard on a hard earth, pulping what it fell on into mud; unfructifying. He lived in Kreuzberg; he had a job in a bookshop in Kreuzberg, minding the shelves, three afternoons a week; he drank and went out and saw friends in Kreuzberg. He had no children, or none he knew about; had never slept with the same girl more than five times; had written nothing; had no money; owned nothing; no family, now; was replaceable. He wondered how he had planned his life when he had first left Cologne, years before; he wondered how anyone planned any of their lives, and with what success, what result. He looked at the foreigner, driving them through the midwinter unpopulated roads. All he knew was that tomorrow would be a new year.

They drove on, and in time they came to the crossing point.

'I hate this,' Daphne said when they were through. 'It gives me the creeps. I'm going to sleep.'

She was right; it was a frightening road. The temporary blocks of the road surface, laid coarsely next to each other, made the car thud with the regularity of a muffled ticking clock, not soporifically, but angrily. There were few cars on the road. Friedrich wanted to drive faster, to escape the sense of being watched from all sides, by the silent grey foreign country which called itself Germany; on this coarse temporary road, they were an insect on a miniature race-track, watched from above, going as fast as it could, and not fast enough, their path decided by others. Because roads can be frightening. It had an unmappable quality, taking them only, without alternative, to Berlin. Daphne lay down, her booted feet pressed against the door, a position which made Friedrich worry. Her knees were uncomfortably drawn up. She lay on her side and managed to sleep.

Picker was looking ahead. It was so dark with the lack

of headlights on this unfrequented road, it was possible he was not thinking at all; possibly he only needed to concentrate on driving.

'What do you do?' Friedrich asked.

'This and that,' Picker said. 'I have various projects.' He had the air of someone who let out information with care; a man who, speaking carefully, seemed to control what he said.

'What sort of projects?'

'Various things,' Picker said. 'I'm interested in Berlin.'

'Are you studying it?'

'In a sense.'

'You're very mysterious.'

'Do I seem mysterious? There's nothing so very interesting about it. I live in Berlin because it suits me, and because I'm interested in the political situation. I talk to people and I see what comes out of it. I don't really do anything. I'd like to write, but I don't seem to be able to get started.'

'How do you live?'

'I manage to live.'

'And –'

'You seem to want to know a lot about me, if I may say so.'

'It's interesting. You said yourself it was interesting finding out about other people.'

'And so it is. The thing is,' Picker said, 'who are you? Where do you come from? What do you do?' The road ahead was perfectly straight and almost completely empty. Picker turned right round in his seat to look directly at Friedrich. 'I don't know anything at all about you. All I know is that you turn up wanting a lift. You don't tell me who you are, or why you want to get from Cologne to

Berlin; why you want to travel with me, and not with anyone else, or go on the train. Like anyone else. Why don't you go on the train, Herr Kaiser? And you want to know about me. All these things. What do you do? Where do you come from? Who do you work for? All I want is a quiet drive, and some money for the petrol. Come on, Herr Kaiser, what do you want? Who are you? Who sent you?'

It was in this way that Picker was not facing the road when the tyre burst.

'How long, do you think,' Daphne said politely, 'it would take to change the wheel?'

'I don't have a spare wheel,' Picker said. 'We'll have to try to flag someone down and try to buy their spare wheel off them.'

He got out of the car, slamming the door behind him.

'He said he hasn't got a spare wheel?' Daphne said.

'That's what he said,' Friedrich said.

'There's no one on the road, though,' Daphne said. 'I mean, absolutely no one.'

'Oh, I wouldn't say that,' Friedrich said. 'There's two or three cars passing every minute, at least.'

Behind the car, Picker was waving with both furious arms at an oncoming car, which drove straight past. It was difficult to blame anyone for not wanting to stop on the transit road.

'What's he doing?' Daphne said, with what seemed like real curiosity.

'I don't know,' Friedrich said. He started to wonder how long it would take to walk to Berlin. Twenty-five kilometres, maybe thirty. No chance that anyone would stop to offer him a lift, and he would rather not think of the penalties for hitchhiking in the German Democratic

Republic. He envisaged his aching thighs; he thought of the ineffective cardboard texture, the pointless stiffness of his donkey jacket against the now fierce snow. He still wondered if it was worth it. He started to think of the complicated conversation at the border. He could see himself approaching the checkpoint, and the spotlights trained on him, something never seen before, a man walking along the transit road; a small crowd of stiffly armed border police, the GrePos and their hungry dogs, standing, and looking at him as he approached. It had to be a wait of indefinite length in this car with a fat foreigner of paranoid tendencies, and a girl who called herself Daphne.

'I promised Mario,' Daphne said. 'I promised him.'

'Who is Mario?' Friedrich said. 'Do I know him?'

'I shouldn't have thought so,' Daphne said, apparently surprised. 'He's a friend of mine. But I promised him, I absolutely swore I would be back by nine at the absolute latest.'

'Did you get the lift through the Mitfahrzentrale?' Friedrich asked, for something to say.

'Yes,' Daphne said. 'You?'

'Yes,' Friedrich said. 'It's always been good before.'

'My parents would kill me if they knew I was doing this,' Daphne said. 'They gave me the money for the train. But I need the money. Never again, though.'

'Yes?' Friedrich said. He would have said that he needed money, too; but he was too aware of the fact that when anyone admits anything interesting in their conversation, invariably the person they are speaking to finds something comparable but dull in their own experience with which to respond. 'Look, Picker's got someone to stop.'

A man drew up behind them. After a short conversation, he and Picker stood gazing at his tyres, then the tyres of the

English car. All the time, they scratched their heads and shrugged, conventionally. Finally, after a great deal of effortful crouching and squatting, the man stood up, got into his car and drove away.

'I'm cold,' Daphne said.

Picker opened the door and put his head in. He was still mildly sweating; there seemed to be no temperature so low it would not make Picker sweat.

'There seems to be a problem,' he said. 'I didn't realize that wheels weren't a standard size.'

'No, they're not,' Friedrich said. He was oddly pleased.

'I thought they were,' Picker said. 'I'll try stopping some more cars.'

'I'm cold,' Daphne said. 'And no one's going to want to stop on this road. Everyone just wants to get off it as soon as possible. I'm cold.'

'And can we have the radio on?' Friedrich said, taking a little pleasure in childishly joining in with Daphne's whining demands on Picker. The next thing he was going to say, he decided, if Daphne didn't get there first, was that he and Daphne were hungry, and wanted some food. He might even remind Picker that he'd refused to stop at the café just before the crossing. He saved it up.

'All right,' Picker said. He handed over the keys, and shut the door. Friedrich turned the radio on.

'No, not that,' Daphne said. The first station was some unexpected heavy metal music. It was hard to imagine it being Picker's customary station. Friedrich started to turn the dial. 'No, I hate that. No, not that. No, I can't stand people talking on the radio. You know, when I was little, I used to think that when you were in the East you wouldn't be able to get radio from the West, that it would somehow just stop at the border, as if there was some invisible Wall on top of the real one. It's odd just going through the air-waves and hearing some things from the West and some from the East and trying to guess which is which. Yes, that one. That's nice.'

'No, I don't want to listen to that,' Friedrich said. He was mildly piqued that she had turned down a snatch of Italian opera with such confidence; it was something he quite liked, and was emboldened to refuse the whingeing ecological protest song by a eunuch with a guitar and one finger stuck in his ear which she preferred.

'All right, carry on. Oh, chat show. No, stop, DDR chat show. That's nice. I really like this stuff.'

He left the dial where it was for a minute and a half, while they listened.

'That's nice enough. Next station.'

He kept on going through the airwaves. He was beginning to think, despite himself, that the choice between New Year's Eve with Daphne in this by now heavily per-fumed car and New Year's Eve in an East German jail was a fairly clear-cut one; that Daphne might, in the end, turn out to be quite all right.

'Stop, stop,' Daphne said. He had hit on an American pop song, an old one. 'I love this.'

'Me too,' Friedrich said. He liked the incongruity of listening to Lou Reed, taking a walk on the wild side, and looking out at the snow, at a fat foreigner semaphoring in the semi-dark, his bulk periodically illuminated by an approaching car.

'Plucked his eyebrows on the way, shaved his legs and then –' Daphne said. 'Do you think this can be an East German station?'

'I don't think so,' Friedrich said. 'Do you know what it's about, the song?'

'A bit,' Daphne said. 'It's not much of an advert for Western civilization, is it?'

'I don't think it's meant to be,' Friedrich said. 'Do you think they're broadcasting it as a dreadful warning, or something?'

'And the coloured girls sing –' Daphne said.

'"Say", isn't it?' Friedrich said.

'What do you mean?'

'I think he sings, "And the coloured girls say".'

'Does it matter?'

'Maybe not,' Friedrich said, looking at her in the rearview mirror. 'What do you think of Herr Picker?'

'Herr Picker?' Daphne said. 'Oh –' she pointed at the driver's seat. 'I don't know. I heard you having an argument with him.'

'It wasn't really an argument,' Friedrich said. 'He was just –'

'Here it comes again,' Daphne said. '"And the coloured girls sing, do, be-do, be-do, be-dooby-dooby-do." You see?'

'No,' Friedrich said. 'I couldn't hear what he was saying, because you were singing. It wasn't an argument Picker and I were having. He just thought I was being nosy.'

'Maybe you were,' she said.

'I thought you were asleep,' Friedrich said.

'Just didn't want to join in,' she said. 'He's a bit mad, isn't he?'

'Or just foreign,' Friedrich said. 'He strikes me as a bit odd, no more than that. Look, he's got another one to stop.'

A man drew up behind them; after a short conversation, he and Picker stood gazing at his tyres, then the tyres of the English car. All the time they scratched their heads and shrugged, conventionally. Finally, after a great deal of effortful crouching and squatting, the man stood up, got into his car, and drove away.

'I could have sworn that was the same man as before,' Daphne said. 'But he is a bit mad, don't you think?'

'In what way?'

'Not saying anything about himself, really.'

'Well, I don't know,' Friedrich said. 'After all, you haven't told me anything about yourself.'

'You haven't asked. I would,' she said. 'Or at least I wouldn't have a fit if you did ask. Maybe you're just not that interested.'

'We've got the whole night,' Friedrich said. 'We can tell each other the history of our lives later. What's that perfume you're wearing?'

'Something my parents gave me for Christmas. I put it on to please them. Does it make you sneeze? It made my father sneeze all the time. It was funny. I kept saying that I liked it so much, that it was really the stuff I would buy for myself, and they thought I was wearing it for their sake, or because I liked it. But really I was only wearing it because it made my father sneeze so much. It was so funny. He didn't work out that was what it was. But it doesn't make you sneeze.'

'Not yet,' Friedrich said. 'I like it. What's it called?'

'I can't remember,' Daphne said.

'I didn't mean to be rude just then,' Friedrich said. 'Saying I didn't want to hear your life story. You can tell me about yourself if you want. I want to know. It would pass the time.'

'No thanks,' she said.

'There you are,' he said. 'Just like Picker, refusing to say anything about yourself. You see?'

'Maybe it's your fault,' Daphne said. 'I can see why he lost his temper with you. Pretending not to be interested.'

'Go on,' Friedrich said. 'No, I am interested. I really am. Tell me one thing about yourself, one interesting thing.'

'Just one?' Daphne said.

'Something that happened to you a very long time ago,' Friedrich said. 'Something you remember.'

Daphne thought. 'Just one thing? All right. Once, when I was thirteen, in Cloppenburg, a girl who I thought was a good friend of mine said to me, "Oh, you're so lucky, you know. You'll never have to worry whether boys are interested in you for your personality or your looks."'

Friedrich laughed. 'That's nice. I like that.'

'Well, it wasn't very funny at the time,' Daphne said. 'But I got my own back.'

'Yes?'

'A year or two later, this girl – by then, of course, I wasn't speaking to her, because you can't be friends with someone who says something like that – had a party for all the beautiful people in school. You know what I mean. And she didn't ask me. And I was really furious, even though I wasn't friends with her. So I went round to this photocopy shop, and had cards printed, making it look like invitations to, like, a free music festival, five hundred cards, with the time and place and date of the party. And I went to all these bars, like biker bars, and just left thirty cards by the door in each one, with the rest of the music festival fliers. And she was a really respectable and nice girl. But on the night there were three hundred Hell's Angels outside the front door, all yelling to be let in. It must,' Daphne said, grinning, 'have been quite frightening.'

'Just because she said you weren't pretty?'

'Well, that's quite an upsetting thing when you're that age.'

'Quite upsetting.'

Picker suddenly opened the door.

'This man here's going to give me a lift to Berlin,' he said. Behind him a short man nodded and bobbed. It was as if he spoke a different language, and was doing his best to communicate by gesture alone. 'He's on his way there. I know a garage I can go to, and then I'll come back with a spare wheel. That'll really be quickest.'

'All right,' Friedrich said. 'We'll come with you.'

'No,' Picker said. 'I'll need you to stay here. There might be some kind of problem. I can't leave the car un-attended. They might tow it away. I could take one of you.'

'We'll both stay,' Daphne said, surprisingly. 'It's better for company.'

'It's not our problem,' Friedrich said. 'I don't see why we should have to stay here with your car.'

'It's the easiest way,' Picker said. 'I'm sorry, but I can't think of anything else to do.'

'Why don't you stay with the car, and we'll go to Berlin and come back with the wheel?' Friedrich said.

'Why should I trust you to come back?' Picker said. 'I don't know anything about you. I'm sure you would just get to Berlin and think, oh, stuff it, let him sort it out him-self.'

'Why should we trust you to come back?' Friedrich said, recognizing something in what Picker said.

'Because you've got my car,' Picker said. 'I'm not just about to abandon it. I'll be back in an hour or two. Don't worry.'

'We're not worrying,' Daphne said. 'But how are you going to get back here?'

'I'll face that question when I come to it,' Picker said. 'Don't worry. That's my problem.'

He withdrew his head. They watched him retreat down the road, and get into the car with the nodding man. The American music continued on the radio.

'Christ,' Friedrich said.

'Christ,' Daphne said. 'I hate to say this –'

'– I'm quite scared.'

'Yes.'

'Was that what you were going to say?'

'Yes. Let's not think about it.'

'It might be best. But how is he going to –'

'Let's not think about it.'

'And what happens if the garage isn't open?'

'Let's really not think about it.'

'Do you like this song?'

'I don't know it. Let's talk about something else. Tell me about you. I've told you about me.'

'Nothing to tell. Tell me more about you.'

'I can't think of anything. You tell me about me.'

'Shall I guess stuff, or what?'

'Yes,' Daphne said. 'Guess what I do.'

'I guess you work in a clothes shop,' Friedrich said.

'A clothes shop?' Daphne said. 'How can you say that?'

'I don't know,' Friedrich said. 'I was just guessing. I don't know what you do. I had to guess something.'

'But a clothes shop,' she said.

'Well, there's nothing so bad about that,' he said. 'I know people who work in shops. I work in a shop.'

'What sort of shop?'

'A bookshop, a few afternoons a week.'

'Well, that's not so bad. But a boutique – god, like a yuppy or something. Do I look like I work in a clothes shop?'

'Yes,' he said. In the mirror she surprisingly smiled at

him, not fondly, but because, it seemed, what he said was funny. 'And anyway, the people who work in clothes shops aren't yuppies. Maybe the people who buy clothes in shops are, but the people who work there aren't. And we all have to buy clothes from time to time. You're a student, I suppose.'

'Yes, I am,' she said. 'Did you have this kind of problem getting from Berlin to Cologne?'

'No,' he said. 'I didn't get there with the Mitfahrzentrale. I got a lift. I thought I'd get a lift back. To be honest, it's the only reason I went, because I thought I had a lift there and back.'

'Do you come from Berlin?'

'No, Cologne. I was going to see my mother.'

'Just your mother?'

'Yes, and my sisters and things. My father's gone.'

'Gone?'

'Yes, gone. I hardly ever go home for Christmas.' He needed to go on talking; if he stopped, they would have to turn to the subject of the next few hours. He blanked it out. 'This was the first time for years. I only did it because I had a lift, as I said. With a girl.'

And then there was a useful fiction. That would keep it going.

'A girl? What's her name?'

'Why?'

'I can't follow stories if I don't know the names of the people in the story.'

'I didn't know I was telling you a story. I was just going to tell you how I came to be stuck here right now. Anyway, she's called Charlotte, this girl.' He lied, when he lied, readily, and without thinking too much.

'Charlotte?'

'Yes. Anyway, she said to me that she was going home too – she lives in Cologne as well, goes home every year, wouldn't miss it, and said she thought it was about time I went home as well. She's rather like that. I told you I hadn't been home for Christmas for years.'

'I know this is going to be a really sad story,' Daphne said. He could see her hugging her knees, as if in pleasant anticipation.

'I told you, I'm not telling you a story, so don't be disappointed when nothing much happens. I'm just saying how I came to be here. So Charlotte picked me up and we set off. It was fine for a couple of hours –'

'Can I just ask, how long have you known this Charlotte?'

'Twenty years,' Friedrich said.

'In what way?' Daphne thrilled with the scale of her own intuition.

Friedrich paused in a melodramatic manner. This girl deserved almost everything. 'For the last five we've been sort of seeing each other. Five years in February, it would have been.'

'Go on,' Daphne said.

'It was fine for a couple of hours, as I said, and then I said something to criticize her driving – I don't know, maybe she cut up some other driver – and she had a fit. You know, I hate aggressive driving. It really scares me. And I couldn't keep quiet, I had to tell her she was putting herself in danger. You know, when you can't keep quiet.'

'Sorry,' Daphne said. 'Do you think you could find the news? It's just on the hour.'

'Sure,' Friedrich said, turning the dial on the radio. The next station was an East German one, a small respectable voice reading from a rustling pile of paper. As he spoke,

Friedrich felt a momentary terror, as if what had happened to Picker – though he had been gone for barely a quarter of an hour – would at any moment be broadcast to the Democratic Republic. It was, however, merely the usual banalities of the hourly news bulletin, thrown into the programme with more regard for the exact stroke of the clock than for the timing of records. It was the usual Democratic news of what the leader of the Republic happened to be doing that day, the sweet peaceful nothings of life over the Wall, and – in the absence of any predictable decisions from Parliament – an extended piece about some artist or other who had just died. After a couple of minutes, Daphne said,

'I'm cold. Can we have the heater on?'

'Sure,' Friedrich said.

'Go on with the story.'

'So I criticized her driving, and she just exploded at me. All this stuff started coming out she'd never said before. She said I was useless, that I'd never achieved anything or ever would, that I'd never manage to have any kind of marriage, and certainly not with her, because secretly I hated and despised women, that I felt sick whenever she took her clothes off, she could see it in my eyes.' He stopped. He surprised himself with his invention. He did not know where it came from.

'How awful,' Daphne said. Her eyes were bright with excitement. She's making me say all this; she's making me lie to her, this girl, Friedrich thought; he felt a little pang, not of guilt, but of disgust at his own easy lying.

'Shall I turn back to the other station?' Friedrich said. The news had finished, and the East German station had started to play, with fine incongruity, some dried-peas-in-a-drum Latin American dance music.

'No,' Daphne said. 'I actually quite like this stuff. Did you ever learn to dance at school?'

'Yes, of course,' Friedrich said. 'Yes, it was always a bit like this. I quite like it, too. Anyway – there's not much more to tell – she'd never said any of this, or anything like it, ever before, and I really had no idea that was how she felt.'

'Don't go on,' Daphne said. 'If it's difficult for you to say any of this.'

'No, not at all,' Friedrich said. It wasn't difficult at all. With her eager reflected gaze, it was as if she were sucking each detail out of him, as if she were doing the lying. 'There was no point, really, in saying anything to any of it. I wasn't going to reply to her. It wasn't a sudden outburst, you saw that straight away. She'd obviously been thinking about it for years, storing it all up. So we just sat in silence, and Daphne carried on driving –'

'Charlotte,' Daphne said.

'Sorry?'

'You said, Daphne carried on driving,' Daphne said.

'I meant Charlotte,' Friedrich said. 'We just carried on, and when we got to my house, she said, All right then, and I just got out with my bags and she drove off. My mother came out into the drive, and said Was that Charlotte, driving off in such a hurry? and I said Yes, she couldn't stop, she was late, she wasn't spending Christmas with us after all, she was in a real rush, and she'd come round and see us properly later, maybe the day after Christmas. My mother must have thought it was pretty strange, because Charlotte had spent Christmas with us for the last three years, and she couldn't stand the sight of her parents. But, bless her, she didn't ask any questions.'

He cursed himself for that 'bless her', even more than

for calling his fictitious girlfriend Daphne by mistake; it stamped the whole saga as a lie. Daphne, though, just said, 'You must have had an awful Christmas.' She sounded genuinely troubled, sympathetic. Friedrich felt like a shit.

'Yes,' he said, simply. He left an effective pause. 'The day after Christmas I called her to make things up with her. Her father answered the phone, and first he pretended not to recognize my voice, and then said Charlotte was out. I told him to go and fetch her, and then he got really angry, and said that if she didn't want to speak to me, or see me, that was her business. Then he put the phone down. There was no way I was going to drive back with Charlotte –'

'Even if she'd wanted to,' Daphne said.

'Yes, even if she'd wanted to. So as I'm quite hard up, I had to get on the phone to the Mitfahrzentrale. You know how it is. And here I am.'

'Are you going to have to find somewhere to live?' Daphne said.

It was a moment before he saw what she meant. Oddly, he hadn't considered the question of whether he and his Charlotte had actually been living together. Just then, another news bulletin came on, and they listened to it in silence. He wondered if Daphne had the same dread he did; that they would only discover what had happened to Picker through hearing it on some DDR news bulletin; and that if Picker was safe, in West Berlin, he would by now have decided that the best thing was to abandon the car, and them, and let the DDR authorities deal with the whole mess. He blanked it out again. It was an absurd feeling; of course, it wouldn't happen quite like that; things never happened quite as you expected them to; it was a feeling he couldn't shake off, like a knowledge of truth, an ugly secret.

'Where are you going to live?' Daphne said finally.

'Luckily,' Friedrich said, 'we both hung on to our flats. There'll be stuff to move out, of course, and she'll have to ask this friend of hers to move out of her flat –'

'What's the friend called?'

'I can't remember,' Friedrich said. 'When that's all over, we can start again, I suppose. Tonight I just wanted to go to the Oranienbar and get pissed. But it doesn't look as if we're going to make it back by midnight.'

'I feel like Cinderella,' Daphne said. 'Sitting in a carriage which is about to turn into a pumpkin. That's a really sad story.'

'Yes,' he said.

'What do you think can have happened –'

'I've no idea,' Friedrich said. 'You mean Picker?'

'Yes.'

'Let's talk about something else. Do you like this music?'

'It reminds me of dancing lessons at school. I used to love to dance,' she said. 'Proper dancing, I mean. Tango and foxtrot and everything. I haven't done it for years. In a way I'd like to go and dance, but I don't know if there's anywhere you can go in Berlin.'

'There are places you can go,' Friedrich said. 'There's this club I go to in Kreuzberg called S.O.36, they've just started up a proper dancing night. It's really strange. Every Friday night, ballroom and tango. But drag queens and punks and leather guys and dykes and girls with pearls from Charlottenburg, all dancing together. Sometimes it's hard to know whether you're supposed to lead or to follow.'

Daphne laughed. It was an unexpected surprise, her laugh, an unexpected flash of delight; she had smiled, but she had not laughed before. 'When we get back to Berlin,' she said, 'would you take me there one night?'

'Sure,' he said. 'But we don't have to wait till then. Do you want to dance now?'

'How?'

'Now,' Friedrich said. 'On the road. Turn up the radio, and leave the door open. Pump up the volume.'

'You're nuts,' she said, but she gathered her coat around her as he turned up the sound of the tinny car radio to its not very loud maximum volume. And then she did what he asked of her; she stepped out on the hard shoulder, with a pensive heavy gracefulness, and waited for him, with one arm outstretched, the other curved around some phantom partner in air, waiting for him. He followed her, and, with an unaccountable feeling of bad manners in beginning in the middle of a dance, they started to repeat a long-forgotten foxtrot. He took her perfumed flesh in his arms, the coarse texture of her cheap clothes against his hands, the sudden soft pale flesh of her neck, her hands, against his coarse scrubbed hands, and felt as he felt her that this was what he had wanted to do, wanted to do since he saw her first. Without knowing. Silent they were, and serious, unsmiling; and those few who passed them as they danced in the snow on the fast-cracking surface of the transit road saw something unimaginable, a solemn gesture of absurdity, like the absorbed games of children.

From time to time, they paused, and he said to her 'Tango?' or 'Paso doble' or 'Quickstep', or merely the polite exchange of compliments, 'You're really good at this'; and she followed him; and he let her confident backwards yielding guide him, the yielder and the yielded to, the lied to and the liar. He thought about their need, every need of everyone, to allow themselves, sometimes, to be lied to, sometimes to yield, sometimes to allow themselves to be driven through a strange country, behind walls, guided only by the roads which were there. And they went on dancing, only stopping when the radio gave way to its occasional bursts of melancholy predictable news, and only continuing when, again, the music began. In a foreign country which called itself Germany, in the car of a man who had abandoned them, they sat and smoked, and talked, and after a moment or two, got up and began to dance again.

They were still dancing when midnight struck, and they had not noticed that, an hour before, the snow had stopped falling. Over the silent air, still as the black water of a lake, came the distant brilliant crackle of the new year, making them look at their watches and smile at the noise which could be fireworks, tossed into the bright streets of the island city only thirty miles away, or a giant's sibilant footsteps breaking through the stiff surface of a snow drift, or the approaching noise of gunfire, or anything. And, looking forwards in the now quite empty motorway, in the direction of Berlin, it came to Friedrich that they would not hear if a man or a car came up behind them; that if a stranger or their long-gone English rescuer or the blank-faced authorities shone the lights of a car on them, they would not respond, but act only in accordance with the roles they now occupied, two still figures in a dance, waiting for the music to start, waiting for someone to arrive and show them how to act, show them the steps to take, show them how to surrender in the great arms of another.

PUBLIC TRANSPORT

I T WAS SEVEN o'clock in the morning. It was five days after Peter Picker's puncture. It was in the same city, but somehow quite different. It might have been in Schöne des Tages, or Beer Heaven, but it was probably just the Oranienbar.

'And then,' Friedrich was saying to his now forgiven and now very drunk friend and drinking partner Martin, 'it was getting really cold. And the car's heater wasn't working that well. I had that feeling you get when you're going to die –'

'How do you know?'

'What?'

'How do you know what the feeling you're going to get when you're going to die is like?'

'I guessed. I had that feeling. I had that feeling that before too much longer the heater was just going to pack up and we'd both die of hypothermia, and I'd be found blue round the edges, with pathetic frosty lips, in the middle of the German Democratic Republic with a girl who certainly nobody would have expected me to be with, I mean, I wasn't with the person who was supposed to be driving me to Cologne in the first place.'

'Who did drive you there, as a matter – a *matter* –' Martin said, looking up from his glass with emphatic emphasis, 'of fact?'

'You did,' Friedrich said. 'You remember? Do you remember? You offered to take me. When we were in the Oranienbar.'

'We're *in* the fucking Oranienbar,' Martin said. So they were.

'So we are,' Friedrich said. 'You knew that. You were supposed to take me back but you didn't because you came back before I did for some reason.'

'For some reason,' Martin said.

'For some reason,' Friedrich said. 'So there I would be, frozen stiff in the arms of a woman called Daphne or a fat man called Peter Picker who probably wasn't even called Daphne –'

'Peter Picker wasn't called Daphne?'

'No.'

'You never said,' Martin said. 'You *never* told me his fucking name. Picker's fucking name was Peter. And not Daphne. And he never told you his name was Peter before he went off because you would have told me his name was Peter. So that must mean he came back, to tell you his name. And to drive you over the border to *Kreuzberg* –'

Kreussbach –

'– because you're *here*, aren't you?'

'Not necessarily,' Friedrich said. 'He might have told me before he went, and I just forgot to tell you.'

'But he didn't,' Martin said. 'Didn't tell you. And you're here, aren't you?'

Friedrich looked around him. Martin had a point.

'So I am,' he said. 'And a fat lot you care, abandoning me in Cologne with no means of getting back here, not giving my tragic plight any thought at all, and frankly I don't know why I should even think about forgiving you.'

'Because I'm paying my penance,' Martin said.

'What do you mean?'

'Because my family were so cross with me for going away that they've said to me that this niece I've got who is my sister's child has got to come and stay with me which is a way they always have of punishing me when I've done something really awful like go away from their Christmas.'

'Big deal,' Friedrich said. 'So what kept us going and not freezing to death or dying of boredom was the radio. Because, as you know, what the People's Democratic Republic likes best in the world is the dance music of Latin America, which reminds them of where their leaders are going to end up, so it makes them cheerful. Very very cheerful. And what the radio was playing was Latin American dance music. Now, we were talking, the lovely Daphne and I, and she revealed to me that, along with the People's Democratic Republic of Germany, what she loves best in the world – no, she revealed to me that, along with the People's Democratic Republic of Germany, she *too* loves best in the world the dance music of Germany. Latin America. So I wondered why we hadn't already started dancing on the road. There was no one on the road at all. Because no one travels at midnight on New Year's Eve, not even in East Germany where there's nothing to do except go from Leipzig to Dresden to Magdeburg to Karl-Marx-Stadt in the vague hope that you'll find somewhere that isn't quite so fucking awful as the place you've just come from. And there's no reason at all to go from the Federal Republic to West Berlin on New Year's Eve because the danger that you'll break down and be stuck in a car with no way of escape on the transit road is too strong. But I only found that out later. So there's no one on this transit road. And if you look at it the right way, the transit road is just like a dance floor, exactly like one, exactly as smooth and nice and empty. Except that it's outside and it's covered in snow and no one ever bothers to repair it so it's full of potholes. But it would do. So we got out and we danced.'

'You don't blame me for running away from that family of mine?' Martin said, catching up rather slowly.

'No, Friedrich said. 'Tango and paso doble, and every so often this car would whoosh past and you'd see some kid's face pressed against the window, looking at these two people dancing the foxtrot in the snow and thinking, well, I always knew East Germany was strange but I never knew they danced on their motorways, that's really something you don't get to see in the Federal Republic, and he's going to spend the rest of his life wondering why you don't actually get to see it that often in East Germany either, and wondering why that is and if he really ever saw anything at all, that New Year's Eve.

'The thing was – the weird thing was – that dancing made me start to like this girl. She made me feel – just through walking backwards and doing whatever I made her do – she made me feel like a real man, like a man doing whatever men are supposed to do, to master women, or take the lead, or be dominating. I haven't danced for years. I felt really great. But there was something even weirder. I was leading, and everything – I was doing the big macho thing with the tango and pushing her about. But I didn't feel like I was in charge. She wasn't in charge either. You know at school, in dancing class, there's always this sort of girl who when she's doing the following is really yanking you forwards all the time, so she ends up kind of leading in reverse. She wasn't that girl. It was the dance in charge and this girl was just sinking backwards and smiling, and leading me gently towards her, and I was just giving way.

'We kept it up for hours, it must have been. And at midnight – you could hear the fireworks going off – we stopped and just stopped and just listened to it all. It just strikes me now – I thought at the time it must be the noise of the fireworks from Berlin, but it might not have been, it was probably too close. It must have been – it might have been fireworks in Brandenburg, or somewhere else. Even in East Germany they have fireworks. Chinese fireworks from the Chinese Eastern Democratic People's Republic of Germany. And the fireworks were going off somewhere and I turned off the radio. And we sat on the bonnet of this expensive, beautiful English car and didn't talk or say anything at all. I could have kissed her but I didn't want to. She wanted me to kiss her so much. So much. And I didn't want to at all. Because I had such a good time.

'So we sat there for ages. And there was Peter Picker, who we'd stopped thinking about so successfully that we'd forgotten all about him, with some grumpy bloke going from Berlin to Hannover on his New Year's Eve and not very happy about any of it, and Peter Picker with this perfect wheel for his English car. And it got put on and the man drove off and we all got in. But when he tried to start the car it turned out, of course, that we'd run down the battery by running the heater and the radio for hours. But we only had to wait another fifteen minutes before a car came along, which by some miracle had a set of jump-leads, and off we went, with Peter Picker looking as if he wished he'd never set eyes on us, Daphne crying her head off, but not crying from laughter any more, just crying because she was thinking of her Marco or Mario or whoever and me being my usual happy and smiling self, and then here I am. And by the time I got here everybody had gone I don't know where and I went to bed but I'm making up for it now. What's the fucking time? Time! Time! You, you're *fucking* drunk!'

'He's worse than that,' the barkeeper said. 'He's asleep. You fuck off now. It's eight o'clock in the morning.'

Martin was on the bar, supporting himself by one side of his face, his arms dangling, ape-like, in the direction of the floor, his mouth slightly open. It was as if he had decided to lie down, and, finding a bar in the way, had discovered that it would be better to stay where he was. Friedrich looked at his watch. It was eight o'clock in the morning.

'Ah, fuck off yourself,' he said cheerfully. 'See you later. Hey Martin. Martin.'

He hit Martin in the side. The barman watched him morosely.

'Watch it,' the barman said. 'I know where you live. I know what your name is.'

'I dare say,' Friedrich said. 'Martin, come on, wake up.'

Martin raised his head.

'Kiss me, my darling,' he said. So Friedrich did, and Martin didn't resist, until Friedrich put his tongue into Martin's mouth. That woke him.

Many things gave Friedrich pleasure, but one of the most persistent was the working of public transport. He liked the efficiency of it, and he liked the breakdown of efficiency. He liked to stand on the street and watch two buses of the same line drive past in opposite directions; he liked it when the drivers raised a ponderous hand in greeting to each other, inadvertently witnessing to the world some enjoyable conversation, some after-work drink, some colleague thought well of by another colleague, and, for no good reason, liked. But when, as sometimes happened, two drivers ignored each other, Friedrich was filled with a strange heavy sadness, unable to understand what had led two men to fall out, unable to understand, but interested by his own sadness. He liked to watch, in the underground or the suburban train, the beginning of a conversation between strangers, struck into life like a match by a chance coincidence, like two people wearing the same coat. He liked the arguments between strangers which began as a request not to smoke. He liked the arguments which developed when a passenger passed some ironic remark about the shoving brute behind and the shoving brute replied, in some ironic remark.

Once, Friedrich took a bus from one end of Kreuzberg to another. The bus was full of schoolchildren from Hamburg, on a trip to see Berlin. They all carried a small purple rucksack with the name of their school on it, as if education were a thing which needed to be advertised. The two teachers sat at the front, wearily two days into a trip, allowing themselves for the moment to ignore the growing rowdiness of their forty children. Opposite Friedrich a blonde woman was sitting, thin and pretty, failing to concentrate on the newspaper she clutched.

The children were busy chorusing the names of the bus-stops after the driver's announcements. Unfamiliar with the street names, they mistook them, and riotously corrected each other. Friedrich engaged the blonde woman's gaze; they both rolled their eyes a little. The teachers obstinately continued their discussion of a television programme.

'Next stop,' the tannoy announced, with a certain calm exhaustion, 'as we would happily wish to advise our esteemed guests from the Federal Zone, is the world-famous landmark of Checkpoint Charlie.'

Friedrich and the woman started to giggle; it was the withering scorn of the driver which did it.

'Federal Zone,' Friedrich said, and the woman started to giggle again. As she got off, two stops after the school-children, he noted with a clinical feeling quite removed from anything resembling lust, the narrow ankles, the thin graceful calves in their pale stockings. He wondered what a woman so groomed was doing in Kreuzberg. He noted, looking down, the grubbiness of his unobserved finger-nails.

(It was only a month or two later that, buying cigarettes in the Oranienstrasse, he turned and found her behind him. 'Hi,' he said, knowing her face, not quite placing it. She seemed entirely unsurprised. 'Our esteemed visitor from the Federal Zone,' she said, with a diminished echo of the driver's contempt, and oddly more distancing, more merely flirtatious; and then, of course, he knew her. She did not giggle; she was grave, as if saying something of the greatest importance. He waited for her at the kiosk, waited for her to finish buying her telephone card and come for a cup of coffee with him. But when she turned and found him still there, she mildly waggled her finger, smiling, and walked off briskly down the Oranienstrasse. And this time his lust was like lust, so like lust.)

What else did Friedrich like about public transport? Well, all of it; the shared underground air, the shared diffi-culties, the trust and the mistrust of it. The pleasurable overheard conversation of old ladies when they thought no one was listening, clustered like crows at bus-stops, com-plaining. The bus drivers speeding joyously past un-requested stops. When it, or its agents, let you walk on to the street without seeing if you had a ticket, when it stopped you before you had had a chance to punch your ticket, just to see if you had one. He liked cheating the network; he liked the dubious feeling when he stepped off a train or a bus, ticketless. He liked the equally dubious feeling which succeeded the panic when some unremarkable bloke standing in the aisle suddenly produced an ID card and set about inspecting everyone's tickets; the delicious relief of realizing that, for once, he had got round to buying one.

He liked to contemplate the uncontemplatable intricacy and perfection of the city's transport system, shuttling from border to border, bouncing across the confined city like a pinball against glass walls. He liked the moments when the simple perfection of the system broke down into its ordinary human constituents, and stopped running. He liked those moments, when the carefully orchestrated discipline of the city's transport cracked for a moment, revealing beneath the impersonal world where a bus had only a number and a place in a timetable, a place where a particular tram happened to be driven by a particular man, who, like him, might be bored, or in love, or in pain, or, unknowably, anything at all.

It was two days later. Friedrich was asleep in his flat when the telephone rang. Rummaging through the bedclothes in search of the telephone which so urgently shrilled him out of his morning sleep, he found his mother on the end of the line.

'Friedrich, hello.'

'Hello, Mamma.'

'You didn't call.'

'I thought I tried.'

'I was thinking about you. I was just wondering if you'd managed to get back all right.'

'Yes, no trouble.'

'Your friend –'

'Martin.'

'He called to say he was sorry. I didn't ask what for.'

'When did he call?'

'New Year's Eve. I thought he was driving you back.'

'Well, the thing is – yes, I thought he was driving me back too. But I got a lift back. And as you see I'm here safe and sound.'

'I wish –'

'I wish Martin hadn't phoned you. I didn't want you worried.'

'I just wanted to know that you were all right,' she said. 'That's all.'

'I know, Mamma,' he said. 'But I had another lift. It was fine. I got back all right. Martin had to go earlier than he said and he forgot about me, that was all.'

'You know I worry too much,' she said. 'I can't help it sometimes.'

'I know,' he said. 'But I'm not Papa. I'm not going any-where.'

And then it was said, his father's name.

'I'm sorry for worrying,' she said. 'It's just after –'

'I know,' he said. 'Nothing's wrong. I'm back here safe and sound. I would have called you straight away if I knew you were worrying, or if I knew Martin had called you. I'll kill him when I see him for giving you a fright.'

'No, he was only doing what he thought was right,' she said. 'And you too, I know.'

'I enjoyed Christmas,' he said extravagantly. 'I really did. I don't know why I don't always do it. It was nice to be home.'

'Oh, you say that now,' she said. 'It was nice to have you back. What happened to your friend Martin?'

'He said he got fed up of his family,' he said. 'There are lots of them, and I think the house gets too crowded, and he was sleeping on the sofa in the same room as two of his nephews, and he couldn't get any peace and quiet, and so he just decided to go back to Berlin. And his father, I don't know if you remember the father, he's always having a go at Martin for living in Berlin, he's really critical, and probably they had some kind of a row about the clothes Martin wears, or about him leaving home and not doing much with his life. You know the sort of thing.'

'Indeed, yes, I do,' she said. 'So he went back to Berlin?'

'Yes,' Friedrich said. 'Just forgetting to tell me he was going.'

'Well,' she said. 'It was nice to have you for so long. I wished you'd told me what was going on. I can't help worrying sometimes.'

They carried on for a while, and at the end of the conversation, Friedrich put the telephone down and went back to sleep. His dreams were full of paranoia and worry and uncontrol. He was a soldier – a major or something – who had to lead his thirty men in a parade, but he couldn't get the pace right, he led them in a shambles. When he woke, he had the sense of lying there in silence for a second or two, the sense of failure and recrimination before the telephone rang again.

'Fuck,' he said, or perhaps only thought, in his sleep, as he woke, to the shrill noise, his arm already flailing out in its general direction. In the years to come, Friedrich sometimes thought of the moment as he answered the telephone, a good moment, as a time of perfect meaning and quiet. It was a Janus moment; it was a moment, like some street noise, a foghorn, mounted on a car hurtling down a street heard by an alerted bystander; a moment which, looked forward to, looked back on, was more like two moments than one, just as the alarm, heading towards the bystander, and the sound of the same alarm heading away from him were two different notes. The Doppler effect of memory transformed Friedrich's lying supine on the bed, wondering whether or not to answer the telephone, into two different moments, two different choices, two different worlds; the first, a world where Peter Picker had been forgotten about, had passed into a crowd of acquaintances who might or might not be met with again. And then there was another world, as the alarm-bell of the telephone hurtled backwards into the past; a world where Peter Picker always was there and always had been there. A place where Peter Picker had his plans; plans for Friedrich.

'Had you forgotten, perhaps, who I was?' Picker said.

'No,' Friedrich said cautiously. 'Of course not. It was only last week. Sorry about everything.'

'What do you mean?'

'Sorry it was such a disaster, the whole trip, with the tyre and the battery and that.'

'It wasn't your fault. Well, perhaps the battery could be viewed as being your fault. But it all turned out for the best, and I had actually forgotten about that. Have you seen that charming girl again?'

'No,' Friedrich said. 'I haven't.'

'She seemed very nice,' Picker said, as if conceding something graciously. 'I wondered if you might like to come out to a small party with me soon. That was why I was telephoning.'

'If I would?' Friedrich said. 'Yes, sure. Why not.'

'Why not indeed,' Picker said. 'That would be nice. Tell me, are you interested in art?'

'Not uninterested,' Friedrich said. 'Why?'

51

'I was invited to a *vernissage* here at the museum,' Picker said. 'I wondered if you would like to come with me. That would be very nice. And these things are often quite dull, so it would be nice to have someone to talk to.'

'No,' Friedrich said. 'I just wondered why you ask me.'

'And I was just wondering why not,' Picker said. 'Perhaps that sums up a fundamental difference between human beings, the ones who say why and the ones who say why not.'

'Perhaps,' Friedrich said, plucking idly at some fluff off the mattress, 'though it hadn't occurred to me to wonder whether there was any difference between us.'

'Oh,' Picker said. 'I didn't mean that. I meant. Oh well. Or anything between us.'

He giggled, nervously.

'How did you get my number?' Friedrich said.

'From the book, of course,' Picker said. 'You said you lived in Kreuzberg. You were the only one.'

'I'm a bit surprised to hear from you,' Friedrich said. 'To be honest.'

'Because of the battery?' Picker said. 'Yes. To be honest, I'm a bit surprised to hear myself calling you. No, I'm joking. But I like to meet people and talk to them. And it would be pleasant to have a drink and look at some paintings. It's on the 23rd of February.'

'That's a long time away,' Friedrich said.

'I wanted to be sure of you,' Picker said.

'Let me have a look,' Friedrich said. He put the telephone receiver down on the bed, walked to the other side of the room. He looked out of the window for a minute at the leafless trees and the scrubby few metres of mud and half-grass, three floors below, to which the noise of some men chainsawing branches lent a faint air of countryside.

He went back to the telephone. 'Just fetching my diary,' he said. 'No, that's fine.'

'Six o'clock?' Picker said. 'Let me tell you where to come.'

'Don't tell me now,' Friedrich said. 'Call me on the twenty-whatever of February.'

He looked at his flat. It was all a bit much. If he sat here, he knew, he would start to think about his flat; or about his mother's telephone call; or about his father. He closed his eyes, sinking backwards. Sleep, on the whole, was always to be preferred.

CHANGED

DAPHNE HADN'T WANTED to be back in Berlin so urgently just so that she could see Mario. She wanted to be back because Sunday – and New Year's Day was a Sunday – was her day for class war.

Sooner or later, it had to be admitted by any friend of Daphne, as, usually pretty quickly, it had to be admitted by Daphne herself, that Daphne was not Daphne's real name. Or not her original name. Now, of course, it was as real as names usually are, ordinarily expressive of desire and aspiration which the bearer so pathetically fails to live up to. They usually represent the parents' aspirations and desire; in Daphne's case, they represented only Daphne's. Her real name was Charlotte; the name her parents had given her, the expression of some ambition, lost over twenty years in the past, or more. At some point, both she and Friedrich Kaiser would begin to see some kind of comedy in their names; but it wouldn't be just yet.

Unlike Friedrich Kaiser – and, having been told his name only once, it was hard for her to believe she had heard his name correctly, and she was satisfied to wonder what, exactly, was odd about his name – Daphne didn't come from Cologne. She had little attachment to the place, and when, at Christmas, she went there, it was with a faint cheerful sense of holiday, of going somewhere she didn't know and wouldn't necessarily go back to. Cologne was always interesting to her, since she wouldn't stay there for more than a week. This was the third Christmas she'd spent in Cologne; it was the third Christmas her parents had lived there. Once she had arrived, Daphne had shed her Berlin self by the minute, with an anticipation which belonged to an arrival in a festival town, one of unfamiliar and interesting customs, rather than a city where her parents lived and to which, in some sense, she was coming home. Her Christmas week was usually taken up with sightseeing; she would suggest the picture gallery, or a palace nearby or even a park. They were both shorter than her; they were both exactly the same size (something she'd never thought about, something she found weirder and weirder with each returning visit); they held hands. It was hard not to think of them as bewildered children as she led them over the lawns of some palace they lived half an hour's drive from and had never thought of going to, lawns dark and wet as spinach.

'This is nice,' her mother would say, decidedly, as if with relief, anxious to appear grateful. Daphne wondered why it was like this; why her parents, in retirement, were so grateful to her, why she seemed to have taken charge. She tried, sometimes, to imagine their lives when she was not there. Fifty-one weeks a year in Cologne, a life of such quietness she could not conceive of it. A new recipe, tried out, was an event to be commented on over the telephone. 'Your father said it made a nice change,' if it wasn't very successful, or 'your father said, we must have that, when you come home next,' if it had proved a small triumph. Much of their conversation was made up of the events of television programmes, something which Daphne normally took some pride in knowing nothing about. A new scarf might be enough to talk about; daringly going out for dinner in a restaurant would be discussed, repeatedly, until Daphne's ordinary cruelty got the better of her, and she said, 'Mother, you've told me that before.'

They had no friends in Cologne. 'The lady in the flat below seems terribly nice,' her mother often said, vaguely, though they hadn't seemed to be able to find her Christian name out. Other than that, how should they get to know anyone? When people entered into her mother's narratives, over the telephone, they were waiters in cafés, girls in supermarkets; they might be neighbours; they might be relations, they might be people her parents had known before they moved, and kept in touch with. As far as Daphne could see, they had met no one new, and she could not see how such people – how her parents – could meet anyone new.

Why had they gone to Cologne? She could understand why she had run away from where they had all lived; she could not see, however, how they had managed to pull off the same trick, or why they had wanted to. Until she was eighteen, they had lived in Cloppenburg. It was a small town, which one had to describe as being 'near Bremen'. It was remarkable for only one thing, she had discovered subsequently; being the cheapest place to buy a house in all of Germany. Her childhood and adolescence seemed to her to be conducted calmly, in the secrecy only possible in a place with a flat curving earth and a sky which could have seen everything. There was nowhere to go, and nothing to see, except yourself, in a field, and the effects of the wind, blowing, every day, in the same direction. The grass grew at an angle of forty-five degrees.

She remembered what people said about her. She always did. And everything people said to her, about herself, she picked over for insults, for hidden rudeness, for a chance, when she got old enough, to revenge herself. A friend said to her once, 'You're a truly beautiful person and you mean a lot to me.' A black mark, for insincerity. Another girl said – who knows what she meant, who knows anything except what Daphne took from her comment – that Daphne was lucky not to have to worry whether boys liked her for herself or for her looks. Sometimes what she remembered was not quite right; she was capable of brooding over a casual remark until she believed, quite firmly, that a boy had called her a fat lesbian, and with equal solidity, that one day soon she would slap his face, or call him something which would hurt him as much. Something; she didn't quite know what would hurt anyone as much as things hurt her.

The wrongs done to her and the revenge she would take ruled her thoughts. She thought on revenge as other girls planned their weddings. But no revenge would ever be enough. She knew that. The world had done terrible things to her; made her itch alone, at night, with the certainty that it was always going to be vile, that she would never get what she so much deserved. And revenge would never be enough; because, she knew, of all the people in the world, she was the only one who ever lay in bed and burnt at a remark someone had made, and no one would ever be hurt by her as much as she had been hurt, twenty times a day, by everybody. No, no revenge would ever be enough. Something had to be done about the world. The world was unjust to her, and when she read that the world was full of injustice, she nodded, and counted herself among the wronged. She would fight against injustice, of course she would; against the rich who trampled on the poor, against all the dictators, against the wrongs of history, against the girl who said *You're so lucky*. All of them. The world had to be put right.

She was still young when she saw the trap her classmates were falling into; she heard them describing the town of Bremen as a place to go to, a place where excitement might be had. She would not fall into that trap; she would rather stay in Cloppenburg and cycle along the flat roads, braced against the wind in her oilskins, and think her thoughts, and find pleasure and freedom in her imagined power, her staircase rejoinders. At some point, she would know where she had to go to, and she would go there. Not just yet.

She was not popular at school; people thought her arrogant, and they knew her to be a liar. They were not interested in what she was interested in, herself and the political life, and did not see the simple reasons she was interested in them. She was not arrogant, just afraid; and she was not, or not quite, a liar. She did not invent alternative versions of events which had already taken place, she did not pretend that she had not broken windows or farted. She only invented one alternative version of events; it was an alternative version of her own life. It was a simple one, a well-known story, which people often tell; it was the story of the good dead twin. Many children like to believe in a dead twin, into which all the badness, all the virtue may be offloaded; it is how they make themselves. She believed in her story of the dead twin; she believed with such force that she barely had to invent it. She told her classmates that she was adopted (*must* have been, *had* to have been); she thought, in lesser flights, that she might be the illegitimate daughter of her mother and some more vital, more outward man than her father. Into these banal inventions, having no access to any other, she poured an ecstatic measure of what she wanted to be, what she wanted no longer to be. It went on for years; she would still be telling people about her dead siblings as she was handing out leaflets against environmental disaster, against animal experimentation, against the abuse of human rights, against, in short, against the world, in the shopping street of Cloppenburg.

She saw too little of what everyone knows, that the tale of the dead good twin is too important ever to be invented by just one person. It is the one tale which everybody knows before they hear it, because they have already told the story to themselves, only half-understanding why. It is the only lie everyone recognizes, the only lie everyone knows to be true of themselves. She was stung when the story came back to her, and, somehow, she had a sense of the tone in which someone had said 'That girl there says . . .'; it hurt more than if it had been fed back to her in a wave of incredulous laughter. She thought about the story again. There was more to come; there was too much she wanted to become. One dead twin could not bear the load of all that wished-for villainy, all that virtue. She was the last of a series of children, none surviving. That was right; that was what had happened. Babies came, and died, each exactly three months after their birth, every single one called Charlotte. That was what had happened, and nobody could ever explain why. 'Why?' her open-mouthed audience would say; amazed, gripped by the magical detail of *exactly three months*, but still unrespectful of the lying *diva*. 'Nobody could ever explain why,' she would say. They grew out of it, she saw that afterwards; she went on, as if she were obliged to go on telling it.

There was something strange about this story. It was true, or almost.

One day – she was almost grown-up – her mother was waiting for her at the gate of their house, and she knew – knew from the end of the street – what had happened. Knew exactly what had passed between her mother and a neighbour, in the baker's; *my daughter says your daughter says*. Daphne felt shame, of course, but also a strange little fit of excitement, a boost. The eye-widening feeling, better than any revenge, of being discussed, of fame, of her story being told by daughter to mother, by mother to mother. Her mother would not reprove, could not, but she was crying by the end of it anyway. Daphne could not see why her mother would cry; embarrassment was what she felt, but she also felt, with a fine sense of the dramatic, the possibilities of the scene, the beautifully fulfilled directions she could push it in. She sat, and watched her mother cry.

'It's all right, mother,' she said. 'I'm sorry. I didn't mean to upset you. I didn't do it to upset you.'

'No, you never do,' her mother got out. 'But you did upset me. How can I go and talk to anyone now? When I know what they know about us? How can we carry on living in this place?'

Daphne said nothing. She could not see what had changed.

The strange thing about the story of the line of Charlottes, all dead at three months – and she found this out, not from her mother, but from her father – was that it was true, or almost. He brought it out because she was telling him that she wanted to change her name; brought it out with some obscure sense of wrongness, of duty unfulfilled. There was a sense, never spoken, that Daphne was too old for this sort of thing; that a lying child was one thing, but a girl of eighteen, still telling these things, still knowing better; that was beyond contemplation. There

had, it was true, been other children. They hadn't made it
into the air, not at all, not the exactly three months Daphne
had envisaged; they had not been there to serve the
dramatic purposes of a narrative. They had got as far as
fourteen weeks, once to twenty, and that was it. 'How
many?' Daphne asked. Her father shrugged; too much
untellable ordinary pain to recall.

And now she wanted to change her name from a name
she had been given to a name she had chosen, had invented
for herself. And she wanted to leave them. Her name had
been Charlotte. It came from somewhere in the past, from
some date before her conception, before her birth. Who
knew how many foetuses it had been so hopefully attached
to; who knew how often the little wished-for child had
been taken away by the hospital, the flap of surgical waste
destroyed and the name Charlotte, written neatly on a list,
underlined and ticked, preserved in a drawer somewhere
for the next time, the next chance.

It was time for her to leave Cloppenburg, and, with her
new name and her school results, she went to Berlin.

'Hello,' the boy said. They were in a queue at the university registry. This was the way your first days went; in
queues, making friends.

'Hello,' Daphne said. 'Have you just started here?'

'Yes,' the boy said. 'I'm studying literature.'

'I'm studying literature too,' Daphne said. 'I'm
Daphne.'

'I'm Mario,' Mario said.

'Have you come straight from school?' she asked. The
boy looked older; he was even slightly balding.

'No,' he said. 'I've been doing other things.'

'What sort of things?'

'Cycling,' he said, amused.

'Cycling?'

'Yes,' he said. 'Not so much now.'

'Where do you come from?'

'Berlin,' he said.

'I don't think I've ever met anyone who came from Berlin,' Daphne said. 'Everyone you ever meet here seems to have come from some other part of the country.'

'Not me,' Mario said. 'I'm from over there.' He seemed to make a point of being opaque, as if he liked to have information dragged out of him.

'What do you mean?'

Mario gave a brief, odd twitch of the head, tossing it sideways. 'The other side of the fence.'

'The east, you mean?'

'Yup.'

'How –'

'The usual way,' Mario said. She had never met anyone from East Germany before. 'Not surprising, since you've never been anywhere,' Mario said, much later, when she admitted to this. 'Who would leave the DDR and choose to go to Cloppenburg?' And she had never even thought of going over the border. So when Mario said 'the usual way', she envisaged daring escapes, tunnelling, snorkelling through canals, pole-vaulting over the Wall itself, which she still hadn't seen. What she didn't know was that there were some people who had simply found themselves in the right place, and had walked into a police station; there were others who the Democratic Republic had judged sufficiently worthless in economic terms to permit their exit without a great deal of fuss. Daphne hardly knew this, and her mind filled with derring-do. No wonder she agreed to go out for a cup of coffee with him.

Mario liked his own name; it was a mark of where he came from.

'Everyone I know is called Mario or Pierre or Nicole or Sandra,' he said in the cafeteria. 'They like foreign names in East Germany.'

'It seems eccentric,' Daphne said.

'Not really,' he said. 'Think about it. And you don't have a German name.'

'No, but I made it up myself,' she said. 'Why Mario, though?'

'No reason in particular for Mario,' he said. 'Maybe it's because you can't travel. You can't go to Italy, but your son can have a wonderful Italian name. You might bring a bit of freedom, of abroad, into your life, even if your daughter's called Nicole Spangenberg.'

'Come on, though,' Daphne said. 'Why is travelling all that important? I've never been outside Germany in my life.'

'You can be really frivolous, when you try,' Mario said. He looked at her luminously with his great sad eyes; the wonderful thought came to her that he had seen almost everything, every concreted-over misery the People's Republic ever contained. 'It's not having travelled that's important. It's having the freedom to, if you want to. Look, Daphne, do you care about social inequality?'

'Yes,' Daphne said. She would have said yes if he'd asked if she cared about boiled bananas.

Something very strange happened. A letter arrived, soon after she had gone to Berlin, from her parents. They had decided – they didn't say why, as if it were obvious why – that they were going to move to Cologne. But they told her their address, so that was all right. She had thought ambitiously of not telling them where she had moved to – to break the bond with Cloppenburg decisively – but it was rather difficult to carry out the step. She was living, in fact, with her mother's sister, who had a nice flat at the far end of Charlottenburg; a part of Berlin disappointingly unlike the Berlin she had imagined and dreamed of, but too comfortable to leave.

Daphne cared about social inequalities. She had cared about rabbits being forced to smoke and nuclear power and fur coats and the tribesmen of Papua New Guinea or wherever. So she cared about social inequalities. Of course she did. She cared about the inequality between her aunt's house and the places everyone she met lived in; Kreuzberg, Schöneberg, Wedding, Spandau; grey flats, two hundred marks a month, and a grey view of walls. And then to go to the street her aunt lived in, and her aunt's building, a palazzo of fantastic window sills and doorframes fanged with stalactites of stone like the mouths of dragons, and, inside, a padded pink flat of girly plush and unfaultable central heating. She didn't mind living there, exactly, though she thought it would be better on the whole not to, and the question *where do you live* stirred in her an embarrassment, an aggressiveness she was sure no one else felt. She cared about social inequality. Of course she did.

'I go to this group,' Mario said, one Thursday afternoon.

'What sort of group?' Daphne said. They had settled into a routine of a cup of coffee at four o'clock, like a pair of old women breaking off from nothing in particular for coffee and cake. Nothing agreed, nothing remotely habitual, but there was a regularity Daphne had noticed about the way Mario would come up every afternoon at ten to four and say, 'Fancy a cup of coffee?' And, a couple of times a week, he would ask in some ordinary way over the afternoon coffee if she wanted to go out for a drink that evening. She said yes four times out of five; she didn't want to seem too eager.

'It's the group I go to,' Mario said. 'This friend of mine got me into it. It's a sort of political group, supporting the rights of the workers, direct action, protest, all that.'

'Sure,' Daphne said. 'Fighting against social inequality.'

'It's good,' Mario said. 'You should come. The thing we aim for is starting here, in Berlin, fighting inequality in Berlin.'

'What sort of stuff?'

'Like the way all these places in Berlin keep turning into some kind of middle-class suburb.'

'I don't know,' Daphne said. 'I mean, I didn't know that was happening.'

'Well, it is,' Mario said. 'You haven't lived in Berlin long enough to really notice it. But it's happening. All the money men are moving in and all the ordinary people are being dispossessed. You would only notice it if you had some sense of the irreconcilable differences a part of a town contained within itself, had a sense that the district was in a state of change. Do you see what I mean?'

'Yes,' Daphne said. 'I see.'

He looked at her; she was abruptly embarrassed, and dropped her eyes to the floor.

'Come to this group anyway,' Mario said. 'We'll talk about all this properly. Only you've got to understand it's not just talk, we have action against all this shopping, all these yuppy bars, all that plate glass that's taking over most of Berlin right now.'

'It's taking over the world,' Daphne said.

'Too right,' Mario said. 'And we can stop it.'

The thing about Mario — well, Daphne sometimes thought there was a thing about everyone. A single fact

about them which, if you uncovered it, would explain
everything in them, the whole of their personalities, their
charm, their awkwardnesses, their difficulty. Something
which, if you understood it properly and fully, would
enable you not only to say *the thing about her*, but to pre-
dict their actions. It was an idea she'd thought up herself;
she was proud of it, and never mentioned it to anyone. She
understood *the thing about*, she understood it for so many
people, and she was so often right, she found. Her parents,
the thing about her parents was that they believed outside
was full of terror, full of a strangeness and a fear you could
only avoid by staying inside; and when outside was full of
people you knew, people whose blood you shared, full
of people you had talked to since you were all five years
old, then you moved from there to find the strangeness you
always needed and feared; needed to fear. The thing about
her favourite teacher at school was that she hadn't had sex
for ten years, minimum; hadn't had sex and wanted it. But
what she didn't need was her celibacy, and it wasn't doing
her good, and she hadn't given in for the sake of any hidden desire for sexlessness; no, the thing about her favourite
teacher was that she just wanted sex.

The thing about Mario, she had quickly understood, was
that he was amazingly beautiful. If Daphne had had a face
of such loveliness and fragility, she would have tried,
almost to run from it, to hide it in case other people were
scared of its sharp-edged intelligence. It was almost gaunt
with the deep set of Mario's eyes, the dark-powdered edge
of his horizontal jaw, the strange kink in his nose which in
others might be a cause for embarrassment or disavowal
and in him, she felt, must only be a cause for indifference.
She knew his face so well it was as if she had held it and
not, simply, looked at it quietly. Looked at him, listening to

what he was saying, whatever he was saying. Nobody had ever said to him, *Mario, you're so lucky*; nobody had ever said to him that he would never have any doubt whether he was loved for his looks or his personality. There was never any doubt about that, and there could be no doubt that Mario had no regret about any of that. Looks, on the whole, were best. That was the thing about Mario; the unfair beauty he had so strangely acquired in a country where beauty was not to be bought; only engendered. Beauty, in him, was like goodness; it was a benefit which he chose to bestow on the world, and had now chosen to bestow on one world rather than the other; a benefit which he could, if he wished, withhold; it was a benefit which, in the end, time would withdraw from him, but which, at twenty-three, he only withheld, when he chose, from the world, in hats and scarves and mufflers.

And the thing about Daphne was . . . She often began sentences like that, in her head, and faltered before her tongue could complete the sentence. What was the thing about Daphne? It might be that she was called Daphne now and had been called Charlotte – and that, perhaps importantly, was not something she could have told Mario, and, following a definite instinct, she had not told him. It might be that she was a student, or had chosen to live in Berlin. The thing about Daphne might reside in her invented dead twins, the surprisingly real dead Charlottes who had come before her, the fact that she was the repository of all her parents wanted all their children to become. It was her choice, perhaps; it was up to her whether *the thing about Daphne* could be all that, or whether people would begin to describe her as a nice girl from Cloppenburg who lived with her aunt and did the work she was supposed to. The thing about Daphne had to be something she had chosen for herself, something she had invented. She couldn't have borne it if it turned out to be something that had been there all the time.

Maybe that was why she first went to Class War.

Of course she didn't put it like that to herself. She went to Class War because she cared about inequality and she cared that the influx of the rich into Berlin should not drive poor people away. It did not occur to her, because nobody ever asked her, where the rich were to live, or whether the rich had not always lived in Berlin; certainly in Charlottenburg, where she lived, where rich people lived, there were streets where the rich had always lived and where the poor never had lived and never would. But that was the thing about the rich and their money. There was so much money, and there were so few rich people. The money didn't need people; the people needed the money. And all that money could take over as much space as it wanted; all the space there was; every corner of every city, until there was nothing left for people with nothing, just, perhaps, a place called Kreuzberg.

Daphne could change that. Not on her own, but with Class War she could change things. She thought of herself as poor just because she had no money. It took Mario to make her realize that of course she was not poor; she had always been on the side of the rich, had always been rich, though she had no money at all. Living in a comfortable flat in Charlottenburg was enough to make you rich. It took Mario to explain to her that poverty was an effort of mind, an effort of choice. When he remarked that students were rich, it took some doing not to remark back that it was not the students who were rich, but their parents. But Mario was right, and Daphne took to her unvoiced vow of poverty like a nun. Her parents had always kept up an appearance of decency, of middle-class comfort by a brave show, by effort. Not by extravagance, but by saving up for purchases. Daphne took to poverty, to plainness and to the novel discipline of not buying what she could not afford with a sense of doing the right thing. She didn't want to save the money she didn't spend; she just didn't want to spend at all.

Part of her self-improvement, in this regard, was Mario's group.

The group meetings were held in the back room of a bar which had been there forever.

'No direct action tonight, right?' a man said, sitting at the far end of the table with a beer. 'I'm a bit knackered after all that. I mean I think we should give it a rest for a week. Who's this?'

'This is Daphne,' Mario said. 'She's all right.'

'Right,' another man said. 'We'll talk about that in a minute. I want to raise the issue of –' ironic voice – 'the actions of the heirs of Andreas Baader and the honourable victims of the class struggle.'

'If it was them,' someone else said.

'They've claimed responsibility,' the man said. 'I saw it on the television news tonight.'

'Who's claimed responsibility?'

'The Red Army Faction,' a girl at the end of the table said. 'I saw that tonight too.'

'Or what passes for the Red Army Faction these days.'

'What's happened?' a fresh-faced boy said. 'I've been in the woods for two weeks with my men's group. I haven't seen any papers at all.'

'Some members of the Red Army Faction –'

'Some people claiming to be Red Army Faction –'

'Some members of the Red Army Faction got into a

branch of a bank in Frankfurt and walked out with half a million Deutschmarks and quite a senior official of the bank, who happened to be paying a goodwill visit to that branch on the morning the Red Army Faction were also paying their visit.'

'What happened?'

'Got away. The fairly senior official got shot in the head and left by the side of the motorway three quarters of an hour later.'

'To the best of my knowledge,' Mario said, 'there is no reasonable grounds for doubting that anyone who claims to be the Red Army Faction really is the Red Army Faction. There only is one claimant to the title of Red Army Faction. I seem to remember we discuss the issue of the Red Army Faction and what attitude we ought to take to it every time anybody in Europe kills anyone.'

'Yes,' a man said. 'We do because it's an important issue.'

'Why is it an important issue?'

'Of course it's an important issue,' a girl said. 'They are killing people. We may not disapprove of them simply because they are killing people, because we may democratically consider that they are correct to kill people, but it is wrong to attempt to stifle debate within the group of the rightness of their actions simply because we have debated other actions of theirs on other occasions.'

'And have we debated the question of whether these supposed actions,' another, twitchily bearded man next to Mario said, 'are actually carried out by anyone who might be considered in any ideological sense the heirs of Raspe and Baader, or whether every murder has been carried out by the hired agents of the West German Government for the express purpose of discrediting the radical Left.'

'Yes,' someone said. 'We always debate that. That's your belief, and no one else ever thinks it could be true.'

'And I seem to remember,' Mario said, 'that we then go on to debate whether the acts of the supposed or real Red Army Faction could, indeed, be supposed to discredit anybody, or whether murdering international capitalists might in fact not be thought to enhance the prestige of the radical Left, but that debate usually collapses because nobody here actually thinks that. Unless Daphne does.'

They turned to Daphne.

'No,' she said. 'I don't think I do believe that.'

'Good,' Mario said. 'That shortens proceedings. Can we merely abbreviate the proceedings at this point, since democratic views on the actions of the RAF have been extensively displayed by every member of the group on previous occasions, and unless anybody believes that there was anything so very different about this murder and robbery –'

'Liberation of funds,' the bearded conspiracy theorist said.

'Or liberation of funds, according to taste, then could we all express a view on whether our assent should be cast behind this expression of the radical will, or whether we generally believe, as I do, that murdering and physical violence is an undesirable hangover from the violence trained into individuals by the capitalist system and we should have nothing to do with the Red Army Faction, no way.'

'Hold on,' the bearded conspiracy theorist said. 'I want a vote on whether we believe that the Red Army Faction actually exists, or whether we think the whole thing is mounted by the West German Government.'

'In a moment, Thomas,' Mario said. 'I seem to remember your position last time something like this happened was that the murder was carried out by the West German

Government in the name of the now defunct Red Army Faction, but that we should nevertheless throw our support behind the agents of the murder since the name of the Left should be in support of radical actions, whatever the intentions of the participants, and a bogus Red Army Faction is as good as a real RAF.'

'Yes,' Thomas said. 'That was my position, and I think it remains my position in the light of these events.'

There was an outbreak of tittering around the table.

'Very well then,' Thomas said. 'If no one will take my views seriously, I feel I have to leave this group.'

He got up and left the table, stalking out with all his dignity.

'People are always doing that,' Mario muttered to Daphne. 'It doesn't matter.'

'Will he be back?'

'Shouldn't have thought so. He'll probably go and form some absurd cheerleading group of his own now. Now –' Mario said, to the group generally. 'Supporters of the first view?'

Everyone raised their hand.

'Of the second?'

Nobody raised their hand.

'Right,' he said. 'This is Daphne.'

The agenda had, clearly, been progressed upon.

'Do you know what we're here for?' a man said.

Daphne composed her face into an expression, she hoped, of serious intensity, of political concern. She tried not to worry about scowling.

'You work against yuppies in Berlin,' she said.

'That's what we do,' the man said. 'But why? Why do you want to work against yuppies in Berlin?'

'I don't know,' Daphne said. 'You tell me.'

'No, I want to know why you yourself want things to change for yuppies here in Berlin.'

Everyone seemed to be looking at her. She concentrated on her sentences.

'I want,' she said slowly. 'I want Berlin to stay as it is for the people who've always lived here.'

'Yes,' Mario said. She hadn't thought that he might be there to test her correctness too. 'But why? Wouldn't it be better for the people who live here to get rich too, rather than just let a lot of rich kids from Hamburg get even richer?'

'No,' Daphne said. She went for naive charm. 'I don't really know the right vocabulary or anything. I mean, I don't know about economics or anything. But I think it's more complicated than that. The thing is, I think, if there are rich people there have got to be poor people too. There's never going to be a world where everybody's rich. You need to work against the structures of oppression – do you see what I mean? – and you need to give people their freedom without turning them into oppressors first.'

'Now we're talking,' the man said.

'Look,' the barman said. He had come up while Daphne was talking. 'You've been sitting here for two hours, and there's only one of you' – he pointed with disdain – 'who's drinking anything. I don't mind, and I wouldn't want to give you a hard time, but, you know, I've got to make a living. So what will you have?'

There was a cascade of fumbling round the table.

'Yes, okay,' Mario said. 'I'm skint, though.'

'And you come from East Germany,' the other man said.

'Yes,' Mario said. 'I come from East Germany.'

'And I'm skint too,' someone else said.

'Hey, look, I'll get this. I've just sold some textbooks back to the shop,' Daphne said, lying. She was thrilled at having made any kind of mark on them.

'Great,' the man said. The barman went off. 'So you understand that we're after a bit more than just wrecking some cunt's *brasserie*, that we're doing something a bit more serious than that. We think – we want to dismantle the structure of the late-capitalist system, and the structures of the West German State.'

'And the East German,' Mario said. He had his eyes closed, as if anticipating a sudden immersion in water.

'No, I don't accept that,' a girl cut in.

'What's your objection?'

'In the first place, we haven't struck against the East German state at all, and we haven't and don't plan to go over the Wall.'

'The oppression of the late-capitalist West German State –'

'It's always like this,' Mario said to Daphne. 'They always get into those pointless arguments about theory, as if that was all there was to get interested in. The thing is that if you grew up in the sorts of places I grew up in you get completely sick of all of this.'

'It's interesting,' Daphne said, not sure if Mario was seeing how committed she really was. 'I used to go to these groups when I was at school, but they were really kind of naive in a way. I mean, they were single issue groups, fighting against racism or boycotting South African goods or whatever.'

'Well, this lot can be quite naive too,' Mario said. 'Where do you live?'

'I'm living with my aunt,' Daphne said. 'She's got a nice flat in Charlottenburg and it doesn't cost me anything.'

'It's quite different, if you look at it from a psychological and political standpoint, the freedom of individual action in the Democratic Republic is quite in *excess*' – thumping the table – 'of that available to the subject in the Federal structures of oppression –'

'But you're forgetting the illusory nature of the, the essentially illusory nature of the State –'

'Precisely, that's what I'm *not* forgetting, that's the thing which in the Democratic Republic, the state apparatus in the East is acknowledged by the forcefulness of the machinery of oppression, I mean, it's so forceful it becomes absurd, it becomes something nobody could take seriously, none of its subjects, it becomes risible to its subjects, reducing, in the end, the meaning of the state through nothing more than over-statement, I mean –'

'I don't know how much more of this I can take,' Mario said. 'I just get really bored when they start debating how many angels can dance on the head of a pin.'

'I don't really know,' Daphne said. 'I'm not sure I'm really following. When that man walked out –'

'An idiot.'

'Yes, I thought he was an idiot,' Daphne said. 'But I didn't like to say.'

'Are you saying,' someone at the far end was shouting, 'the Democratic Republic is in essence, in some sense an anarchist state?'

'*In potentia.*'

'*Ab ovo.*'

Daphne looked at Mario, leaning back and shutting his eyes, not listening to any of this, to the opinions around him, which all seemed to be agreeing, despite the forceful-ness which made their conversation so resemble a violent argument. What they seemed to be saying was that the

DDR was bloody awful and the Federal Republic and West Berlin were even worse. There was a small pause as two dark excitable men at either end of the table produced their Latin tags. The beers arrived. She wondered how familiar these opinions, or rather these statements of opinions, were to everybody around the table apart from her.

'You're all talking,' Mario said in a measured way, and turning from Daphne to the whole group, 'about things you don't know anything about. When, for instance, did any of you last go over the fence into the DDR?'

'Last week,' a girl said triumphally. 'I had to buy some books.'

'And where did you go?'

'There's a shop just off the Friedrichstrasse I go to.'

'Unter den Linden. A showpiece for tourists. I repeat. You're all talking about things you know nothing about. When did any of you last go to the DDR? When have any of you even thought about living in the DDR?'

'Don't you think,' one of the excitable men said, 'that the essential absurdity of the state apparatus is more sharply revealed to its subjects by the excess of the East German state machinery, don't you think the East German state more accurately and inevitably predicts its own inevitable demise?'

'No,' Mario said. 'Fuck off.' He was not the leader here, Daphne saw, but he carried an unusual and unquestioned authority. The nearest to a leader, in this ideologically unled grouping, was the man who had so ferociously quizzed her. But it was obvious that Mario's obviously East German name and his excitingly-hinted-at sufferings on the other side of the border – not to mention his amazing looks – gave him a secondary authority which the others wouldn't quibble with or think of challenging. 'Do we all agree that we can stop talking about all this crap and start discussing next week's direct action now?'

The others barely glanced at Daphne; there was a general sense of imperceptible nodding.

'Right,' Mario said. 'Let's get down to business.'

That had been two and a half years ago. It was in this way that Sunday nights became Daphne's nights for Class War.

Her aunt always looked forward to Daphne's Sundays, because she had a bit of peace and quiet for the TV – not that Daphne wasn't a nice girl. And whatever she got up to, Daphne always got home in time for *Derek*. They had a cosy, two-year long argument about *Derek*. Daphne swore blind it was a German series; her aunt always agreed in the end, but privately carried on thinking it was actually an American series, made in America with German actors. But they both liked it.

THREE LIES

Pierre Stifter had the knowledge. He knew so many things. He had the knowledge – of course he did. He knew that the paintings of the reign of Jahangir were to be preferred to those of the reign of his son Shah-Jahan. He could tell you the names of ten alchemists from the court of Rudolf II. He could recount without repetition, correction or giggling the plot of *Flegeljahre*. He had heard of Henry Green and had read *Green Henry*. He knew that Pope Alexander VI thought that he was descended from the Egyptian god Osiris in a direct line. He knew that Wagner was only inspired when he stroked silk and Schiller when he was sniffing rotten apples. He knew what the octatonic scale was and what sfumato was and how to say hello, goodbye, thank you, no thank you and fuck right off in English, French, German, Italian, Spanish, Portuguese, Czech, Polish and for some reason Arabic. And yet he was standing serving drinks at the gallery and rolling his eyes at the people, the utter unutterable low-life white-trash riff-raff who had managed to get themselves into the private view this time and wondering what on earth had led him to this pass, facing Friedrich, and trying to dredge up some part of his knowledge which would help him to deal with Friedrich.

Friedrich, too, knew so many things. But Friedrich's knowledge, though perhaps more immediately useful, was less likely to be classified by him or Pierre Stifter or anyone else in the white cavernous halls of the State Gallery as knowledge at all. He knew how you could make money out of strangers in bars armed with two dice or a pack of cards. He knew the sorts of sentences girls said (*No one's ever made me feel like this before, how can you bear to live like this, don't you think you've drunk enough*) which ought to make you think about not seeing so much of them. He knew the hot places you could go to on holiday which balanced maximum cheapness with acceptable levels of squalor and degradation. He knew how you got drunk quicker if you wanted to or stayed sober longer. He knew which drugs were basically all right and which would basically fuck you up. He knew to a minute the times of the month when the inspectors descended on the public transport system. He knew the streets and he knew his way around. But it was unlikely that any part of his knowledge was going to equip him with the way to respond to a fresh-faced and floppily bewildered blond boy at a state-funded piss-up at the state art gallery to which he had not been invited. The two of them faced each other, making small twitching motions with their hands; they might have been brought together by Peter Picker, a man whose knowledge extended to many things, many things unknown or suspected by other people. But, by now, Picker was on the other side of the room, his fat back presented to the company, and was no help.

An hour before, Friedrich had found himself in front of a blank-faced short apartment building. It was in a part of town somehow between districts; technically it must belong to a quarter, must be Schöneberg or Charlottenburg, but had no feeling of locality. It was on a quiet road off a busy road, heavily lined with trees, and anonymous; its name was not one he recognized, and it could not, he felt, convincingly claim to belong to anywhere in particular. It was a place from the first sentence of a Russian novel, specifying nothing except the millenium in which it existed: *Our hero lived on the —— strasse, in the —— district of the town of ——, in the year 1——*. He walked up to the door, and before he could press Picker's button, the door buzzed open. He had been observed approaching, and Picker had buzzed him in without waiting for him to announce himself. Just as eagerly, he was standing at the door of his flat when Friedrich reached the landing.

'Come in,' he said. 'We won't stay long.'

'I had a bit of difficulty finding the road,' Friedrich said. 'It wasn't a road I knew.'

Picker nodded, and motioned Friedrich into the sitting room. The flat seemed more or less entirely without character. There were no books or records to be seen, and the few pathetically small pictures on the wall, the occasional anonymously abstract stone objects (all fist-sized, none, quite, raising themselves from the status of ornaments to something which might be regarded as sculpture) did nothing to suggest that anyone lived or had ever lived here. In the corner of the sitting room there was a large grey filing cabinet. There was something unchosen about the flat and its surroundings, as if acquired and decorated without reference to anyone's personal taste.

As he went into the room, Friedrich's legs were suddenly battered from behind. He turned in half-alarm, and there was a small boy, blond and pyjamaed.

'Oh, he ought to be in bed,' Picker said. 'I put him to bed half an hour ago.' He spoke to the child in English. The child looked back, interested. 'He's got to the age where he likes new people.'

'Most children are too shy,' Friedrich said. 'They always want to hide behind a chair for the first half an hour.'

'Yes,' Picker agreed. 'Not this one, though.'

'Music man,' the child seemed to say.

'What did he say?' Friedrich said.

'He asked who you were,' Picker said. He said something to the boy, who looked seriously at Picker for a moment and then replied.

'What's his name?' Friedrich said.

'Tom,' Picker said. 'I'm sorry about this, but he wants to tell you his joke. I would explain to him that you don't understand English, but it would be quicker if you just listened, all in all. He's just learnt his first joke, and I don't think he understands it, because he always gets it wrong, but he knows it's a joke, and he wants to tell everyone he meets. Do you mind?'

'No, not at all,' Friedrich said. 'Fire away, Tom.'

Picker said something to the boy. The boy concentrated for a moment, then produced, with a miniature stagey air, a sentence.

'Now you say,' Picker said, '*I don't know*, in English, so he understands.'

'Doesn't he speak German?'

'No,' Picker said. 'Just say, *I don't know.*'

Friedrich did his best. The boy said something else, then looked at Friedrich nervously, waiting a response.

'It would be good if you laughed,' Picker said.

Friedrich tried to laugh; it came out wrong. 'Very good,' he said, loudly. 'That was very funny.' Then he ruffled the boy's hair, as adults are supposed to with children. The boy looked at him, almost horrified, then turned and ran away into another room, tottering as he went.

'What was the joke?' Friedrich said.

'Oh, it's too hard,' Picker said. 'It only really works in English, it's a very bad pun. I don't think he understands it at all. Literally, in German, you say, *Why are there no aspirins in the jungle*, and the other person says, *I don't know*, and the other one says, *Because they are all eaten by the parrots*. But in English the phrase for *all eaten by the parrots* sounds like the name of a painkiller, like this, *parrots eat them all, paracetamol*. I'm sorry, it's a very bad joke, but he knows it's a joke, and he knows jokes are funny, so he insists on telling everyone just now.'

'Your English sense of humour,' Friedrich said.

'Perhaps,' Picker said. He was looking at the door through which Tom had gone, not listening to Friedrich; when he turned back, his face was lit with pleasure and happiness, a pleasure so full that it was as if Friedrich had ignited it, and not that he, a mere bystander, was splashed by the happiness which existed between Picker and his boy. Picker was changed by the proximity of the child, his shell for the moment was gone like an egg's, broken. 'We'll be back by eleven,' he called. 'Is that all right? The baby-sitter,' he confided to Friedrich.

There was a small noise of assent from behind the kitchen's half-open door. Friedrich had an impression of big blonde hair.

'Let's go,' Picker said.

They were in the taxi before Picker said anything.

'You must be surprised that I have a son,' he said.

'No, not especially,' Friedrich said. 'Although I don't remember you mentioning him.'

'I must strike you as an unlikely person to have a son, that's all,' Picker said.

'No,' Friedrich said. 'Not really. And his mother?'

'She's in England,' Picker said. 'We don't talk. It was a mistake. We never married or anything. It was just once and afterwards she couldn't cope with Tom so she gave him to me. I never see her. The thing is –'

'Yes?' Friedrich said.

'The thing is that I was always a homosexual before, and I was always a homosexual afterwards, and it was only the once, and it was really, all in all, very bad luck. I hope you don't mind me telling you all this. Some people are embarrassed, but I think it's important to be honest.'

'But you don't mind having a child, I suppose.'

'No,' Picker said, amazed. 'Of course not. When I say very bad luck, I just mean it never occurred to me that you could make a woman pregnant with just one go. Anyway, that's why I thought you would be surprised that I had a son.'

'No,' Friedrich said. 'I didn't think that you might be a homosexual. I didn't give it any thought, to be honest.'

'And you?'

'And me?'

'Are you homosexual?'

'No.'

'Ah,' Picker said. 'Here we are. Can you get this?'

He was out of the taxi and up the steps of the State Gallery before Friedrich could object. It had not been far from Picker's flat to the gallery, and it was not much money; still, Friedrich hadn't thought that he was going to have to pay for the ride. It took a couple of minutes ransacking of his pockets before he came up with the seven marks, and by the time he had paid and got out of the taxi,

Picker was inside the gallery and nowhere to be seen, and Friedrich found himself confronting a floppily bewildered and fresh-faced blond boy, a functionary of the gallery, at the entrance, and wondering what part of his knowledge was going to equip him with the way to respond to him.

'Hello,' the boy said.

'Hello,' Friedrich said.

'Can I introduce you to anyone?' the boy said.

'Sure,' Friedrich said. The boy looked at him expectantly. 'And you are?'

'And I am?' Friedrich said.

'I'm sorry?' the boy said.

'I thought you were saying something.'

'No,' he said. 'I was asking you who you were, actually, but it doesn't matter awfully if you *absolutely* don't want to tell me.'

'No,' Friedrich said. 'I'm a friend of Peter Picker. I came with him, but he got in before I could.'

'I don't know your name, though,' the boy said.

'And I don't know yours,' Friedrich said in what seemed, just then, the peak of wit.

'I'm Pierre Stifter,' he said. 'And who are you?'

'Friedrich Kaiser,' Friedrich said. 'Peter Picker brought me. Is there a problem?'

'No, plenty of room,' Pierre said. 'Not so sure about there being enough to drink, but, frankly, what can you do with the budget we have to struggle along with? Sorry, your name – Friedrich?'

'Kaiser.'

'Kaiser?'

'Kaiser.'

'Well, as I was saying, can I introduce you to anyone?' Pierre said, flapping his hands a little. 'Or do you just want to talk to Peter Picker? I'd *quite* understand. Have you met Mme Fitelberg?'

'Is she the painter?'

'The painter – you mean –' Pierre gestured at the walls – '*this* painter? No, no,' he said, evidently a little shocked. 'Don't you know whose *vernissage* you've come to, even? He's coming along a little later. No, Mme Fitelberg's the author. You know, Solange Fitelberg the author. *Brothers*. She's French, very successful over here, novel about a pair of brothers, one German, one French, separated in the Second World War, one ends up in a concentration camp, the other becomes a Nazi general, you know the sort of thing, the tragedy of France, the tragedy of Germany, an IQ like her size of *brassière* and her book's as thick as your wrist. Terribly good, everyone says, though frankly I wouldn't know.'

He gestured in the direction of an immensely tall woman, yellow as parchment, her smoke-stained hair and face and hands, the only smoker in the small gawping crowd around her. A faint feeling of dread came over Friedrich at the mention of France, a feeling he could not quite pin down, until Picker's returning form reminded him that he had claimed, while sitting in Picker's car, to speak very good French indeed; a lie which had at the time seemed unlikely to be tested. He put it from his mind.

'I've never heard of her,' Friedrich said. 'And now you're wondering –'

'Have a drink,' Pierre said.

'Thank you, I will,' Friedrich said. 'But you're wondering how I happen to be here since I've no idea who anybody is here or who even the painter who the party's for or anything much at all, and I'm obviously not the usual sort of person you get at this sort of thing, and I'm probably not on the list, or anything –'

'Well, heavens, don't mind *that*, don't let me put you off or anything, and, you know, the more the merrier, and, in any case, didn't you say Peter Picker brought you?'

'Well, there is that,' Friedrich said. 'Did I say that?'

'Yes, you did,' Pierre said. 'And here he is.'

Pierre performed an intricate manoeuvre, something like a figure of eight in a dance, leaving one partner behind, twisting adroitly round a new partner and, immediately, was halfway across the gallery; it was a pleasure to be the victim of the ordinary party-ditching when it was carried out with such a flourish. The ordinary accepted semi-rudeness, in the hands of this slick boy, was like a tactful withdrawal; and with a shiveringly emphatic, hardly observed running of the finger down Friedrich's right arm, he seemed not to leave him with Picker, but to produce him like an impresario pulling back a curtain.

'Oh, I'm sorry,' Picker said. 'I thought you were just behind me, and then I look round and I have to come and rescue you. Was that man just giving you a hard time?'

'No, not at all,' Friedrich said. 'Do you know him?'

'I don't think so,' Picker said.

'He knows you,' Friedrich said. 'What's this all for?'

'Some painter,' Picker said. 'Do you want to have a look at the paintings? I don't know anything about him. They send me invitations all the time; it's just that I got on a list a year or two back and now I quite like coming to them. Of course, I know very little about painting, and I was trying to make head or tail of these, without a lot of success. I don't mean to say that my three-year-old son could do them, as people are said to say about painting, or that it wouldn't matter whether they're hung upside down or the right way up. But I don't know what they're all about.'

'Well, let's walk round and have a look,' Friedrich said.

They began to walk round. 'I quite like that. This one's not so nice. What's that painted on? Do you know, I think it's painted on bubble-wrap – you know that stuff?'

'I wish you hadn't said that,' Friedrich said. 'I want to start popping the bubbles now.'

'Yes, rather irresistible,' Picker said. 'So, Herr Kaiser.'

'Yes,' Friedrich said, wondering what on earth they were going to talk about for the rest of the evening.

'So, you live in Kreuzberg,' Picker said. 'You see, I remember.'

'As I see,' Friedrich said. 'Perhaps some time you ought to find your way there.'

'Perhaps during daylight,' Picker said, taking what Friedrich said seriously. 'I haven't been to Kreuzberg. I don't know.'

'It's full of danger and excitement,' Friedrich said.

'That's what people say,' Picker said. 'Of course, I wouldn't go to somewhere where I don't know exactly what to expect. It's odd in another way that I haven't been there, because, you know, I like to travel, to go round in Berlin, at the weekends. It's interesting. Thank you.'

'Yes, thank you,' Friedrich said, as they both swapped their empty glasses for full ones from the waiter. 'Cheers.'

'I've been to most of Berlin now,' Picker said. 'Last weekend, for instance, I went to a place called Lübars. It's this village, very quiet, exactly next to the Wall, but a long way in the opposite direction to here. It's almost tucked away in this tiny little dip, quite invisible until you get right to it. And then you come out from this farm, with a blacksmith's, into a field, but then, golly, there's the Wall, in the middle of a field, just cutting directly across it.'

'I've never heard of it,' Friedrich said. He knew the place; it was a done-up mock village where American soldiers went on Sunday afternoons and sat at café tables with bowls of whipped cream and looked at what was probably the only horse in Berlin outside the zoo, morosely plodding up and down for their benefit.

'Look at that,' Picker said. 'What do you think that's all about?'

Friedrich looked at the label. 'It's called *Paganini*,' he said. It was a long canvas, painted on some sort of pre-printed cheap curtain material; at one side, a black and extravagantly horned devil was playing the violin. At the left, a skeleton in a clown's outfit was juggling, juggling with skulls which, in the fountain of his circus ability, turned back into the nuclear symbol, turned back into the swastika. 'I don't know, really,' he said.

'I don't know about painting at all,' Picker said. 'But sometimes I like to look at it.'

'Do you like to look at this?'

'I don't know,' Picker said. 'Is the painter here?'

'That boy –' Friedrich jerked his head leftwards – 'said he was coming later. If you want to meet him.'

'I've got a sort of ambition,' Picker said. 'Not about painting. About Berlin. I'd like to walk round the Wall.'

'A lot of people want to do that, I suppose,' Friedrich said. They carried on walking.

'No,' Picker said. 'I don't mean that. I mean I want to circumnavigate it – is that right? I want to walk round the whole of the inside of the Wall, keeping it on my right hand all the way round, walking round clockwise.'

'Of course,' Friedrich said. 'If you kept it on your right

hand and walked round clockwise, you'd be walking backwards. Which would be a sort of record, I suppose.'

'Keeping it on my left hand, then,' Picker said. 'I've never heard of anyone doing it. I don't know why.'

'Probably because it must be two hundred kilometres round,' Friedrich said. 'Maybe not quite so much. But it's a big place, Berlin, you know, even cut in two.'

'Having a lovely time?' Pierre said, coming up with a bewildered short dark boy in tow. 'Another drink? Would you like some food? It's gorgeous food, they've been up *all* night stuffing prawns, and nobody's touching it at all, can't think why.'

At the back of the room a large dark wooden table, densely polished, somehow as incongruous as the cigarette smoke in this gallery, was laid with food. Two whole salmon, bowls of salad, bread, cheese, cold roast game, sides of beef, none of which had been started.

'No thank you,' Picker said, stiffening slightly, but taking both the glasses of wine Pierre was offering.

'Maybe later,' Friedrich said. 'No, don't go – oh, too late.'

Pierre had swished off already.

'Of course,' Picker said. 'It must be a long way round, the Wall. I'd thought of that. I wasn't thinking of doing it in one go. Just a bit every weekend, maybe spending the whole summer doing it.'

Friedrich regarded him with equanimity, contemplating the idea of an out-of-breath Picker returning from his sweating fifteen-kilometre Sunday segment, getting out the map and drawing another line along the line of the Wall. He wondered why anyone would want to do such a thing.

'Why?'

'Because it's too big to do in one go,' Picker said.

'No,' Friedrich said. 'I meant, why do it at all?'

'Don't you think it would be interesting?'

'No,' Friedrich said. 'Most of it would be the Wall on one side and some scruffy bit of land on the other. There are more interesting things in Berlin than the Wall.'

'Maybe,' Picker said, thinking. 'Maybe this thing about Berlin is that there aren't any cities with walls round them. I mean, there used to be – in the Middle Ages cities always had walls. But now only Berlin has. Has a proper wall. There's something really interesting about a city that can't grow at all, beyond this Wall. And if it grows at all, it's going to grow in ways the Wall makes it grow.'

'Or stops it growing,' Friedrich said, looking round to see if there was anyone else here he knew. It seemed unlikely. 'There are nicer places to walk, and at the end, you wouldn't have got anywhere. You'd just be back where you started.'

'But you can't go anywhere in Berlin,' Picker said. 'You always end up banging into the Wall.'

'Have you been to the East?'

Picker shook his head.

'Haven't you been to Potsdam?'

'No,' Picker said. 'I never have. I once went over the Wall, but I just went to Unter den Linden and looked at the embassies. I thought it was really scary.'

'They want you to think that,' Friedrich said. 'It's not particularly scary.'

'It's not very adventurous of me,' Picker said. 'I just hate the idea of the East, and all those people living like that.'

'That's not much of a reason not to go.'

'Perhaps it isn't,' Picker said. 'You know, if you come from outside Germany, it's really striking that all the intelligent people in the West are always running down the

West and praising the East, though it's obvious to everybody that the difference between the East and the West is that the West more or less works and the East more or less doesn't. I wrote an article – well, more than one article – saying this, and I sent it to all the papers, offering it to them, but none of them would print it. I'll show you the article some time, it's just taking pot shots at all these intellectuals, sitting in the West in comfort and saying that the East is a much better sort of society though of course they wouldn't go and live there. And it was a good article but no Western newspaper would print something like that, even though it's obviously true.' Picker seemed to recall himself. 'Do you go?'

'From time to time,' Friedrich said. 'It's not all that bad. It's expensive to go, of course, having to change twenty-five marks every time, and you can't spend twenty-five Ostmarks if you spend the whole day trying. I had a bet once with a friend that we couldn't drink our way through twenty-five marks' worth of beer.'

'What happened?'

'We had to give up. We were just too drunk and they wouldn't serve us any more. Never been to Potsdam, either. It's supposed to be nice, but it's a bit complicated getting there, because the transport's so terrible.'

'I hate it,' Picker said. 'I really do. If I could do anything to get rid of a country like that, change it, I would.'

'What do you hate more?' Friedrich said. 'The Western intellectuals or the Eastern authorities? Neither of them are very easy to change.'

'Well, I would change the East if I could,' Picker said. 'I really would. I just don't think it's very practicable. But I really would get rid of it. I think it's absolutely loathsome, and I don't know why nobody ever says how detestable it is that half of Europe should have to live in such a way.'

'But you can't,' Friedrich said, faintly alarmed at Picker's enthusiastic tone. 'You can't get rid of it, just like that. So relax. It's all for the best. Things happen or they don't happen. Nothing's going to change whatever we think about it.'

'I don't believe that,' Picker said. 'I don't believe in the idea that things happen because of invisible forces. I don't believe in historical inevitability. I think I could change the course of history single-handedly if I chose to.'

Friedrich looked at Picker, seriously worried. Then Picker abruptly boggled his eyes in a comic face. There was no humour Friedrich could see in what Picker said, no reason for Picker's disconcerting lapses into merriment, and Friedrich shrank from him involuntarily. It was as baffling as Picker's son's joke.

'So,' Picker said eventually. 'Do you have a job?'

'Yes,' Friedrich said. 'I work in a bookshop. A few afternoons a week.'

'That can't pay very well.'

'It pays the rent, and it buys me enough to drink at least. Yes, thank you,' Friedrich said to a passing waiter, removing two glasses of wine and giving one to Picker.

'Oh – yes, thank you,' Picker said, swallowing what was left in the glass he held. 'And food?'

'Well, beer is food,' Friedrich said. 'And do you have a job?'

'Not really,' Picker said. 'Or in a manner of speaking. I'm self-employed. I gather and reap. I plan things and see what happens. I'm interested in political situations. I might write something one day. Or I might try to change things. You never know. I told you I wrote an article. I'd really like that, to break into journalism or to write pieces about my opinion about things, that would be really good. But I don't think I stand much chance, because all the newspapers here are in the grip of this liberal consensus, and they none of them have any time for anyone saying what's obviously true, that West Germany works and that East Germany doesn't.' He suddenly seemed to shrink; Friedrich wondered, afterwards, what remembered rebuke made him add, 'At least, that's my opinion.'

'I see,' Friedrich said. 'I'm not sure that there really is a conspiracy, or anything. You quite often read these general sorts of attacks on the DDR. You want to work here in Berlin?'

'Where else?'

'Where else.'

'I come from England,' Picker said, placidly, as if continuing a conversation. 'I've never lived abroad before, only now, in Germany. I never thought I would live abroad, actually. I always thought I'd live the rest of my life in England.'

'And,' Friedrich said, 'you speak German well, I think.'

'I do,' Picker said, not acknowledging the compliment. 'I think I do. I learnt it at school, and I liked it, and I carried on. I had conversations with a man, three times a week, conversation lessons, for five years, and every holiday I had, I came to Germany. But always the West, never the East. I don't think I would like the East very much. I went to Cologne at Christmas and the New Year. I like to travel. Oh, of course, you know I was in Cologne, I drove you back. What do you think of this?'

'I don't know,' Friedrich said. It was an almost blank white canvas; the upper right-hand corner had been filled in with a black triangle. At the bottom, in a careful imitation of old-fashioned typewriter print, was written 'The higher powers commanded; paint the upper right corner black!'

'Nor me,' Picker said.

'Maybe that people are always under instructions from something else,' Friedrich said.

'Or maybe it's supposed to be funny,' Picker said.

'It depends whether you think the higher powers really told him to paint something black,' Friedrich said.

'Or rather,' Picker said, 'if he had the willpower to choose to resist the invitation and put his paint where he chose.'

'Maybe,' Friedrich said. 'You ought to go to the East.'

'I don't really want to,' Picker said. 'I just think –'

'Well, it's much the same as it is here,' Friedrich said, his attention drawn by a smiling blonde waitress. He wondered whether everybody else here knew each other, or whether, like he and Picker, they were all condemned to go on talking to the people they came with.

'Much the same?'

'Pretty much.'

'But how can you say that? How can it be?'

'Well, it is,' Friedrich said. 'How can you doubt it, since you haven't been?'

'I don't need to go' – he took a swig of wine – 'to know how wrong it is.'

'What's wrong?'

'East Germany. The DDR. It's gone wrong. It never was going to be right, but it's certainly wrong now. It won't last.'

'It's lasting quite well so far.'

'So far,' Picker said. 'It can't go on. It's too *wrong*.'

'I thought you didn't believe in historical inevitability.'

'I don't. That's not believing in historical inevitability. It's just thinking that frankly most people wouldn't put up with that indefinitely. Sooner or later people are going to get fed up when they realize what they're missing. That's not invisible forces. That's just knowing what people are like. They want what they can't have.'

'If they want things they can't have,' Friedrich said slowly, 'why can't they want it in the West just as well as in the East?'

'Oh,' Picker said. 'If you're going to make fun of me I won't go on.' Friedrich looked at him; he hadn't noticed that Picker was losing his temper.

'Come on,' Friedrich said. 'You haven't been there.'

'No,' Picker said, regaining his pale colour. 'You don't need to go to prison to know about crime.'

'It's not like going to prison,' Friedrich said. 'Not much. And it's not exactly a crime.'

'The way you talk,' Picker said, 'anyone would think you didn't care about East Germany.'

'Care?' Friedrich said. 'I don't think much about it. They seem to do all right on their side of the Wall and we seem to do all right on our side. If they were really bothered about the way they were ruled, they'd have a revolution or something. There are plenty of East Germans. They only need to band together.'

'They need some kind of incentive,' Picker said. 'That's all. What things do they have to care about, to get bothered about? The truth is, they don't really know about freedom. They don't know about ordinary things like what it's like to go on holiday wherever you like or whenever you like, or getting drunk in the street –'

'Well, you certainly haven't been to the DDR,' Friedrich said. 'That's one thing they're the world experts in.'

'– or sex –'

'Well –'

'– or good food, or having a choice of cars, or a choice of washing powder, or – isn't it better to have –' Picker gestured extravagantly, knocking a man, who was just passing, and sending a glass of red wine down his shirt front – 'I'm so sorry, excuse me, isn't it better to have fifty paintings rather than two?'

It was a rhetorical question, but Friedrich still took a moment to look, eyebrow raised, around the gallery.

'Or in any case,' Picker said, ignoring the victim of his semaphoring and his viciously dabbing companion, 'if there are fifty washing powders, the washing powder will be better, and it will be cheaper, because of the competition. The best of fifty washing powders will be better than the better of two washing powders.' He was patient and careful as if explaining something to an idiot or to a child. 'Of course, it never would get to that point, because there wouldn't be enough call for fifty different washing powders, but if someone wants to chance their arm – sorry, I'm wandering off the point. But you see – but they would be happier if they could choose whatever washing powder they liked, rather than have the government decide for them.'

'So, instead of the government, there would be great big soap powder manufacturers who decided on their behalf what washing powder they could have.'

'Yes,' Picker said. 'Maybe.' Then he threw back his head and roared with laughter. The people around them looked round, staring at the head-back fat man, roaring like a hippopotamus. 'Here we are, a pair of homosexuals, nothing better to talk about than washing powder.'

'I'm not homosexual,' Friedrich said. 'I said I wasn't

homosexual. And I didn't think we were talking about washing powder, not just about washing powder. I don't have any views on washing powder.'

'No, you're right,' Picker said, unabashed. 'I'm sorry. I forgot. We weren't talking just about washing powder. It's really about pleasure, which we have and they don't.'

'Are you having a lovely time?' Pierre said, coming up with two more glasses of wine and without the bewildered boy he had been with earlier.

'Oh, yes,' Friedrich said. He wanted to go.

'And have you met *Madame*?'

'No,' Friedrich said. 'We've just been talking here.'

'Do you want to meet her?'

'Who is *Madame*?' Picker said, raising his eyebrows in his heavy manner.

'A French novelist,' Pierre said, 'terribly good, awfully nice.'

'I don't speak very good French –' Picker said, shrugging regretfully, as if it were only his lack of French which would make him less than an ideal interlocutor for the novelist.

'She speaks German,' Pierre said.

'– though of course Friedrich here speaks French very well,' he went on. 'Don't you?'

'That would be lovely,' Pierre said. 'I'll drag you over in a minute. She's being charming tonight, considering what an old bag people always say she is. I can't think where he's got to, the painter. He's definitely coming, he promised me he would – or rather his secretary promised me, or rather promised someone who I share an office with – that he'd be here by now. I can't think why. Still, it makes the party nice and thrilling, him not being here. Can't you just sniff the excitement, the anticipation, everyone just twitching by the door, waiting for him to walk through it?'

They said nothing.

'Oh, I'm interrupting,' Pierre said. 'I'll be back.'

Picker walked over to a painting and examined it from a few centimetres away. Friedrich watched him dispassionately, never having quite understood why people ever wanted to do this. Watching him stand there, bending in towards the half-reflecting surface of the canvas and the paint, looking at his sausagey rolls of fat pressing against the side of his pale grey jacket, the damp patches of sweat which plastered down the dull-dyed black strings of hair, like dried blood, on to his pink scalp, Friedrich wondered where such a man could have come from and how he had failed to notice how little he resembled anyone else on the planet, and why he had failed to do something about it. He wondered why Picker had called him up and asked him out; he would not consider the line, which still hung in the wondering air of the now crowded gallery, just now turning away from him; a line which suggested not only that Picker was homosexual but that he didn't believe Friedrich wasn't homosexual too. What unspeakable things Picker might want from him, or want to do to him, were thoughts he would not entertain. Then he wondered, more or less simultaneously, what he was doing standing here with him, and what else he could be doing instead.

'Where do you come from?' Friedrich said when Picker came back. He asked this as a way to encapsulate, inadequately, all his concerns.

'Palmers Green,' Picker said.

'I don't know it,' Friedrich said. 'In England?'

'Yes,' Picker said. 'In London. Do you know London? I try to forget all about it. Everything good that's ever happened to me has happened to me since I left England. I never speak English now. Or only to Tom, my boy, you know. I wouldn't be able to live as I do if I lived in England, my life wouldn't be half as interesting. You know, I was one of those people who never had much in the way of friends when I was a child. I thought I had friends at the time. But now I know they weren't really friends of mine because I know if I met them now I'd have nothing to say to them.'

'Nobody ever has anything to say to friends they had when they were children,' Friedrich said. 'Were you always fat?'

'If you think you could call me fat,' Picker said stiffly. 'But all the real friends I have now I've made since I came here. I've just come to understand how the world works. I suppose that's it. That's what I do. I'm trying to understand how the world works. And I've met people and I want to meet more people who I think understand how the world works. And how things change. That as well.'

'Were you always homosexual? Apart from the once?'

'Always,' Picker said. 'I'm just going to the loo.'

Friedrich watched him go, and let the thought slide into his mind that this was the perfect opportunity to leave. He stood there, swaying slightly, enjoying the thought; and, instead of acting on it, he set off on a tour of the room. Circling the pictures, he found he could not look at them; he just read the titles, and that was oddly enough. Small groups got out of his way, looking at him with more intensity than he thought he deserved. It was hard to know how people knew he was drunk. Sentences came to him, as if floating over the tranquil pond of heads, rippling through the rich and brilliant light of the gallery; *it's the texture of the paint, I saw him in Kassel last year, they're spending all their time in.* All spoken, all disappearing, not recorded, not remembered, not, sometimes, even heard, except by him. He found the thought intensely sad; he found the thought, which came to him, that there were millions of people outside the gallery who would never hear any of these comments, millions of people, even in this city, who would never know that such an event as this party had even taken place, even sadder. And then he was face to face with his new friend Pierre, who seemed to have his hand down the back of a startled boy's trousers. He widened his grin at Friedrich, the grin of a conspirator whose plot is about to come to fruition.

'Have a drink,' Pierre said eventually, withdrawing his hand and modifying his smile as the boy took the opportunity to escape. 'Go on, do.'

'Thank you,' Friedrich enunciated. 'I think I will.'

Friedrich found it almost incredible that he was in the grim position of being the only person hopelessly drunk at a party at the state art gallery at not much beyond ten o'clock in the evening. Ten o'clock, and taking another drink off some feyly fresh-faced boy, so fresh-faced and twinkly it made you wince like toothache just to look at him. It was the time when, normally, he would be just stretching and thinking about whether to go out or stay in and contemplate his horrible flat. He blamed Peter Picker, personally.

'I blame you, personally,' he said, in the general direction of Picker, standing with two glasses of wine, looking about him for Friedrich; a shaven-headed woman of remarkable knock-kneed thinness, who was apparently about to address a remark to Friedrich, walked away instead, recoiling from the unsolicited rudeness, alarmed, or perhaps only revolted at Friedrich's drinker's dog's-breath.

'You blame me?' Pierre said.

'No,' Friedrich said. 'I was thinking aloud. Don't you think, if you thought about it, that Peter Picker is quite appallingly fat?'

Pierre brightened. 'Our Herr Picker? Would you call him fat?'

'I don't know another word for it,' Friedrich said.

'Splendid fellow, Herr Picker,' Pierre said. 'Appallingly lecherous of course, and *those clothes*, though I see there is an argument for saying it's not the clothes but what's inside them, but a splendid fellow, and what he does all day long but troll around trying to pick up boys I really don't know. Still, it's lovely of you to come out with him. How did you get hitched up with him?'

'He drove me from Cologne to Berlin at the New Year,' Friedrich said, foreseeing he was going to have to repeat the explanation soon, and probably have to repeat it at regular intervals until the end of his life. 'Did you know he had a son?'

'Don't be absurd,' Pierre said. 'Is that what he told you, about some nineteen-year-old he was holding hands with on the Kurfurstendamm?'

'Not exactly,' Friedrich said. 'And what's he doing here?'

'Well, what are you doing here, if it comes to that?' Pierre said, putting his hand in the small of Friedrich's back. 'As far as I know, he's someone who lives in Berlin that's managed to get himself on various lists for parties and turns up at openings and anything remotely official regular as clockwork. Never seems to know anybody, apart from me, though I'm always introducing him to people, but every now and again he has some very attractive young man in tow. His *son*, indeed. Of course, it's not difficult to get yourself on to all the lists if you're foreign, vaguely presentable,

accent on vaguely, don't mind turning out in all weathers.
He told me once he goes every single morning to the English
library and reads all the English and the German newspapers, and makes photocopies of absolutely anything that
interests him. Mad as a house. But if you didn't have people
to your *vernissage* just because they were mad you'd soon
have no party at all and now I come to think of it if you
didn't use people because they were mad you wouldn't have
any artists to show either. God knows where this painter's
got to. Come and meet Madame Fitelberg.'

Sinkingly, Friedrich allowed himself to be pushed forward by Pierre towards the tall smoke-yellowed French
woman. She had been engaged in intense conversation by
Picker. Her mouth kept falling half-open, as if to make
some point or objection which never quite arrived; her
eyes flapped desperately from side to side. The small and
diminishing crowd were nodding in that unsynchronized
and nervous way people have just before they find they
have to go and get another drink. Friedrich was quite
suddenly there and Pierre, again, gone.

'– a charming sort of village,' Picker was saying, 'with a
very remote feel, but bang up against the – oh, Friedrich,
hello – a young friend, *un jeune ami de moi*, Friedrich –'

The crowd, and the woman writer, had, in the moment
of Picker's turning to Friedrich, taken their unwitting cue
and opportunistically dashed for safety; Friedrich and
Picker were left alone.

'Ah, Friedrich,' Picker said, unabashed, as if he hadn't
seen him for days. 'An agreeable woman, that. A writer,
apparently.'

'Yes,' Friedrich said. He was overcome with relief. 'She's
called Solange Fitelberg.'

'Is she famous?' Picker said. 'I haven't actually heard of

her myself – I was just saying to her, do you know, I haven't read any of your books – but I dare say that's probably my fault. But an agreeable woman, very agreeable and interesting. Perhaps now I will read her books. Do you suppose she's going to come back? She said she was going to get a drink.'

'No, I shouldn't have thought so,' Friedrich said.

'No, perhaps not,' Picker said. He simpered horribly. 'A pity. I hate to think of you being stuck with me, an old bore like me all evening.'

Friedrich could not bring himself to respond.

'So how are you going to bring about the fall of the DDR?' he said lightly.

Picker laughed. 'A wonderful idea. Tanks, do you think? I don't think I could quite stretch to that.'

'But remember, it's probably only them now. The Russians aren't going to come and save them.'

'Really? Do you think so?'

'Wasn't that what that Russian was saying a few weeks ago?'

'Something like that. You know, I used to think all this was some game plan, some trap to get us to throw our weapons away and then they'd all come marching over the border. Now I don't know. Maybe you're right, maybe they wouldn't come. But the Russian soldiers are still there, aren't they?'

'True,' Friedrich said. 'But it would be only you against the soldiers that are still there. You wouldn't have to worry about the Red Army as a whole.'

'Oh, well, that's all right then. No, you'd need to do something much subtler. Give them something which would make them think they're really missing something. Give the people something.'

'They already see loads of West German television, of course, and the adverts for fridges.'

'Well, that's probably merely extremely peculiar if you have no means of buying any of the advertised products. It must be odd making up your mind whether you'd rather have a BMW or a Mercedes if you can't buy either, just on the basis of television advertisements. You probably wouldn't know how tempting the whole thing is.'

'Well, not very,' Friedrich said. 'You'd need to give them something which is completely wonderful, but which isn't going to last. No point in selling them fridges. Something disposable, like a pack of really soft toilet paper. Wouldn't that be simplest?'

'I see what you mean,' Picker said. 'That's perfect. You buy loads of the most incredibly soft lavatory paper –'

'– in a lovely shade of pink –'

'– and go and give everybody in East Berlin one roll each.'

'And they all wipe their arses on this fabulous lavatory paper for a few days, and of course they can't believe it because all their lives they've been wiping their arses on old bits of wood, sandpaper or, on good days, copies of the *Berliner Zeitung*.'

'Brilliant.'

'And then it's finished, and they have – this is the brilliant part – to go back to sandpaper because the supply's disappeared. And now they know how people wipe their arses in West Berlin and they can't stand it. And they all take to the streets with banners calling for softer bog roll and the right to choose a better life for your arse. And then the government resigns and there's a painless revolution. The Arsewipe Revolution. I can see it.'

'Perfect,' Picker said. 'But there's the problem of getting all that lavatory paper into East Berlin. You'd need lorries.'

'There is that,' Friedrich said. 'Better to use something very small, that pretty soon you could persuade them that they couldn't do without.'

'I think I've got it.'

'What?'

'Drugs.'

Friedrich looked at Picker; he seemed overwhelmingly excited with his excellent idea; a smile not far removed from sweet reasonableness was on his face.

'Not very moral, of course.'

'No, but perfect. You know East Germany.'

'I think so.'

'You know what they lack in the DDR.'

'Freedom. Fun. Money. Food. Whatever. Go on.'

'Pleasure.'

'Oh yes.'

'So anyway,' Picker started. 'We find some really reliable seller of drugs –'

'A dealer?'

'Sorry, can you say the word?'

'Dealer,' Friedrich said carefully. Picker got out a small red notebook from his pocket, from which a stub of pencil on a string dangled. He made a little note, holding the book up as he did so. 'Spell it, please. I don't know the word,' he said. Friedrich spelt it. 'That's the English word,' Picker said. 'Yes, that's what I mean. And we find a dealer and buy a lot of some sort of drug that young people will enjoy. I know; do you know this new drug, this drug they're all taking? It's called something like Pleasure.'

He used a German word.

'No,' Friedrich said. 'I don't know about that stuff. Is it new?'

'Yes,' Picker said. 'In English we call it *Ecstasy* –'

'In German we use the English word,' Friedrich said. 'Dealer, Ecstasy. I'll soon be speaking English. I've heard of it. It's for dancing.'

'Exactly,' Picker said. He beamed. 'So, this is what happens. You get a lot of this stuff, and just take it to East Berlin and create a lot of instant addicts, who enjoy the whole experience and want to take the drug again, but very quickly they find they can't, and so they have a revolution. I like the idea of the Dance Revolution better than the Arsewipe Revolution.'

'Quite good,' Friedrich said. 'But the problem is they've got no money in the East. I mean none at all. They couldn't possibly afford to buy it. It would probably all fall into the hands of incredibly rich people who like the system exactly as it is. So the whole thing would collapse. The sort of prices East Berliners could afford – for most of them it would be a choice between twenty minutes' worth of cocaine or two weeks' food.'

'No,' Picker said. He thought for a moment. His face was right up against Friedrich's; he almost hissed with the excitement of his own invention. Friedrich was aware that Pierre was watching them with unhealthy fascination. It was almost involuntary, the way his whole body tipped backwards, away from Picker's odours and his drunkenness. 'I've got it. This is how it works. You buy it here and take it over and give it away. Think of it as a sort of charity. I mean, your aim isn't to make money but to bring down the DDR. And it would be cheaper than buying tanks, and probably less conspicuous.'

'More expensive than bog roll, though,' Friedrich said.

'Yes,' Picker said. 'But you give it away for nothing. And they take drugs once, and they're happy and dance or whatever they want to do, and afterwards they'll want more, but of course they won't be able to get it. And they'll start to ask why not, and come to the conclusion – goodness me, this is such an excellent plan – that their whole political system is against pleasure, that they haven't been allowed to see more than a fragment of what life could be like.'

'Perfect,' Friedrich said. 'And then they take to the streets and chant *We Want More Drugs* and the government resigns and it becomes an utterly hippy sort of place and everybody stops caring what sort of government they live under anyway.'

'There is that,' Picker said. He obviously thought hard; the labour of it looked like someone trying to move wardrobes. 'Of course, if your objection to the political system in East Germany is that you're not allowed to take drugs, then that's also an objection to the political system in West Germany. What fun. You know, I feel most peculiar.'

'Well, you're probably at least as drunk as me, since you started earlier.'

'What do you mean, drunk?'

'You know, falling over, all that.'

'I thought this wine was alcohol-free.'

'Well, I don't think so,' Friedrich said. 'I mean, of course it's not. I wondered at you drinking it. I mean I remembered you saying you don't drink.'

'Do you know –' Picker, a perfect stage drunk, gestured at the far end of the room – 'he told me it was alcohol-free. He swore to me it was.'

'Who?'

'That boy, over there.' He gestured at Pierre, now talking to the lady novelist. He, in turn, raised his glass; it was not possible to say whether he did it in warm mockery or ordinary half-acknowledging kindness. 'He – and I'm supposed to go home and talk to the babysitter – and he promised it was –'

'He might have been mistaken,' Friedrich said.

'Go home and talk to the babysitter –' Picker went on, perfect fat tumbling embodiment of outrage, 'in *my* condition – I'm going to –' and Picker was shouldering Friedrich aside, moving weightily towards the novelist and Pierre and the small shy coterie. Friedrich, following, quite suddenly felt appallingly drunk.

'There are no Proustians,' the novelist was just then saying. 'There is only Proust.'

A little pause, and then, from the patient group, led by Pierre, came the glass-breaking laugh produced by people who do not share a language, who want not to laugh in pleasure, but to show politeness and appreciation.

'The trouble. The trouble with you is –' Picker began.

'Excuse me, sir,' the lady novelist chillingly said. The room seemed to turn at the sound of Picker's voice; it was like the ripple on a hot day when wind strikes a field of long grass, a noise both silent and emphatic.

'Friedrich,' Picker said, turning. 'Explain to this lady what the problem is. Tell her.'

They all turned to him, and, as they looked at him, all his non-existent French suddenly failed him.

'Can you do something?' Pierre said, and quite suddenly Friedrich saw that Pierre was utterly, appallingly sober, and knew exactly what he was doing. *Can I?* he wanted to reply, but it was too late; astonished, without any warning, he found himself laughing and holding on to something – a chair, a bookshelf, Pierre's shoulder, the lady novelist's bosom, a painting – for support; laughing not with the private-view shimmer of appreciation but at something, and who knew what, that was truly, killingly funny. There was something almost patient in the way they looked at him, and, unable to do more, Friedrich gave Picker a shove, pushing his indignant back out of the door, and all the while, Picker and Friedrich and Pierre, who was pushing Friedrich, talking.

'You know,' Pierre was saying – and even at the time it seemed to Friedrich like a sentence which would come back in daylight and torment him – 'it's really good that Picker's met someone like you. I'm sure you'll both be *perfect* for each other. I can just see it.'

'Here he comes, here he is,' a woman was calling in Friedrich's ear as he and Picker and Pierre, propelling each other and resisting and pulling, fell through the door, and it was hard to know who was evicting whom, and all he could see was a car drawing up at the foot of the steps and three or four photographers letting off their blameless harmless weapons, flashing in the unassuming face of the half-smiling pale painter, arriving at last; it was as if they had expected the Holy Roman Emperor, risen from the grave, and got only a mild little clerk, and were making the best of it. And with a deft choreography, the Museums' Director of all Prussia was shaking his hand and then behind him and helping him up the steps towards the *vernissage*, and meeting only Picker and Pierre and poor falling Friedrich. And all the time Friedrich was saying, 'And I suppose you think this is part of all the pleasure and freedom, the limitless pleasure we have here, and everyone knows that our lives are nothing but pleasure and freedom and rolling in piles of money and drugs –'

'So sorry,' Pierre said, as he stepped back from them and opened his arms wide to the painter, executing the casual manoeuvre of a prestidigitator, a dancer, as he let them fall catastrophically into the advancing entourage, greeting and stepping back tactfully in one move.

'– and women all day long, and if they get one whiff of that in Leipzig and Dresden and Karl-Marx-Stadt, just one whiff, then, why then –'

And there was the horrified ramrod of the Museums' Director of all Prussia, with the weight of Picker suddenly draped around his neck, and falling, and Picker calling, 'So sorry, so sorry,' and the great painter, as if he had never in all his life seen such a thing, and now almost running up the steps as Picker fell and Friedrich falling over his own feet, and the last thing of all the willowy undrunk figure of Pierre turning with the door behind the gorgeous brushing-down entourage and waving a half-kiss in their direction, and –

God, the next morning.

SHIT

DAPHNE ALWAYS PUT on the same dress for her Class War evenings. It was very unlike the rest of her clothes: a clinging black dress which transformed her, when her hair was brushed back and oiled into a sleek tight cap, when her proper shoes were out of their box, when – of all things – she had put her carefully preserved tights on, transformed her into something respectable, unnoticeable, acceptable. It was the end of February.

'You look nice tonight,' her aunt always, without fail, said to her. 'Anything special?'

'No, not really.'

'Or anyone?' her aunt went on, knowingly.

'Oh – aunty –'

'Don't mind me,' her aunt always said, a little, though not enough, under her breath, settling back with her book. (She knew what she thought. It was obvious, when you thought about it.)

But in fact there wasn't much reason for Daphne to dress up for the Class War evenings. Perhaps originally there had been – perhaps at first she had thought that it was better, before you perpetrated whatever this week's outrage was going to be, not to dress in any way that might draw attention to you. Really, the heavy boots and scrunched bleached hair her aunt always fondly tutted over could well announce an anarchist who might order a beer, but would certainly trash the place before paying. So, instead of dressing, as usual, like half the female population of Kreuzberg, Daphne made herself perfectly invisible in drop-dead, fuck-off, fuck-me glamour before she went out.

Anyway, that was what she thought.

The truth was that they never hung about before carrying out the evening's deed, her and Mario, who was now her regular partner in the lightning-action lark. The idea of announcing themselves as innocent customers for an hour before they got up and trashed some yuppy-bar was too absurd a double bluff to risk. It was the logic of girls who, secretly sleeping with a married man, seek to deflect attention from the identity of the lover by mentioning him and praising his wife at all opportunities. It never worked and never had. So Mario and Daphne saved a lot of time by walking briskly in off the street, trashing some place that definitely shouldn't, no way, be in Berlin, and walking briskly out again, never knowing if the faces behind showed outrage or fright or despair or what. You never knew what people would think of the class war, and it was better not to bother imagining.

There was one simple reason why Daphne dressed up like this for her Sunday nights. It made her feel incredibly sexy; and when she felt sexy she felt strong; and when she felt strong she knew she was in the right, throwing a brick through a window, dumping ten litres of red paint on the floor of a shop. Dark red paint; it had been important, in the elegant boutique just off the Savignyplatz, to make the assistants and the hapless manageress, scurrying from her little office in the back with a dulled look of what-now, think for just one moment that it could be blood.

So she stood in her warm bedroom at her aunt's, in her dress which tightened at the hips and made her run her palms down her sides, made her feel how her clothes embraced her, held her tight. The sexed-up feeling of a dress so tight you could only walk in it because it was so short; she stood, ecstatically smoothing her palms down her sides, down her restrained tightened ribs. She scowled, irresistibly, in the mirror.

'You look nice tonight,' her aunt said.

Mario, who had a taste for eccentric meeting places – never, naturally, the same one twice – had suggested the foyer of the Philharmonie at seven. The foyer was beginning to fill when Daphne got there; she walked around as if waiting for her date. After a couple of minutes, afraid, as usual, of seeming conspicuous, she bought a programme for the concert. No one, certainly, seeing her, would have thought anything of her, anything at all remarkable; she looked exactly what she was, a girl, a student, who had taken care to put on her best clothes for the evening, a girl who looked exactly her age of twenty, a girl whose clean and eager expression could so easily be explained by her anticipation of a fine piano trio that no other, more surprising explanation could be entered on.

When she saw Mario he was watching her – had been, clearly, for some minutes with an expression scrupulous and judicious, not the fond gaze she would always have wished for. She wandered up to him with deliberate casualness, through the now crowded room, not speaking until she was standing next to him, both looking at the room like bored party-goers assessing the social chances.

'Hi,' she said.

'Don't overdo it,' he said. 'This is Caspar.'

'Sorry?'

'This is Caspar,' Mario said. 'He's coming with us.'

Next to Mario, leaning against the wall, was a short man, bonily featured, who looked as if he had slept in his clothes, and stained them while he slept. Unshaven apart from his razored scalp, he nodded to Daphne, eyes half-closed, as if in sleep, or suspicion.

'It's okay,' Mario said. 'They've cleared it. It can be three of us tonight.'

'It's a problem,' Daphne said.

'Why?'

'There's only ever supposed to be two of us in the actions,' Daphne said. She was obscurely furious at the idea of having to talk to this Caspar, to have him there diluting her time with Mario.

'It's okay,' Mario said. 'I said so. It's not just that I cleared it. They asked me to take him along. He's okay. Now let's get going.'

'If you want to know,' Caspar said, drawling behind his cigarette, 'it's you that's being allowed along as a favour. If you're really worried about there being three of us, solve the problem. Shove off home.'

'No,' Daphne said. 'It's okay.'

'Or you could always stay and hear the Beaux Arts,' Caspar went on, reading from her tightly clutched programme, 'Piano Trio.'

'Come on,' Mario said, evidently a little embarrassed at Caspar's bad manners. 'We want to be finished by ten.'

'I'll go ahead,' Caspar said. 'Meet you out the front in five minutes.'

Daphne looked at Mario.

'Don't worry,' Mario said. 'It's okay, really.'

'I've never seen him before.'

'He's okay,' Mario said. 'He's just passing through Berlin.'

'No one just passes through Berlin,' Daphne said. 'Who is he? Is he called Caspar?'

'Why do you think he's not?'

'I don't know,' Daphne said. 'He didn't seem to respond straight away when you said his name.'

'You're a fast one. I don't know – I don't know his real name. The same thing had occurred to me.'

'It all sounds a bit peculiar. Do you know him?'

'No,' Mario said. 'But he came very highly recommended.'

'Are you sure he's not some kind of –'

'Some what?'

'Some policeman.'

'No,' Mario said. 'I'm sure of that. He came very strongly recommended. He's certainly not the filth. He's from the Ruhrgebiet. I think, reading between the lines, things have been hotting up over there a bit, and he's come to have his fun over here for a while.'

'Is he in trouble?'

'I don't know.'

'That would be just great,' Daphne said. 'Carrying out an action with someone the police are already looking for. Brilliant.'

'I don't think,' Mario said, lowering his voice, 'things are quite as bad as all that. I don't think if they were he'd be risking anything over here. But he's supposed to be perfectly reliable, and I believe it, and frankly, I've been more or less instructed, from very high up, to take him along. There's no avoiding it, I'm afraid.'

Daphne looked at him. He puzzled her so much sometimes; the idea that the wiseacres they occasionally met for their argumentative and frugal drinks could have been so ranked in a hierarchy to allow the use of an expression like 'very high up' was quite amazing. And the ten of them was all there was, she had always thought.

'How did he know about us?' she said.

'How did you, come to that?'

'A completely different way, I hope,' Daphne said. It was a joke between them – at least, it was a joke Daphne told to Mario – that she was only in Class War because Mario had seduced her into it. 'Come on, let's get on with it.'

'Look –' Mario said. He held her in his gaze. 'Look, if you're worried about this, and, god, maybe you really have a point, maybe it would be best if you didn't risk it. The whole thing – why don't you really not risk it? It might be best, you know. It really might.'

'Oh, it'll be fine,' Daphne said. It was so like a protective fondness, the way he sometimes considered her periodic nervousnesses. The way he always let her stand at the back, to make the fastest exit; the way she had seen, even mid-action, he took care not to splash her with paint or acid, made sure she was standing somewhere the glass would not shatter over her. His consideration, protecting him from their own violence and destruction; how little the perfect manners of a lover it was, how like the concern of love.

Caspar was standing outside, stamping his feet, though it wasn't cold at all.

'You took your time,' he said.

'We had something to talk about,' Daphne said.

'Sweet,' Caspar said. 'Where's the shit.'

'Left it in Kreuzberg,' Mario said. 'It's in a courtyard behind the café we're hitting.'

'Will it still be there?' Caspar said.

'No one would go near it, let alone steal it,' Mario said.

'You never know,' Caspar said.

'Besides,' Daphne said. 'If you want to ride on the U-bahn with six plastic bags full of pigshit, you're welcome to. But count us out.'

Caspar grunted.

They were in Kreuzberg before they spoke again. The target for the evening's action was a bar on the Dresdener-strasse which practically all the group had noticed and picked out as a high priority. It had opened six weeks before. All of them had had some difficulty remembering what, exactly, had been there before, the building work had been going on so long. Finally, someone said,

'An electrical shop,'

and they all said 'Exactly'. It was perfect. The scruffy electrical repair shop had been there for years, serving a useful purpose, mending broken-down stuff, keeping stuff on the road for ordinary people, people who could afford their services, but not the inflated exploitative price of a new vacuum cleaner. Now Daphne thought of it, she could envisage the man who ran the shop; a man nearly sixty, with greying hair yellowing at the front with ceaseless cigarettes. A moustached man – was that right? – ageing badly, heavy and tired in the face, looking up as the door opened as if he only wanted to be left in peace, but carrying out his useful job patiently and, in the end, kindly.

Of course, Daphne remembered none of this, but it was probably right, or something not a million miles from it. And something functional and useful like that, to be replaced by this. They all agreed. Something had to be done, and quickly. It was bad enough yuppy bars opening up in some square in Charlottenburg, and they got round to those as well, but something as exploitative and contemptible as this in Kreuzberg; something had to be done.

The bar that was there now had replaced the whole of the front of the former shop with a huge sheet of plate glass. On the lower right of the glass, in lower-case sanserif, was modishly tattooed the name of the bar: *Schöne des Tages*. You just wanted to put a brick through it. The bar itself was dimly, luminously lit; as you walked the street, behind the thick glass the people in the bar seemed to be moving, slowly, silently, in another dimension, gliding about the dim space, until picked out by a periodic brilliant pool of light, uplighting their startled or composed faces in a thick gust of cigarette smoke. The dimness, the unexpected silence from the street – they never played loud music, and the thick glass muffled all rumble of conversation – turned it into a blue and peaceful aquarium, its exotic strange life so strangely and roughly set down in this quiet grim street. In a way it was magical. She could see that.

None of the group had ever been there. It was just unmistakably a good target.

Mario had left the bags of pigshit in a courtyard behind the café.

'I put a pig's head in one of the bags as well,' he said. 'To make the point.'

'That's right,' Daphne said, lifting two bags with great care. They seemed already to be dripping, though the plastic bags were the reinforced and solid sort you had to pay extra for at the supermarket. 'They are pigs, these people.'

'Where did you get the head from?' Caspar asked.

'Schöneberg,' Mario said. 'Don't worry, it was three weeks ago. They won't remember me.'

'And the shit?'

'Oh, that was *much* harder,' Daphne butted in. She was determined to make a show of not taking this man seriously. He glowered, but did not press the point.

The three of them stood just inside the entrance to the courtyard, invisible in the mid-evening gloom. The Dresdenerstrasse was almost deserted; at the far end, some middle-aged women were standing without talking, as if struck with amazement, prematurely. Daphne felt, as always at this moment, waiting for a street to empty, waiting for the right moment to launch the action in silence, as if a performance was about to begin. Waiting for the moment when any observers were gone, she felt as if the city, the audience, was about to assemble and quieten down, to attend to her action, her scripted and scrupulous account of a violence seen everywhere, a violence everywhere, in the lives of every one of her invisible and, it must be said, largely apathetic audience.

'Okay,' Mario said. 'We split after the action, and run, don't walk, to the garden behind the Oranienplatz. Wait exactly three minutes, then, if no one else shows, clear off.'

'Why do we need to meet up?' Caspar said. 'Wouldn't it be safer –'

'Yes, it would be safer,' Mario said. 'But that's what we do, because that's what's good to do. It helps if we know straight away if anything went wrong. Ready? Hey – you – it's my show. Okay? Ready?'

'Ready,' Daphne said. Caspar merely nodded, like a professional singer, drafted in, determined to regard everything as beneath him. He just nodded, and ignored Daphne's eagerness.

The time before leaving the dim place of safety and bursting through the door of the site was, for Daphne, a time without boundaries or measurement, an ecstasy of

119

action, of doing which could have continued for long delirious minutes. It wasn't the destruction which contained the joy; it was the brief moment when action was imminent and could not be reversed, and it was the sense and the joy of being right, of acting to set things straight, as they should be, as they always had been. And doing it with Mario, and, perhaps, in front of him; perhaps, she thought as she strode forwards with a bag of shit in either hand, perhaps it was Mario, him alone, who was her audience, and not the assembled city, gathered around her in the empty street.

They were straight through the door, walking quite normally, and then, in a line, they began to throw the bags. Throw left, one two three four five, throw right; so simple, so ordinary an action, and in five seconds six piles, unbagged, of shit were all over the café, and the three of them were out, and running. So quick; and nothing to take away; nothing, just a sudden impression of a girl at a table, her face turned away, her black hair splattered with yellow shit; the faces at the tables at the side, just beginning to turn, blank with the beginnings, only, of curiosity and, behind the bar, a man and a woman, both young, he neatly moustached, she with a smooth glossy bob, dark and carefully, nervously elegant, with the empty look of oncoming terror as something, some solid heavy *thing* the size of a cannonball hit the floor with a thud, or a crack, and the beginnings, only, of stench.

Daphne ran straight ahead, cutting behind the cheap baker's, and only slowing to a walk when she was out on the Kottbusserdamm and in sight of other people. She doubled back, avoiding the Dresdenerstrasse and the irresistible sight of their carnage; she knew about the temptation to contemplate, coolly, what they had done from the other side of the street, knew enough to resist it with the thought that she could always read about it in the newspapers. Normally, after an action, she had a strong urge to be alone in a street, and to laugh at the sheer clean beauty of the action, the ruin so quickly created, so easily left behind. Not today. All the time, there was a voice, swearing in her head. How the fuck could they have got it wrong? Whose idea had it been to launch the action at this place, and why hadn't they found out anything about the bar?

Caspar was already at the Oranienplatz, skulking about with a fag in a hopelessly suspicious way. *Amateur*, she thought, contemptuously.

'He's not here yet?' he said.

'He went in the other direction,' Daphne said. She couldn't hold it in any more; it hadn't been Caspar's fault, but she needed someone to blame. 'They were *Turks*.'

'So?' Caspar said. 'They should know better.'

'They do,' Daphne said. 'We shouldn't be attacking Turks.'

'They're capitalists too,' Caspar said. 'They're capitalists before they're Turks. End of debate. That's just not the point, where they happen to come from.'

'I just think –' Daphne said. She paused; out of breath with excitement and rage and running.

'You just think,' Caspar said. 'Well, it's too late for thinking now. I just think you're not that committed to changing things, if you want to excuse people because they're kind to their dogs and children, or because they're friends of yours, or because of where they come from.'

'There's a difference between people who are trying to make a living and people who just exist to exploit the poor.'

'Oh?' Caspar said. 'A difference? Where is that difference,

then? What side of the difference are people who sell over-priced drinks? Or overpriced magazines? Is that acceptable? Would you refuse to make a strike against a newsagent's? What about people who are *just trying to make a living* by selling cars, or owning newspapers, or selling guns? You could say, and I bet you do, that anyone's *just trying to make a living.*'

'They were Turks, though,' Daphne said.

'Oh, really?' Caspar said. 'And if they were Turks sell-ing guns to Nazi hooligans, would that be a good enough excuse for you?'

'No,' Daphne said. 'But they never would. Of course they wouldn't.'

'You don't know,' Caspar said. 'You know nothing, if I may say so, about the world. These things happen. People should know better, but they don't. Saying *oh, they're Turks, leave them alone*, that's the sort of thing that people always come out with to defend anything really evil. You know; you prioritize race. I don't. Which of us has got over the racist structure of society, do you think? Just think about it, and listen to how much you sound like someone defending a Third Reich murderer.'

'I don't think,' Daphne said, 'they're as bad as all that. They only opened a café.'

'Not as bad as all that? Don't you think, don't you realize that capitalism is the biggest evil there is?' Caspar said. 'Don't you realize even that?'

'I just think a couple of Turkish immigrants can do with-out all this,' Daphne said, and faltered, recognizing too well the beginnings of sulk in herself. Perhaps he was right; and what were a couple of oppressed Turks doing trying to make money out of an outmoded system instead of trying to change it by violence?

Caspar didn't trouble even to respond to this. 'Here comes your friend,' he said at last. Mario was scurrying across the road, appearing, as ever, from an unfathomable direction. She marvelled at how his unfamiliar quality had been domesticated, made even warm and sympathetic and lovable by the simple proximity of someone as mad as Caspar.

'Everything okay?' he said, rubbing his hands together.

'Fine,' Caspar said firmly. Daphne said nothing.

'When are you off?' Mario said.

Caspar looked a little surprised. He dropped and trod on his cigarette before replying. 'It's set for next Monday,' he said.

'I won't see you before you go,' Mario said.

'I'm not going far,' Caspar said. 'And it's all sorted out now.'

'You're going far enough,' Mario said, and it was with a strange gesture of benediction that, in the dark of the Oranienplatz, he took Caspar's small shaven head between both his hands and kissed him, first on one cheek then the other. It was as if Daphne were not there, and she had the sense of seeing some secret rite, of some act of election which neither participant and no onlooker could completely understand. Caspar submitted to Mario's kiss, and in his face was the knowledge that he deserved nothing less; but Daphne could look at nothing but the beautiful terrible strength in Mario's dark eyes as, silently, he said goodbye to this man; this nameless man.

His concentration, when it broke, was like the end of a dance. He seemed to become aware of Daphne again, to step out of his role as some unheard music came to its unheard end, to become no longer aware of his own movements, his entrancement in his own body.

'Listen,' he said. Caspar was already halfway down the street, with a scurrying limp; his walk branded him the guilty coward he so unarguably was. 'Don't mention Caspar to the others, even if they seem to be asking. They don't know about him, and it's better, really, that they don't.'

'I thought,' Daphne said. She thought. 'I thought they asked you to take him along with us tonight. I thought you said you had instructions.'

'Not from them,' Mario said. He seemed entirely unconcerned by what she said. 'See you next Sunday.'

He headed off, disappearing quickly, hidden by the thick trees lining the street. Caspar was too far off to see now, and she reflected that he had said, as the instructions required them all to do, nothing in the way of goodbye.

Mario's habitual disdain of the official instructions (he *always* said 'See you next Sunday' at precisely this point) was unarguably a part of *the thing about Mario*; to make a point of breaking the rules of an organization which declined to believe in rules or, actually, organization. She sort of admired it. She'd long ago stopped trying to make sense of the other thing she admired about Mario's 'See you next Sunday', the fact that it wouldn't be, in fact, next Sunday the next time they saw each other, but Tuesday. Because for one year, two months and three days they'd been seeing each other for the purpose of sex every Thursday, Saturday and Tuesday afternoons, regular as a knife through butter.

THINGS WORTH SEEING

'WHAT,' MARTIN ASKED his nine-year-old niece, 'do you want to do today?'

The niece tipped her head on one side, looked at the inexplicably grubby ceiling of Martin's flat. She gave a good performance of someone thinking hard about what she would like to do. Martin waited, his arms folded, as if he had something better to do than watch her perch on a chair and swing her legs.

'I think I'd like to see some more of Berlin today, Uncle Martin,' she said eventually.

'What do you want to see?'

'Things worth seeing,' she said. She had put on something which could only be regarded as a party dress: a blue velvet dress with white lace at the neck and cuffs, with matching white tights and a pair of shiny black shoes. Her hair was pulled up into two bunches. She smiled brightly. The whole effect she had contrived herself; the day before she had asked Martin to help her dress, but only once. All in all, there was very little to be said in her favour.

'Things worth seeing,' Martin said.

———

'Yes,' the niece said. 'I'd like to see the famous land-marks of Berlin.'

Martin regarded her sourly. His niece's visit was a penance he was paying to his family for running away from Christmas. His father had not, as he had hoped, forgotten about it, but had taken to telephoning him to remind him of his unacceptable bad behaviour. The suggestion that he might like to have a niece to stay for a few days was the latest in a series of outrages he felt unable to resist. This niece was apparently keen on history at school, liked museums, was cheerful and liked by all the cheek-pinching old ladies of the neighbourhood. A school project about the history of Germany was mentioned; the girl's extreme excitement at the prospect of staying with her uncle and seeing Berlin for herself was adduced. Martin was not entirely sure which of two nieces was in the question; he could not, however, use his feelings of dread and horror as a reason to refuse.

'What sort of things?' he said. 'We can't see everything worth seeing in Berlin. There's too much.'

'Well,' the niece said. 'I'd like to see the Wall.'

'Come here,' Martin said. She scrambled off the chair and scampered to the window. 'You see that big white wall over there? That's the Wall. All right?'

'Tell me about it,' she said. 'I want to write about it in my school project. You know, Uncle Martin, I'm writing a project for school about the history of Germany. I want to know about it all.'

'The whole history of Germany?' Martin said, just as he had yesterday. 'I don't know about the whole history of Germany. You'll have to ask other people about that. Well, the Wall has been put up by the people who live on the other side of it as an Anti-Fascist Barrier. And it works very well.'

'What does it mean, Anti—'

'Don't be winsome, child,' Martin said. 'I'll tell you. About thirty years ago, the people who ran things in East Germany started to get worried about two things. The first one was that there were too many West Germans going into the East and telling the people who lived in the East bad things, and spoiling everything for them. The second one was that people in the East, when they heard about all the bad things in the West, naturally wanted to share in all the bad things, so they were all crossing over into the West. Some of them came into West Berlin, and some of them didn't bother, they just went straight to West Germany.'

'You know,' the niece said. 'I used to think a very silly thing, when I was little. I used to think that Berlin was on the —' she struggled a bit — 'on the edge, between West Germany and East Germany, and the border went through it. But now I know there's a big circle round West Berlin, a big wall.'

'Right,' Martin said. 'How interesting.'

'Can we go out?' she said. 'I want to go for a walk and see things.'

'Are you going out dressed like that?' he said, without much hope.

What a little cow she was, the niece; what a little *historian* she was, the little cow . . . standing there holding the ingrained hand of her Uncle Martin and smiling at any- one who expended any sort of gaze on her, whether in horror or amazement or sad lechery at her party frock and her pert expression; just knowing what she wanted was the attention of an adult, what she most wanted was to turn what she saw with her pale and shocked Uncle Martin, twitching slightly at this ungodly hour of the morning, turn what she saw into prose; yes, what a little historian she was, the little cow. Trolling her through the galleries, one room full of brown Dutch interiors after another, the best thing he knew to exhaust her, and all the time, exhausting himself only, telling her history, all the time dragging her back from one Reichskanzler to another, Kohl to Schmidt to Brandt to Hitler to Scheidemann, back into the Kaisers, back to Wilhelm and Friedrich, back into a time before Germany, to Frederick the Great, to the Electors of Brandenburg, to the Holy Roman Emperors, to the Thirty Years War, to the Defenestration of Prague, and growing vaguer and vaguer, and backwards and backwards into a great accelerating storm of half-remembered things, of half-invented, half-recounted events; and then, and then, and then, feeding the maw of the historian, feeding the eager snout, keeping it going, trying, above all, to explain, to keep the thing going . . .

And on the other side of Berlin a small boy was sitting on a sofa; holding a book, though he was too young, surely, to read. It was his favourite book, and he walked round with it, wanting someone to read it to him, though he knew every word. He was sitting on a sofa, and looking at his father's broad back, his father, bending over the desk, and doing what fathers do. He was patient, Tom Picker, and would wait as long as it took for his father to finish, and get him a glass of water, perhaps, and read to him, read from his favourite book. Some things about the story puzzled him, puzzled him every time he heard it. Nobody in the story ever went to the toilet, and they seemed to eat much less than Tom did. Every time Tom thought of it, he wanted to ask, but it was not always the right time, and often he forgot to ask. He looked at his father's broad back. His father was big. After a time, he stopped being patient, and went over to the desk. He only ever had to stand there for a second before his father turned to him, and put his pen down, and came to sit with him, and read to him as long as Tom wanted him to, and afterwards, if Tom wanted to, they would go for a walk in the woods. That was good. Yes it was. It was good.

TWO

GENUG

ENOUGH

THE DAY AFTER the *vernissage* at the State Gallery was a complete write-off, during which Friedrich spoke to nobody and nobody, if they had any sense, spoke to him.

The whole thing was just unspeakable, Friedrich thought, looking with nausea at his flat. He had a sense that something had happened the day before, but the idea of dragging it out into the daylight and actually trying to recall what he had done, and whether there had been anybody at the private view – anybody, in short, who he actually cared about ever speaking to again in his life – was a thought he found altogether too much too soon. To cap everything, it looked like the neo-Nazis were moving into Kreuzberg. Everyone was talking about the racist attack on the Turkish bar where he sometimes bought his cigarettes. The word was that the Nazis had dumped a pig's head covered in shit on the bar. The whole thing was just too crap to contemplate, he thought inarticulately, shutting his eyes with faint but pervasive suffering against the horrible sunlight, and the thought of the pig, and the shit, and the noise, and the necessity of having to buy his cigarettes at the not very nice or polite or likeable Turkish bar for the rest of his life, out of the usual weak-willed solidarity.

But the day after that he woke up laughing with a memory, fully formed, as if he had invented it, in an unusual moment of brilliance. It was less like a memory of a conversation than an imagined conversation, the conversation Friedrich usually conducted in his head, improving on messily unstructured real conversations; head-conversations in which the better was got and points were irrefutably made, to the satisfaction of observers and Friedrich alike. One of Friedrich's infallible beliefs was that after a particularly heavy night, you felt absolutely fine the day after; it was the day after that you had to watch. And, wandering in his pyjama top and pants round his flat, he felt quite capable of acting out, for the benefit of the flat, the hangover he had quaked and moaned under the day before. He clutched his head, and muttered, and from time to time threw himself back on the bed and laughed extravagantly. 'Fucking hell,' he muttered, or 'bog rolls – a million quilted bog rolls' or 'christly fuck'. It was much more as if a further conversation had taken place between him and Peter Picker, carrying on with the joke, than as if Friedrich was simply remembering the original conversation.

'Let us see now,' he said, quite in Picker's manner. 'If I were to wish, as I do, to bring about the downfall of the governments of the entire Eastern bloc, how would I carry it out? We'd give something away. What shall we give away? We'd give away signed photographs of Ronald Reagan, which would be lovely. Or perhaps we'd give away the collected speeches of the Christian Democratic Party of the Federal Republic of Germany. Or perhaps we wouldn't do that, since the only possible use for the collected speeches of the Christian Democratic Party of the

Federal Republic of Germany is to wipe your arse on them. So let's give them lots of proper stuff to wipe their arses on, and then they'll know what freedom means and when they go back to the usual DDR sandpaper they'll have an insight into what suffering means. Let's give them lots of lovely pink quilted lavatory paper to wipe their lovely pink DDR arses on. But just one roll each, of course. Only one thing. It's hard to smuggle bog roll in, unless you do it one roll at a time. So let's have lovely drugs. Lovely lovely drugs. So we plan to accomplish this rather ambitious task of destroying the German Democratic Republic by the means of giving away a lot of drugs. Do we approve of drugs? No, since we don't even drink. So why are we planning to give away drugs? Because we *don't* think giving away the collected speeches of the conference of the Christian Democratic Party of the Federal Republic would be half so successful or as popular an introduction to the freedom which exists in the West. So – tune, *Deutschland über alles*, everybody – *Cannabis, cocaine and heroin, Ecstasy and LSD, In your arm and nasal passages, Freedom in a pill for me –*'

Friedrich paused, alone in his flat. A rather brilliant idea had come to him, slightly painfully. And the idea was this: *Well, why not?* It would work, of course it would work. That was always the best thing about these plans; they would work if you could be bothered to do it.

But his thoughts were off and running. Who cared about the DDR, really; who cared what happened to it? His thoughts were all on Picker. An absolutely perfect, a dream scam was forming in his head. Picker, at some level, meant it; it was a joke, but all it would take would be Friedrich calling him and saying, well, you know what you were saying, how to bring down the DDR, well, it's not such a bad idea, is it, and you know, you had a really good idea there, Picker, old mate, and it wouldn't take so much, just, what, fifty thousand marks, but, of course, you'd have to give it away, they couldn't afford to buy it, and in any case, it would be great to persuade them that all this fun would be there for the having, that you wouldn't have to pay for any of this, that in the West people had all this fun all the time. And of course, my dear Herr Picker, I'd be very happy to acquire fifty thousand marks' worth of the drug Ecstasy, or as we low-life scum refer to it, E, and take it personally over the border and organize distribution, only I don't have fifty thousand marks, and I wondered, if you were really committed to the project, I mean, given the importance of the project, you know, fifty thousand marks is nothing at all, and what a brilliant idea this was of yours, my dear Herr Picker, and how splendid the rewards would be, all in all. Christ, fifty thousand marks, handed over to him to do whatever he wanted to with it. How few tablets of Ecstasy could he get away with buying for fifty thousand marks? A thousand? Five hundred? Would Peter Picker believe that a tablet of Ecstasy – top notch stuff, sir, Friedrich could hear himself saying – would cost – he worked it out – ten thousand marks?

What about five?

What about none?

Why not disappear with all Picker's money and enjoy it? Fifty thousand marks – he enjoyed even saying it. How would he feel if he actually had it in his hand? It was more than he earned in two years. And, my god, that was just one shipment. There might be a constant supply of fifty thousand mark notes; he lay on his bed and looked at the ceiling and envisaged what a fifty thousand mark note would look like, held between his hot fists, broad as a newspaper.

Well, there wouldn't be a constant supply of fifty thousand mark notes if he just disappeared with the first one. And of course he had made the whole thing too concrete; he did not actually know, he reminded himself, that it had been anything more than an elaborate two-bottle plan of the when-I-rule-the-world variety. But there was something in it; he could almost feel it when he thought of Picker's amused and yet energetic, excited eyes as they had splutteringly explored the ramifications. No, all it would take would be a small walk in Charlottenburg, and a persuasive, light-hearted manner, and fifty thousand marks would be his for the taking. He did not know precisely how much money Picker had, but he knew that he was about to find out. And Picker would never ever know that he had been stitched up. Of course he would not.

He told himself a joke. 'What would you do if you were suddenly made Kaiser? Kaiser Friedrich Kaiser. I would steal fifty thousand marks and run as fast as I could.'

He lit a cigarette and contemplated the inside of his head. No, fifty thousand marks wouldn't be enough. He looked at his flat. That was the best argument for the fifty thousand marks.

Friedrich had lived in his flat since he first came to Berlin. It was not difficult to find somewhere to live; Berlin was cheap and most people who lived there had to. Anyone who wasn't born here, wasn't here to get out of the army, but actually worked here, got paid more than anywhere else; money supplied by the government. And still nobody really wanted to live here, and flats were cheap.

Friedrich's flat was the cheapest of the cheap and looked it. He took it at first because he had no money – none at all – and could not envisage paying even two hundred marks a month, which was what it cost. It was a single, oddly shaped room. The kitchen was another room, a wedge in shape; at the broad end was a table where Friedrich sat and ate, when he ate. At the narrow end was a pile of bottles, which grew all the time and now was too big to throw out all at once. From time to time Friedrich carried out a raid on this kitchen bottle-dump and, by throwing out thirty bottles, made appreciable inroads on the horrible mountain. He thought of the pile of bottles not as waste, more as a hungry plant, or a crop which, from time to time, might be pruned or harvested, but which would always grow back, feeding on god knew what.

The main room had a bed in it, a desk and a bookcase; there was also a sink and a draining board, not in the kitchen, where it might have been more useful. A corner had been sealed off with hardboard and in here – in something not much more than a cupboard, really – was a lavatory, which in seven years Friedrich had cleaned three times. Each an occasion never to be forgotten; he practically celebrated the anniversaries. There was no bathroom. Friedrich washed each morning at the sink, and from time to time used the bathrooms of whichever neighbours had one, were still speaking to him, and didn't actively object to the idea of Friedrich. If he had fallen out with all his neighbours, which, due to bad planning, occurred from time to time, he had to go to the Kreuzberg swimming pool – not to exercise, but just to wash. Or he just stopped washing. This was one of the many things which annoyed him about the flat and the way he lived.

He absolutely never thought about his flat, and when he did, it depressed him. He disliked the way it smelled when you first opened the door, before you got used to it in a minute or so. (Perhaps other people, when they came, never got quite used to it; perhaps his was a tolerance it took only a few minutes to relax back into. What best friend did he have to tell him tactfully his flat stank?) He particularly disliked the way the flat very noticeably narrowed from the end with the door in it to the end with the window. It reminded him constantly that his flat, the middle one of three on his floor, was only squeezed in between ampler apartments. Most of all, he disliked the fucking landlord and his attempts to persuade Friedrich to go somewhere else, so that his flat could be divided into two bathrooms for his neighbours. Legal recourse and threats would fail, as Friedrich and his landlord both knew, with different feelings; the landlord, Helmut Meier, evidently supposed that persuasion might succeed where force would be useless. He needed to go for a walk – a walk in Kreuzberg – to sort things out in his head.

Kreuzberg was a place more talked about, perhaps, than lived in; it was a district better known to most Germans than whole towns twice the size, a bleached witch of a place, a bleached witch in a fairy story to scare the blond good children of the West with terrors, and which, seemingly, instead, only lured them in. These things happen in Kreuzberg, the mothers of Westphalia, of Bavaria, Hamburg, Stuttgart and Hannover said, and their wide-eyed children looked back at them, remembering the name, dreaming of escape. They told jokes about it – it was the third largest Turkish city in the world, if you thought that was a joke or even funny – but mostly it was there to warn about what would happen to Germany. What, in one corner, already had. It was surprising no one ran coach tours there.

But even within the bounds of Kreuzberg, Kreuzberg was a place more talked about than real, somehow; the people who walked in the Oranienstrasse and sat in the

Oranienstrasse bars seemed, if you judged by their conversation, to think that the streets might vanish, might never have existed, without the constant evoking of the name of the square mile or so. An overheard snatch of conversation between strangers always offered the word *Kreuzberg*, brought in at some length; a town of lovers, it sometimes seemed, separated from their beloved, fated to go on saying the beautiful name, in the street, in a bus, inside their narrow walls, in the open air, to anyone who would listen and many who wouldn't, until the streets seemed filled with the nutcracker-noise of the name, *Kreuzberg*, produced by a thousand tiny yelling voices, a crowd of dwarfs, the hundred European accents of those same blond children who had heard of the walled witchy town from their warning mothers, and remembered. When they talked of it, people often liked to think of it as something interior, imagined; not bricks and streets, but, as they said, a state of mind. There was something satisfied about the way they said this, and Friedrich never did. He had come there not because it was a state of mind, which he could have attained in Cologne, but because it was a place; a walled place; a quiet, distant one. That was why anyone went there, and why no one was born there.

It was a real place, too, bounded on some sides by unremarkable unheard-of districts – and one couldn't think of Kreuzberg as a mere district, more of a crux to ponder, a mountain to climb – and on others by a wall. It had a postcode, or even two – 61 and 36 – two postcodes in which people found, or claimed to find, different qualities. It had been there before Friedrich arrived, and would be there after he left. If he ever did; if he had anywhere else much to go to.

He never went to Cologne now – that was what he said

– and when he did go there, he did not look at it. For Friedrich, now, and since his father had disappeared, Cologne was a place he only dreamt about, and never thought about; and, waking up, it was a place he felt he had dreamt about unwillingly. There was too much there, too much to remember and fill with dread, and if Friedrich ever said to anyone in Berlin that he never went back, he would follow it by saying 'Too much history'. He watched them nod sagely, always understanding what he meant; always understanding that what he meant was the buildings, the immaculate palaces and cathedrals, immaculately restored from piles of rubble, the gilt and the spires, the perfect fake stories for tourists and the perfect fake preservation of the tourist vistas. He never bothered to correct them. In a way he meant that too. But it was his own history, walking the streets, the memory of his skulking father, cigarette between thumb and forefinger, always somehow appearing, always somehow waiting; coming from nowhere, unmoving, the appearance of his father on the street always made Friedrich, that distant boy, now almost a ghost on the far side of his father, jump; just as his father's apparition, now, in his occasional Cologne dreams, made him jump in his sleep, and begin to fear, all over again.

It had been his father's way, whenever Friedrich or his sisters came into a room, to say 'What do you want?' Friedrich never said, like his sisters, 'I don't know', or 'nothing', and he was not old before he never went into even an empty room of the flat without a purpose, a reason to be there, an excuse. His father was a man with a purpose, and the purpose was this: not to be spied on. There are few spies in the world; there are many, and Friedrich's father was one of them, whose manner always suggested threat, always implied that he was being watched. Perhaps, by saying silently that he thought he was being watched, being threatened, in the end he invited it. The way he looked round; the way, self-protecting, defeated, he walked.

Most of all – and there was a shame Friedrich could never free himself from when he realized that this, most of all, was how he remembered his father – it was the sudden inexplicable wrong furies he gave way to when threatened on the road. That was something Friedrich never understood; never understood his father's rage, sudden as it was and succeeded by a silence. A silence like whimpering, a silence like someone who maybe wanted to apologize. He never understood his own terror; it wasn't a terror at danger – it was years before he even thought that his father might have seen any kind of threat in other people's driving. Nor was it a terror at his father's recklessness, but a fear of what would happen when the car journey was over; the knowledge that his mother would get out, slamming the door, and his parents, unable to row, unable to apologize, would sit in silence for too long. Beyond that was the knowledge he had that one day he would simply step out of his father's car and say, 'I never want to be driven by you anywhere ever again.' And, after that, what would be left of the two of them? What would they have to say to each other?

'It's fine, Franz,' his mother would say. She had a knack of noticing the sorts of minor infringements of other drivers which irritated his father. His father drove on. A few miles further on, perhaps, the same driver, or a different one, did the same thing, or something different. It hardly mattered. It might be overtaking Franz's car, which he usually tried to prevent by placing the car as squarely in the middle of the road as he could. It might be preventing Franz from overtaking, on the other hand, by driving squarely in the middle of the road.

'Did you see that?' Franz said.

'It's fine,' Friedrich's mother said.

'It's not fine,' he said. 'I'm going to get the bastard.'

'Franz.'

'Bloody bastard!'

'The children.'

'The children, the children,' he said, ridiculing her, and in his rage a strange note of jollity entered, knowing what he was going to do and how much, in the end, he might enjoy it. Enjoy being in the right. And that was it; his father's brief and unshared merriment preceding the familiar awfulness; a brute dash, overtaking some other car, flashing and hooting in a kind of glee. Friedrich always hung on to something, to the back of the front seat. He was always aware of the futility of hanging on to something in the car when what he really wanted was to get out; to stand in a quiet field forever and watch everything go by, peacefully.

His father was a carpenter. And *his* father had also been a carpenter, Friedrich's grandfather whom he hardly remembered. It was a steady sort of business. Most of his customers had been using him for years; most of them had first used him when he was a boy, working for his father. The business wasn't expanding, but any shrinkage was too slow to hurt. It was enough to keep them going, the few dozen regulars with their occasional demands for a bookshelf or a cupboard, people who were mostly getting on and didn't mind that Friedrich's father had been using the same styles for twenty years and wouldn't be persuaded to change by his customers' tastes or prejudices.

'I'd like a nice new kitchen cupboard,' one of the old ladies might say, after the necessary inquiries after the health and the grandchildren had been got through. 'With shelves,' she might add, with the appearance of helpfulness.

'With a solid front or with glass?' Franz said, pencil in his mouth.

'Oh – I hadn't thought – solid, perhaps, to go with the other cupboards you made for me – or perhaps glass-fronted, to make a nice contrast. No, I think maybe solid. Do you think –'

'Yes, I think solid,' Friedrich's father said. 'Perhaps something like –'

And then he was off on the thing Friedrich could never stand, the fake inspiration of the drawing, drawing as if he hadn't drawn the same cupboard a hundred times before. Franz couldn't really draw; he couldn't imagine something new. But by god he could draw a cupboard. A square box, neatly finished off, two suggestive, elegant squiggles for handles and an absurd little set of finials, for the elegant appearance.

'For the elegant appearance,' Franz said, breathing heavily as he finished this last detail and added the slanting lines – at thirty degrees exactly – and cross-hatching which, as he had once told Friedrich, made the cupboard seem more real to the customer.

'Are you watching, young man?' the old lady said to Friedrich. 'A real talent it is, your father's got. Are you hoping to follow in his footsteps?'

Friedrich said nothing. He didn't need to look. He had seen the same cupboard too many times.

'And we can polish and varnish it, or the boy can paint it, any colour you like,' Franz said. 'Any colour of the rainbow.'

'Oh –' the old lady said.

'And we can have it ready for you – let me just look at the order book – ready two weeks tomorrow, if that suits.'

It was always two weeks tomorrow, whatever the state of the order book, which was always in the same state. Friedrich was quite old before he noticed that, though the old customers of Franz and of Franz's father mostly carried on using him, they didn't seem able to persuade their children to use him when they left home and needed cupboards and shelves in their turn, though cupboards and shelves, as Franz regularly and complacently remarked, are things which people have always needed and always will.

He must have been hit hard by the appearance of ready-made kitchens, Friedrich sometimes thought when it was all over. A whole new kitchen had been a big deal for him, something to keep him busy for three weeks and pay for a summer holiday. It just stopped; it seemed quite abruptly, though in retrospect it had been more like a steady decline. In the course of five years, Friedrich found himself called out less and less to paint whole ranges of cupboards, more and more for the occasional small piece. His father was around too much, morose and unoccupied; fiddling with the grubby little windowboxes, sitting in his chair, going for a walk for the paper and not coming back for three hours. From time to time Franz would suddenly announce some scheme of improvement for their own house, some new system of wardrobes. No one answered him, and silence returned.

It was the bright ideas that were so embarrassing and shameful; even thinking back Friedrich was made sixteen again, blushing for his father's hopelessness. It was the sense he had, the mistaken sense that there was something which could be done about this and not, as Friedrich saw and had always seen, an inevitability about the downward path which had better be met with equanimity and patience and acceptance. Because when failure and death came, it was always better not to pretend to oneself that there was anything which could be done about it. *It's not the despair I mind*, Friedrich said to himself, watching some American schlock as the screaming heroine with the twisted ankle struggled to free herself from the path of the shark. *It's the hope I can't stand*. No, it was the bright ideas that were the worst.

'Did you say,' Franz said one day, rousing himself, 'that Frau Strich had died?'

'Yes, I heard the other day,' Friedrich's mother said. 'A good age, though.'

'Mmm,' he said. 'What's happening to that big old house out in the hills?'

'Maria – it was Maria who had heard – she heard that the son was going to move into it, because, of course, they only have a flat here in Cologne, and his poor wife with three children and a fourth on the way –'

'They're going to move in?'

'Yes, in fact, now I remember Maria said they already had, moved in only a month after the poor old lady –'

'Still,' Franz said, 'doesn't do to be too tactful, and who is there to be tactful to? No sense in leaving a great big old house like that empty for months. And it can't be in that good shape. It must be ten years since I did any work for her.'

It was clear what was coming.

'I wonder if him and his family need any work doing on the house,' Franz said carefully.

'Well,' Friedrich's mother said in the end. 'There's only one way to find out. Why don't you give them a ring and ask.'

'Or better,' Franz said. 'Maybe I should go round there

and say hello. I was thinking of going out there some time soon. In any case. I could take the boy.'

Unaccountable, the dread produced in Friedrich by the words *the boy*; unimaginable how the same dread, preserved, surfaced in him at the dead memory of a sentence.

It was a good day. Too hot, perhaps, to drive; a day for a quiet desultory sort of walk, and not to put on your black jacket which already you were growing out of, and too hot for your father to put on his pimping-for-business suit, to sweat in. It took too long, as ever, to get out of Cologne.

'Terrible, the traffic, for a weekday,' Franz said.

'Yes,' Friedrich said.

The house was a good hour out of Cologne. It was not, quite, in the country, nor, quite, the grand old house Franz had vaguely indicated; a big square pastel-painted house, ugly and new, not more than forty years old, seeming older, if at all, only because it was so uncared for. There were gates, but they stood open, and Franz drove confidently in. The yard was empty, and quiet, giving no sign that anyone had taken over the house. Perhaps – it was a thought which appealed to Friedrich – they were all out and his father and he would have to go home without any embarrassment.

'Wait here,' Franz said.

He got out of the car. All at once a crowd of dogs appeared from nowhere. Friedrich sat, gripping his seat tightly while the dogs howled into his immobile father's face. It was a mystery to Friedrich how his father could be so confident the dogs would not bite, and would stand there in this heat indefinitely, as if in patience.

A man appeared at the kitchen door. He leant against the wall for a while, smoking and observing the scene. The dogs' energies for this pointless unbiting yelling seemed inexhaustible, satisfied to roar and terrify only. Franz simply stood there, let the biggest of the dogs, a huge Great Dane, mount on his back legs and engulf his face in his open roaring mouth. The man seemed rather interested than concerned, or hostile.

'Please!' Franz finally shouted.

The man disconsolately wandered over to the car, as if deprived of a mild but engaging entertainment. He clapped twice, and shouted a couple of syllables. The dogs ignored him, and carried on. He shouted again, and this time the Great Dane seemed to hear something; it pricked its ears, then dropped down and ran off quietly, followed by the other dogs. The sudden silence rang in the ears.

Franz rapped on the window and made a thumbing gesture. Friedrich got out, still slightly shaking.

'My son,' Franz said, as if this would explain his presence.

The man nodded. 'And who are you, actually?'

'Franz Kaiser,' he said. 'Am I right in thinking that you must be Herr Strich?'

'That's right,' the man said.

'I remember you when you were so high,' Franz said, beaming ingratiatingly. Strich did not smile back. 'You won't remember me, I'm afraid.'

'I don't,' Strich said. 'I'm afraid.'

'May we come in?' Franz said. 'We've come a long way.'

Strich shrugged, but led the way into the house. The dark kitchen was littered with papers; a start had been made on bundling up cutlery with string. Strich began to gather the loose papers together from the kitchen table, gesturing with his head that they should sit down.

'I don't know who you are,' he said. 'I'm sorry.'

'Well,' Franz said. 'The boy and I – I heard about your

sad loss the other day, only the other day – and we felt we had to come and present our regrets. Merely that, just our regrets.'

'Thank you,' Strich said, sitting down. 'Of course, she was a good age.'

'How old was she?' Franz went on nervously. 'We were trying to work it out all the way here.'

'Eighty-six,' Strich said. 'And of course she'd been ill for some years, so it was a relief rather than anything else, to all of us, including her, when she finally went. Had you seen her recently?'

'No,' Franz said. 'In fact, not for many years. It must be – when was the last time we did any kind of work for Frau Strich, boy?'

'Ten or twelve years ago,' Friedrich said. He had checked.

'Oh –' Strich said, as if placing them now. 'What kind of work was it that you did?'

'Odd bits and pieces of carpentry,' Franz said. 'An occasional cupboard, the odd bookcase or shelf. To tell the truth, to tell you the truth, they were much smaller jobs, always much smaller than the firm would normally even consider, but we did them for Frau Strich, with pleasure, and do you know why? Because of our admiration for her, our fondness for her. It was always a pleasure making even a small cupboard for her. What a nice lady she was, really.'

'Yes,' Strich said. 'Of course, she was my mother. It must be years since anything's been done to the house.'

'Yes,' Franz said. 'Like the boy said, it must be twelve years at least since we've touched it.'

'She wasn't very concerned about home improvements in her last years,' Strich said. There was something about this man which made it clear to Friedrich that the conversation wasn't going as his father hoped, that Strich wasn't about to turn round and order thirty thousand marks' worth of new kitchen cupboards. It was just a sense he had. He hung his head; it was difficult to understand why his father didn't want to leave as badly as he did.

'There must be a great deal of work needs doing in the house,' Franz said.

'Quite so,' Strich said with great briskness. 'Naturally, I will call you for an estimate if we decide to have anything done.'

'For an estimate?'

'Yes, naturally,' Strich said. 'You, and other firms.'

'And other firms?'

'Naturally,' Strich said, holding his ground.

'I would have hoped,' Franz said, 'that you would use us.'

'And so we will,' Strich said, with an attempt at kindness, 'if you turn out, as I hope you will, to be the best and the cheapest.'

This was so unlikely that, in retrospect, Friedrich could hardly blame his father for going on.

'Out of reverence and respect for your mother's wishes,' Franz said, 'I hope you would use us. I'm sure that if she was with us today she would have wished you to use us.'

'I don't recall, to be honest,' Strich said with exaggerated patience, standing up as he spoke, 'that in her last illness she expressed the faintest kind of preference for one carpenter or another.'

'Perhaps not,' Franz said, with the air of someone generously granting a concession, and half-standing up as well, 'but she always used us.' He was getting fatally angry, Friedrich could see. He wanted to go, before it got worse.

'Nor do I think that I need to be told what is owing to my mother by a carpenter,' Strich said.

'I was only saying out of –'

'And, may I say, Herr Kaiser, that if you are seeking to recommend yourself on the quality of the work you have already carried out in this house, you will not succeed, since the doors of half the cupboards stick.'

'Of course, that's only to be expected, after twenty years, the marshy air, very humidifying –'

'They have always stuck, Herr Kaiser, and they have always been quite astoundingly ugly, and I cannot imagine what possessed my mother to use you once, let alone repeatedly, nor what possessed you to think that anyone, having seen the quality of your work, would wish to use you again.'

'Now, Herr Strich, I didn't come here with the boy to be insulted –'

'No, you come here to insult my good nature. Now, if you please.'

'I came here out of kindness,' Franz said. 'Thinking you would welcome the offer of – and this is what I get.'

'Yes,' Strich said. Quite abruptly, Friedrich saw the difference between them; his father had allowed himself to fall into a pointless and stupid rage, and Strich would not allow himself to grow angry at all, but only to get rid of them as quickly as possible. 'Yes, this is what you get. Now, if you please.'

They went. Franz said nothing until they were halfway home, concentrating, it seemed, on the road.

'Did you see that?' he said suddenly.

'What?' Friedrich said. He was still thinking about Strich.

'That,' he said, nodding in a forwards direction. There

was a black BMW directly in front of them. 'Overtakes then slows right down, like the cunt he is. Look at that.'

'It's all right,' Friedrich said, hearing in his voice with surprise the conciliatory tactics of his mother. 'We're not in a hurry, are we?'

'Oh no,' Franz said. 'No hurry at all. Only he's not to know that. Is he? Are you, you cunt?'

And he was down on the accelerator, swinging out into the left-hand lane, tucking in just in front of the BMW, and, with theatrical panache, slowing immediately to block it.

'Did you see that?' Franz said cheerfully. 'Waved his fist at us.'

'At you,' Friedrich said, surprising himself.

The road was narrowing, and the driver behind signalled, as if to repeat his manoeuvre of overtaking and slowing. Just as he moved out, so did Franz, driving in the middle of the empty road, blocking the man. A furious blow on the horn, followed by the flashing lights of his impotent rage, and he moved back.

'He's met his match here,' Franz said. A line of cars approaching made him move back into the right-hand lane, where he slowed right down to fifty kilometres an hour. There was a sort of relaxation in his unkindness, like a boy torturing a small animal, out of interest, not, quite, cruelty. As the last of the cars passed, the man in the BMW attempted, again, to overtake, but Franz, again, was too quick, moving out into the middle of the road.

'It's not kind,' Friedrich said.

'No,' Franz said. 'I know it's not.' He grinned, wolfishly, and then finally moved back to let the man overtake. But he did not. The car behind them carried on at their own stately pace, although the road was empty.

'Lost his nerve.'

They drove like that for five kilometres.

'I'm going to lose him,' Franz said, putting his foot down. The man behind followed suit, driving close to him as he accelerated. His face could not, quite, be seen, only that he was alone in the car. Friedrich found a kind of terror in this, as though, unlike Franz, he did not have to justify or find sense in this action of his.

'He's overtaking,' Friedrich said. 'Let him go.' It was ten minutes later. They were on a quiet stretch of road. Franz let the man go; he made no gesture as he passed. He did not need to. A hundred metres ahead of them, the man suddenly braked, and, swinging his car directly across the road, blocked it. Franz braked; there was barely enough space to bring the car to a halt, and they stopped in a judder of breathlessness.

'What kind of . . .'

But the man was out of his car, and running towards them with something in his hands, and Franz, scrabbling, as ever, for the reverse gear he could never find in a hurry, revving, hopelessly, at the clutch and accelerator, was sweating and blank as the great iron bar with terrible slow-ness came swinging through the air and the windscreen cascaded on to them like water. It was an iron bar he had. An iron bar. In his hands. He was swinging it at them. He had put it through the windscreen. It had smashed. They were under the blow of the stick and clutching at them-selves. It was there. It was gone. The wreckage. The wrong. The wreckage.

And then he was gone. A single swing, into the car, breaking it, and a leisurely stroll back to his car, and driving off without conspicuous haste or concern, leaving Franz, gulping like a seal, somehow pathetic in his seat-belted security, waiting for security, for calm, to descend, for him to pull himself, somehow, together, and not listening to, not even hearing his son, saying over and over, and constructing what had happened as he was speaking, trying to understand in his mind what had happened, and pulling himself back from his twitching fear, his shake and terror, saying all the time, 'It's all right, he's gone, he's not coming back, don't worry, it's all right, it's fine, it's over.'

Looking back, Friedrich found it impossible not to think of the four months that followed as the four months of a terminal illness. No diagnosis was offered; none, in the flat where they all moved around quietly and spoke only where necessary, was needed. His father was finished, it seemed, by the encounter with Strich. After that, there was nothing more to be said; no pretence to keep up in front of his wife and children; nothing except to bequeath them all the certain knowledge that all lives end in the same way, all lives, it would always unarguably appear to his children, end in failure.

Perhaps it was a small thing, the argument with Strich. But it was enough. The evening they returned from Strich's house, Franz went to the sitting room and turned the television on. This was quite normal. Friedrich's mother came in.

'Well?' she said.

'I'll tell you later,' Franz said, intent on the television.

As the evening went on, he dropped his shoes on the floor and stretched out. He didn't ask what he invariably did, what his wife had prepared for him to eat, and when she came in to offer him some food, he, in fact, refused. She would not pump Friedrich for information; there was so much loyalty in her, knowing that if Franz said nothing, she would not ask. And the evening went on. They stayed in the kitchen. None of them could quite have said why. And at ten Friedrich's mother went into the sitting room. Her voice could not be heard; his carried to the children.

'No, I'll sleep on the sofa tonight.'

'No, nothing wrong.'

'No, it's not you.'

'No, I'll be fine. No blanket, I just want –'

That was all; the carrying request, *I just want*. They didn't know, any more than Franz, perhaps, himself, what he wanted. Now they never would.

And that was it. That was it. He stayed on the sofa, walled up with cushions and curtains against the day, sleeping fitfully at odd times, the television never quite off, the volume only lowered. His life stopped following the acceptable timings. He slept at odd times; he ate at odd times, raiding the refrigerator in his increasingly disgusting underwear; he emerged, blinking, not quite knowing what time it was. A time of things changing, a time of nothing. They looked at the wrapped unresponding chrysalis of him, and tried to show nothing.

What did he do for the four months before things changed permanently, definitively, for good? Now, for Friedrich, the long silent weeks were compressed into a single memory, of tiptoe conferences in the kitchen, sitting, waiting outside the sitting room where his father lay, unspeaking, on the couch, waiting, like heirs outside a Victorian deathbed-chamber for the inevitable and perhaps desired end. The four months are something before which memory, and narrative, withers, where the consequential logic of syntax has to shrug, to say *And nothing happened, until something happened* . . . Here there was no life, no train of events, but simply a fermata, placed over all their lives. Perhaps it was still there, the fermata. Certainly there was no change from the moment Franz immured himself and drew the curtains, for four months; no change, no development, no cure or acceptance, but only the long entropy of the chaos forming around Franz as he lay and thought, and the unknowable entropy, the chaos, in Franz's head.

Was that really how it was? Retrospection permits grief before the occasion; memory flatters the unconsoled, lets them believe that they were always crêped in black, always knew how his stillness, this existence on cigarettes and vodka and refused meals would end. Perhaps they did have a sense that this was not an occasion to improve, a situation with anywhere to go; perhaps they even glimpsed, as Friedrich, in retrospect, always believed he glimpsed, exactly how this would end. But at what point did a diagnosis come against which the survivors could be brave? What doctor was there, to look at Franz in his underwear, eating a herring out of the jar at eight o'clock in the morning, watching some TV exercise show, watching some air-dried blond boy do his physical jerks on the telly, and say *I'm afraid there is no hope*? What the doctor? What the art of diagnosis, except the dry, unknowable, sentimental one in Franz's head, saying *And this is the end. This is it, old chum. You've done your best. And here is consolation. Here is your consolation prize. And your prize is consolation. Here it is. It was always there, and now, here it is. Waiting for you. Just for you. For you.*

It was Friedrich who was there first, and who first saw that what had happened was not, after all, what he had, after all, always been expecting. The flat was silent, but its silence was not the silence that had been there for weeks. He went into the sitting room, and there it was; no blood; no body; no death; no Franz. He was gone. The blankets were bundled up roughly at one end of the sofa. He walked through the flat, making sure of what he already knew, that his father was gone, and then shut the door to the sitting room. He knew he was gone for good, and when his mother came home, he was at the door, and made her sit down with a cup of tea before she could understand that what had happened was not, in the end, what she had known would happen.

There was an awful wait; he could not be reported missing immediately. And he had gone; in the months that followed, no body surfaced from the river, none found on a dump, none on some remote hill. He had gone, leaving everything behind him. And for Friedrich, what was there was a new solitude, and, in the solitude, a new freedom. He felt that it was him who had escaped, who had left something behind him. And he felt alone; and that was good. To be alone in a flat, in a room, to lock the door, and feel you could do nothing, or anything. Had he ever been alone in his life? Always there was the rampaging father, the worn-down grey mother, all of them in a flat too small for them; and no chance, like Strich, that a grandmother would die and leave them a big house in the country. No one would bequeath them the possibilities of solitude; they would have to find it for themselves.

They all knew he was gone for ever. But they did not say it; so it was possible for Friedrich to say, only a few weeks later, that he had decided to leave. He had made his silent decision. He had chosen solitude, and now he only had to find it. He had to act swiftly. Pretty soon his call-up papers would arrive, and his military service would not be delayed on the grounds of a father's disappearance. The death they had all, they found, expected, would have done; a mere disappearance was not enough. Something in him shrank from claiming a depression he did not feel; perhaps even after his father's disappearance, Friedrich did not want to feel in any way obliged to him. There were other ways of avoiding military service, but only one perfect one.

He left for Berlin six weeks later. There he would find solitude; there he could not be called up. For him, the walled city was an asylum, keeping the world and its elementary demands from him. His mother was beyond hurt; his sisters as contemptuous, only, as they had always been to him. And to anyone else, they put up a front. This was what had been planned, long before. There was no point in changing a plan like this, and indeed, to the neighbours who awkwardly offered sympathy, it was not quite clear why anyone might think otherwise. It was probably for the best not to change anything. He left for Berlin six weeks later. He found his way to Kreuzberg.

Meier was, in his characteristic manner, standing on the stairs as Friedrich came back in, staring in his characteristically disconsolate way out of the window. He appeared, as usual, glum, grubbily shirtsleeved and completely distracted, but it was hopeless to try and sneak past the brute.

'There'll be rain before tomorrow,' the landlord observed, as if to nobody in particular. 'Those are mackerel clouds. They think it's fine, they all do, but it'll be rain they'll be facing before Wednesday. Best be putting off the work for a week.'

Friedrich always knew it would probably be best not to respond in any way to Meier's somehow surly back and bizarrely rural observations; but for some reason he could never quite bring himself simply to slip by.

'Yes,' he said, fatally.

'Herr Kaiser,' Meier said, wheeling round with sudden alertness. 'How are you this fine day?'

'Very well,' Friedrich said, trying to carry on up the stairs.

'Not that there's very much of it left,' Meier went on. 'Lovely day like this, almost over. You don't get up, I've noticed. I've never seen you. Never seen you up and about, not till three or four in the afternoon. Best part of the day gone, by the time some people are up.'

'Oh yes,' Friedrich said, since this was merely a throat-clearing exercise on Meier's part.

'You should get a job, you know,' Meier went on, his attention suddenly fixed by an unremarkably bedraggled small bird, perched on a bare and blasted branch outside. 'That'd do. A man needs a job. Or an occupation. Else he'd start getting up at four, nothing else to do.'

'I work in my flat,' Friedrich said. 'I like to go out for a walk around four. I've been out for a walk, now. It's nice to go out for a walk in the afternoons.'

'No time for a walk, no, sorry, far too busy for that,' Meier went on, as if Friedrich had been inviting him. 'Important to keep busy, important to keep on the move. And if he had a job, he'd have more money.' He seemed to have slipped into neutral observation, addressed to the stairwell. 'And if he had more money, he'd want a better flat. How are you getting on finding somewhere else to live, Herr Kaiser?'

'I'm not looking for somewhere else to live, Herr Meier,' Friedrich said. 'I've got somewhere to live. I've got a job, too. I work in a bookshop two days a week. I like my flat, Herr Meier.'

'Bird knows it's rain on the way,' Meier reverted. 'Twitching its tailfeathers, that's a sure sign.'

'Oh yes,' Friedrich said. He couldn't remember ever having seen a bird sitting without twitching its tailfeathers from time to time, but this one seemed perfectly immobile.

'Get on with your neighbours, do you?' Meier said. 'Do you? Only I was just *wondering*, you see, what I would think if I didn't have a bathroom, and the flat on the other side didn't have a bathroom, and I couldn't have a bathroom till some idle *sod* in the middle found himself a place to live. I just wondered what they were thinking, what they'd be thinking.'

'You'll give yourself a heart attack,' Friedrich said eventually.

'Not before I give you one, you twat,' Meier shouted after him up the stairs.

His encounters with Meier always left Friedrich shaking with rage and fear. It wasn't that Meier could do anything much – but Friedrich felt he would prefer a life where something more than the legal regime of the state prevented him from being thrown on to the street by a mentally unstable landlord. No, fifty thousand marks wouldn't be enough. Perhaps a hundred thousand would. But would it? Would half a million do? A million? What was enough? Was money enough? Was *enough* enough?

THAT'S YOUR STORY

'Do you love me?' Mario said.

Daphne paused. She wanted to catch her breath, and to take from her excitement the appearance of considering the question. 'Yes,' she said. 'Yes, I do.'

'Are you not sure?' Mario said.

'Of course I'm sure,' Daphne said. 'Or I'd have said I wasn't sure. Do you love me?'

They were sitting, one afternoon, at Mario's kitchen table. Like everything in his flat, there was a tentative quality to it, as if he had not quite decided that this was where he was going to stay; he had a canvas hanging wardrobe, a bed which was a mattress on a curious cardboard affair, which was solid enough, but slippery, so that two people in bed had a tendency to pull the mattress on to the floor. The kitchen table was a sheet of hardboard, nailed to an old tea chest; it held, but the temptation to grip its sides was hard to resist. His eyes, in the bad light of the kitchen, wide open, seemed on the point of spilling over with tears. 'How can you doubt it?' he said.

'I don't doubt it,' Daphne said. 'I never said I doubted it.'

'But how can you love me?' Mario said. 'I mean,

someone like me? How do I deserve it? You don't know nearly enough about me.'

'I know plenty about you,' Daphne said. 'Maybe you don't realize how much I understand about you just from spending time with you. You're not going to tell me falling in love is a bourgeois concept, now.'

'No,' Mario said. 'That never occurred to me. Do you think it is?'

'No,' Daphne agreed. 'But –'

She looked at him, sitting there, naked; his huge eyes in the drawn dark face, boned and angular as a cat's cradle, the thin arms and the bulbous chest, the big thighs, marked with the deep hollows and gaps of his enormous fitness.

'Look –' Mario said. He pointed out of the window. 'It's –'

'What is it?'

'Nothing. I thought it was starting to snow. It was just paper, or ashes, or something.'

'A bit late in the year for snow,' Daphne said.

'I know,' Mario said. 'That's why I didn't say anything. I realized it couldn't be snow.'

'Do you have anything in particular you want to tell me?'

'No.'

'I mean, you said I don't know enough about you. So tell me something about yourself, if you don't think I know enough about you.'

'Is there something in particular you want to hear?'

'Tell me everything.'

'Everything?'

'Tell me everything, starting from the beginning, your whole life. Tell me the story.'

She had heard it before. But she loved to hear Mario's

story. He told it to her so many times, in pieces, in high-lights, and many times, over lunch, in bed, during immense exhaustive unforgettable walks from one side of the Grunewald to the other, he told her the whole story from beginning to end. He was a good storyteller; a good teller, at any rate, of his own story, which was his favourite. He was used to being asked how he got here, and enjoyed recounting the adventure, happy that people assumed that anyone who came from the East had a good story to tell, and wouldn't mind telling it.

So whenever anyone said to Mario, 'How did you get out?' – and, in fact, though people were always interest-ed, he found that they said this less often than they might, restrained by an obscure sense of embarrassment and tact, as if inquiring after the death of a disliked elderly uncle from whose estate Mario had massively profited – he said that he always felt like saying 'How did I get in, you mean.' West Berlin felt to him – the whole of the West would probably feel the same, if he ever travelled – like a nightclub outside which pale innocents queued, knowing they had no chance of getting past the scrupulous and surly bouncers; a nightclub which, once entered, turned out to be no fun at all; turned out to be so much like standing around and waiting for something – anything – to happen that in the end you were at a loss to know whether you preferred being outside in the queue or inside in the club. In the West or in the East. Except in the end you had no choice, and it was best to assume that where you ended up was probably where you were meant to be.

Of course, Mario never did say, 'How did I get in, you mean'; he only said that was what he felt like saying. His usual response was something rehearsed and flirtatious;

rehearsed flirtatiousness was, on the whole, what he did best. He usually said, 'I rode out. On my bike.' It had the merit of making people look at him strangely, struck by the picture of Mario sitting up and begging on, perhaps, some boneshaker with a wicker basket and handlebars like a cow's horns, cycling in a leisurely way past a bristling checkpoint, startling the bristling guards with a quick tinkle on the bell. And it had the merit of making people ask for more information; which he supplied.

That was his way. He liked to amuse with the jocular word. He liked to say to a girl in a bar, 'Oh, I rode out on my bicycle,' the way it made her listen to him. He had a word for the Wall, a nice understating joke of a word; he called it *the big fence*. Where are you thinking about, a girl would say, or where are you from, and he would look sincerely at her, and enchant her by saying *the other side of the fence*, or *from beyond the big fence*. Always, he saw in the girl's eyes, in the dance and sparkle of her eyes, swarming over his face as he spoke, the success of the jocularity, always thinking this was the way to make people like you. Poor sap, he never knew she hadn't heard a word he said, wouldn't find it funny if she had. These women, they smiled only to be in the same room as such a smile, such cheekbones, such, my god, such *flesh*.

Mario was born in Berlin, or not far. 'It doesn't much matter where,' he said, and people he talked to, thinking he did not want to talk about somewhere he could not return to, did not press him. His life was quite ordinary, until he was eight or nine. Like all schools, his school measured every inch of every pupil, top to bottom, inside and out, twice a year, made them stretch and bend in their underwear, tapping them, winding them about with tapes, as if measuring them for something, not just out of an idle curiosity called science.

One year, Mario was summoned back, and his tests resumed; more tests, more measurements. He was made to hold his breath as long as he could (something he enjoyed showing off with in the swimming pool; once he had stayed quietly underwater so long that the lifeguard, seriously alarmed, leapt in; there *had* been a row). He was made to run on a primitive machine, like a giant hamster wheel, strapped in; made to do hateful exercises with wired-up sticking plaster all over him. It took a whole day away from school, at a sports centre on the other side of the city; he quite enjoyed the day. No one told him what it was all about, or what it was for, or why him. He still, he said, sometimes wondered why him, and had no answer.

A letter arrived. 'For you?' Daphne would say at this point in the story, wondering at the absence of parents in all of this, wondering at the nine-year-old, opening a letter from the ministry. At nine, he had been diagnosed as exhibiting the appropriate physical standards for further development in the appropriate context, and to that end, had been offered a place at a school for sports development from the forthcoming academic term.

'The ironic thing is,' Mario would say, 'that they carried out all these tests, your breathing capacity, your endurance, your strength, without actually asking you any questions. I mean, they just assume so much about what you actually want, what you would be prepared to do. Really, now, I represent a massive waste of money and investment for them. They could have saved themselves all the bother, not to mention the hundreds of thousands of marks, from the start, if they'd just asked the right question.'

'What would the right question have been?'

'One that I've had said no to.'

'But you're glad you did it?'

'Oh yes,' he said. 'I think so. I don't know who I would be if I hadn't gone there. And now cycling is my life.'

'Or was –'

'Is.'

Nothing was just decreed for Mario; he was always asked to agree to things by the fastidious, almost scholarly men in the school at the foot of the Harz mountains. But he did agree; he always did. At nine, with arms like straws and a weirdly bulbous chest, his insect thorax on his childish gangling limbs, he listened to their professional opinion and did not disagree. Merely that.

He was to be a cyclist. And that seemed okay. He knew how to cycle; he had a bicycle at home. 'Fine,' the class tutor said to him. They were in his room on a Sunday night, a few weeks after Mario had got to the school. 'Forget about that, though. We'll start next week.' It wasn't clear whether the tutor meant he should forget about home, or about any cycling he may or may not have done. He forgot everything, anyway.

They were at the base of the Harz mountains. He had never been away from home before; every year a week on Rügen on holiday, that was all. The black remoteness of the place frightened him; at night, to look out of the dormitory window was to submit to a bandage over your eyes, and minutes passed before you knew whether you were looking at a hillside, or over vast distances, or over nothing at all, at a wall ten metres away. Only some nights, the brilliant moon lit up the black land, and a smooth close dimpled forest rustled in the blue quiet light; the noise of birds he could not recognize, calling from trees he could not name. He lay, and the excess of his terror, what it would be like to feel at home here with this emptiness around you, this idea that one could just set off, in whatever direction, and not be hampered, not be directed, just to go. It took years before it started to feel like freedom.

'Did you have friends?' Daphne asked.

'Of course,' Mario said. One more thing not to pursue with him.

The cycling was the thing. Every day to the top of the mountain and back; that was the way the training started, his first day. The instruction was to go with six other boys to the top of the mountain and back. Just that. He set off, the trainer just behind them, saying nothing, pedalling phlegmatically, watching the boys' legs. He said nothing, just watching. They set off quite cheerfully; it could not be so bad, it was something which could be done every day, if his training schedule was to be correctly interpreted. Once past the school gates, there was a silence of almost appalling weight, the quiet only produced by an immensitude of landscape. You could see so far; and you could see nothing; there was nothing there – no town, no building – to see. Nothing but trees and the distant bright snake-flash of a river under the sun; nothing but land. Land to cover; land to cycle over.

The first day he could not believe pain could hurt so much; he could not believe anyone could contain so much incredible suffering and not actually be about to die. And that was after twenty minutes, the trainer prodding his way up the hill, just behind them, hardly even making a noise in breathing. 'Of course,' he called out, 'I've been doing this hill every day for ten years.' Mario didn't respond; he couldn't speak; he could hardly inhale. And twenty minutes after that, he knew he was going to die, and his eyes were fixed on the peak of the mountain, as if he had just been shown a miracle cure, miles and miles above them. The rest of them were suffering, but not like Mario was suffering. His suffering was the worst. He just knew it. They'd been going an hour when Mario fell off his bicycle. He made himself do it – he wasn't able to ask for a halt. He lay on his side, under the bicycle, waiting for the sympathetic hand and the blissful half-hour rest.

'Don't do that,' the trainer said. 'It's bad for the bike. Keep up.' And he was past, leaving Mario no alternative but to strap himself back into the machine and follow, purple, the phlegmatic progress of the little group. At the top, everything was black; great morphous blobs were shifting before his eyes, and his hair was wet as if he had been swimming. 'Look at that,' the trainer said. 'Marvellous, isn't it?' But Mario was beyond that; he hung like washing over his bike and wept in pain and despair and listened to the other boys agreeing with him. 'Two minutes,' the trainer said, and it took Mario a moment to understand that he was announcing the end of the two-minute break, not its beginning, and a moment beyond that to realize that the trainer was standing over his bike, balancing on the pedals, quite patiently, like an abseiler brinking a cliff, with the other boys round him like cygnets round a swan, and all of them waiting for him.

'I've seen worse,' the trainer said when Mario, pale and trembling with the torment of the ascent, the sheer black terror of the descent – and how long had it taken him to understand the one truly awful thing, the truth that only he was stopping himself from crashing and dying – reached him at the bottom and gazed with what can only have been hopeless misery at him. 'We'll do it again tomorrow.'

The next day was, if anything, worse; the sense of remounting the bicycle with legs which could hardly walk was like being pulled apart by horses, and to the agony of the climb was added the agony of yesterday's climb. So how many weeks was it before he noticed that the climb wasn't taking him so long, and how long – perhaps it was the day when his trainer pointed out that the whole ascent and descent had taken him precisely half the time he had taken the first day – before he began to see any kind of pleasure, even to imagine the possibility of pleasure in the circuit?

Six months after he had started, his trainer began to talk. The group had thinned out a little; three boys had been sent back to where they had come from. The three of them left had been chosen, and now it was time to start to talk. Until then, he had imagined that this was how it was to be, up the hill and down again, steadily faster, but his trainer was there to show him the blocks he, unknowingly, had hit, the elementary routes around his problems, routes he would, off his own bat, only discover slowly if at all. Nothing profound, nothing complex, nothing really but abuse, but Mario was quick to see that his comment of 'What are you doing, still in the saddle?' or 'Your gears are all fucked. Start thinking, for Christ's sake' was the only way to get where he was going, and get there fast enough, before the engine of ageing overtook the endless possibilities of swiftness. He saw that so quickly; he saw that he did not have forever, and he saw, exactly, how his career would end. He had no interest in the progress of the others. They were no good. He could see that.

The most important thing his trainer ever said to Mario was simply this: *Look at the road.* He would never have found that bridge on his own; had always, neck creaking, contemplated the peak, hopelessly straining with his head back after the distant pinnacle, his legs breaking, the backs of his legs burning up with pain. And then he heard only this: *Look at the road*. After that he could do it. It was almost like a metaphysical truth, and to himself he recited it like a mantra, a pious proverb: Look at the road. And that is what he did, and it was no metaphysical saying, just a physical truth. Never think about anything but what is before you; look no further than the next twenty metres, only that, and be patient with each unrolling ten metres, and find the joy in your knees. *Look at the road*; and he could do it. The trainer had shown him how, four words. And there was the secret. In another two years it was a secret that let him shed the other two boys, and pass them all, and by the time he was fifteen, it was just him and the trainer. There was the secret. That was it. That was enough.

His name was Hans-Christian. Mario had been at the school for five years before curiosity about the man who had been cycling up and down the Harz mountains with him daily really hit. By then, they were, daily, cycling up the mountain, down the other side and over the two mountains beyond that. Three mountains, translated into one hundred kilometres, or in the way Hans-Christian translated, reduced landscape, six descents, six ascents, and every one, every new ascent, on its introduction into the daily circuit, a shocking augmentation of suffering. But now he waited for his trainer.

'That last descent was a fucking mess,' he said. 'You throw too much away, you're having such a laugh, such a fucking *great time*.'

'Oh, I know,' Mario said, not minding Hans-Christian's tones of disgust. He knew it was true, the way he subdued the importance of speed to the pleasures of flight, and yet he felt somewhere in him that a man who only regarded the vertiginous fall as a tight cling to the

road would, in the end, not be as good or as fast a cyclist
as someone who, like him, could wrap himself round the
bicycle and, at the moment of greatest descent, like a
brick falling down a hole, could by his own decision relax
his arms from the elbow to the wrist, roll his blank eyes
upwards so that he could see not just the road but the
land beyond it, the sky, the earth, and allow the furious
descent, its falling so like flight, to pleasure him. That, he
knew, was why he was going to be so good; that astonished knowledge, in full ecstatic flight with nothing but
air beneath him and before him, great vistas of air, stretching out, unbounded as truth, that he had all the time in the
world. And he knew, too, that his trainer, good as he was,
would never be great and never had been; knew that,
behind him, Hans-Christian was gripping the handlebars,
tense in every muscle, trying to get down by tightening
up and rushing, not seeing what Mario himself could
barely put into words, that the essence of cool speed, the
enchanting secret of flight was to go limp, to guide with
movements of supple slowness, to move like a fish with
the sure knowledge that there was all the time in the
world, to go wherever you wanted, to do whatever you
wanted.

'How far did you get?' he asked Hans-Christian once.

He carried on staring into space, and thinking, as if
Mario had said nothing. 'I'm getting old,' he said in the
end. 'You're beating me too easily.'

'Or maybe –' Mario said.

'I doubt *that*,' Hans-Christian said crisply. 'No, I did
the Tour de France three times. The fourth time I didn't
finish, and after that –'

He didn't go on, just shrugged. It was characteristic,
perhaps, that he knew what Mario had meant immediately,

and Mario reflected what he already knew, that the question *how far did you get* was perpetually at the front of his mind.

'What years?' Mario said. He would know if Hans-Christian had been placed; he was pretty sure he would know if he had even won a stage.

'Aimar, Pingeon, that other guy,' Hans-Christian said. 'And then I had a year off, and the year after that was the second year Merex won it.'

'Why did you take a year off?' Mario said.

'I had an injury,' Hans-Christian said. 'You don't even think about it if you're not all there. It would kill you.'

'And the last year?'

Hans-Christian looked away, and Mario could understand why; what humiliation there was in his gaze he did not care to see, what sharp memory of lying, screaming, by the road, with the blade-knowledge passing silkily through him, that this was it; there was no more; that something, now, had come to an end; the sure knowledge that he had done his best and his best, to tell the truth, was all there was that he could draw on. 'It would have killed me,' he said in the end. 'It would have killed me. It almost did. I could have done it maybe once more. But there was someone else to take my place. There always is.'

'What was the best you did?'

'Finished forty-third the second year. At one point in the mountains I was in twelfth place.'

'You remember.'

''Course you remember.'

'Did you ever win a stage?'

'Ha,' Hans-Christian said. It was as if winning was a toy for children. 'I never cared about that. So I never did. All I cared about was finishing. It's an odd thing; you must have seen something of it. It's not you against them, but all of you against the race. The race is the thing you've got to beat, the thing you're fighting. Every so often it does turn into a competition, and you find, in a sprint, that you're racing against other cyclists, with you against someone else. Then I always thought there was something pointless to it. I cared about finishing, that's all, and three times I finished. 'Course, I can say that now, no one would have dared to say it then, you'd have been out like a shot. No, I never won a stage.'

'I want to win it,' Mario said. Of course he did; he was fifteen. Hans-Christian looked at him, as if on the verge of saying 'Yeah, right,' or 'Fat chance, loser.' But he seemed to think about it.

'That's very much what I would have said, and not meant it.'

'I want to win it,' Mario said.

'I never felt, really, like saying that,' he said. 'And you do want to say it, of course you do, because you want to win. Maybe that was it. Don't ask me how you win the Tour de France. All I can tell you is how to finish the Tour de France, how to finish forty-third in your best year, and end up so you always have to tell people what you've done, because they never know your name.'

'Will they let me go and do it?'

'Maybe. Not yet. There are other races to do first.'

'I race already.'

'And you win, mostly, if that boy from Rostock isn't in the field. Maybe, yes, one time soon. The whole thing is a big nightmare to organize, getting you there and stuff. And from your point of view there's no chance of getting to know the terrain. You arrive knowing it from maps, and do it, and the year after you'll just have to remember all the mistakes you made the year before. We're at a huge disadvantage, all in all.'

'Except that we're better than anyone else. I still want to do it,' he said. 'When I'm ready.'

'Maybe. You might not get that far,' Hans-Christian said. 'You might, but you might not. You have to face that.'

'I'll face it when it comes.'

So there it was; the great unyielding wall against which he could, when the time came, fling his ambition, and see if it came back whole, or what. That was what he was here for; not the crap races, the Polish three-day events, the two-hundred-kilometre rallies which came up every month throughout the season and which he divided up, as if an agreement had been reached, with the pink-faced boy from Rostock. But that; the covering of a whole country, going out to somewhere new, unstopping, unbounded.

It came to him like an unsuspected, hoped-for revelation; like love to a boy. It was as simple as this, his trainer just saying to him, 'It's all right. You'll do it next year.' He was nearly eighteen; it was what he had wanted for almost ten years, and here it was, massive, unyielding gift of a race. Those Polish races; he called them gifts, sailing ahead of the field, and thought them not serious. This was a gift, offered him, waited for, never, superstitiously, expected, precisely because it was serious. Because it could not be now, and what would defeat him would be, at some point, the race. Just to balance in a crowd, just to take part, that would be enough, he said to himself. He knew he lied.

'Listen,' Hans-Christian said. 'We've got a new bicycle for you.'

There was a suppressed excitement in his voice; it was like the voice of an adolescent talking about sex, denying his thrill, and betraying it with the thickness in the voice, the inability not to talk about what he most wanted.

'I've just had a new bicycle,' Mario said. It was true; only six months before, a fine new instrument, taut and resilient, which seemed almost to twang under him like a harp. Every year, a new bicycle, the year-before's reduced to the spare, but this one was fine, a terrific machine. He was almost in love with it, it and its possibilities interested him so much.

'No,' Hans-Christian said. 'No, I know you have. But this is something else. They've produced this bicycle for you.'

'Who's they?' Mario said.

'The usual people,' Hans-Christian said. 'Of course. But they've tried out something quite interesting. They'd like to see what you think about it. It might suit you. They've certainly put some nice detailing into odd corners. See what you think.'

'I like this one,' Mario said, obstinately. 'I've been getting good results on it. I kind of feel I haven't got to the end of it yet.'

'Well, sure,' Hans-Christian said. 'Just give this one a go. There's no obligation to use it if you really can't get on with it. But it's something quite new. In fact, it's so new, we're going to have to check it out with the authorities before we can be sure you can use it on the Tour. They can be a bit funny about changing specifications, and you never know what they'll accept or refuse. Sometimes they just deny that what you're using is a bicycle at all, as if you'd turned up with a skateboard or a motorbike.'

'Well, I don't mind,' Mario said. 'I'll give the thing a go, but don't give me a hard time if I want to stick with this one.'

'Of course not,' Hans-Christian said. 'It's not in any-one's interest to make you use a machine you can't get on with.'

The thing arrived a couple of days later. There was a note in Mario's pigeonhole, just saying *It's here. H.-C.S.* Mario ignored it, and went for his circuit routine in the gym first. At lunchtime, he wandered over to the work-shop. Hans-Christian was chatting to a mechanic. There was a squashed rectangle of a wooden case there, heavily roped around, unopened.

'Thank god you're here,' the mechanic said, breaking off their conversation. 'This one's driving me up the wall. He's been hanging about all morning, like a kid on Christmas Eve. Open the bloody thing and let's have a look at it.'

'What have you waited for me for?' Mario said teasingly. 'I wouldn't have minded.'

'It's yours to open,' Hans-Christian said, cautiously. 'You first.'

Mario took a knife and cut through the thick ropes binding the box up. There were heavy metal clasps holding the case together, and, undone, the box came apart neatly. Inside, the machine was packed heavily with newspaper, and the three of them took a few moments to empty the box. Together, they lifted the beautiful, strange machine out. As they took it and gently tugged it free, each of them almost fell backwards at the lack of resistance, the exquisite lightness which surprised the arms, the strange feeling of emptiness as it fell into the hands.

They set it down. It was peculiarly shaped; it had the air of a bicycle drawn by somebody who had seen one once, and was trying to recall how the struts and beams fell together, with partial success. Mario walked round it as the mechanic pumped up the tyres. Hans-Christian watched him.

'It's something else, this machine,' he said after a minute or two.

Mario said nothing. He took a spanner from the workbench, a small one, a delicate lady's spanner, as it were, and hit the cross-bar. It rang. He went round the machine, tapping gently at each part of it, and at each point, it was as if he had taken a tuning fork between thumb and forefinger and made it resound; the beautiful empty resonance of this thing, and at no point did it clang, or make a thudding empty noise, even at the joints; it was as if it had been carved out of a single piece of metal –

('What's it made out of?' Mario asked.

Hans-Christian just looked at the mechanic, and they both smiled, keeping their secrets, the machine's secret magic.)

– carved out of a single piece of metal, and hollowed and shaped without at any point any weak welding, any vulnerable joining; it was as if the metal had been stretched to the absolute point, the last fine thread of breaking, and then made to hold, and harden at the moment when it would ring, taut as a violin string, and left in this extravagant gleaming perfection, with the sure knowledge that the right touch, just one, would make the marvellous machine sing, and fly. Mario looked at it. His wrists ached with the wish to hold it. He suppressed the excitement he felt, and, looking at Hans-Christian, looking at him, and the mechanic, looking at the machine, he could see that they were mustering a critical gaze, judging the instrument, as best they could.

Mario took it in his right hand, when the tyres were inflated. It took no effort to lift. He raised it six inches, and dropped it; it bounced like a ball, tensile with its contained energies. He mounted it and poised, for a minute, balancing on its pedals like an acrobat about to swing on his trapeze; he swiftly dismounted, then remounted, swinging his leg over the saddle. He executed a tight circle, there in the workshop, almost falling with the unfamiliar lack of weight, the unfamiliar latent swiftness. This would take him, he could feel; it felt like something with some hidden engine, and he looked enquiringly at Hans-Christian's knowing face.

'Off you go,' he said.

'Are you coming?' Mario said.

Hans-Christian shook his head, and Mario was pleased. This was something, just for now, he wanted to be alone with.

He was back four hours later. The two of them were still in the workshop, sitting and chatting. As he came through the door, they got up, both affecting a slight lack of interest.

'Well?' Hans-Christian said.

'It'll do,' Mario said. He could not say more. There was no more to say; and his wish not to gush, his wish to appear stoic in the eyes of these men who had seen everything, whom nothing could surprise, joined with his inability to say enough, the inability to find words for this magical thing, whose secrets he felt he would never quite understand, and whose secrets, he felt, not even its makers had quite understood, quite understood how they had achieved what they had achieved. It would do. It was enough.

'It certainly cost enough,' the mechanic said bluntly. 'Don't mess with it.'

The five months before the Tour were a sudden escalation of training. There were new trainers; Hans-Christian stayed in the Harz mountains, and could not come, to his obvious regret. Mario travelled around, meeting the rest of the team – most of whom he knew anyway, from maintaining some kind of edge over them at the usual races – and going for weeks cycling as much hill terrain as could be summoned out of this small country. The mountains here were not enough, really; there was nothing more, however, to be had, and they had to do. Every fourth day was on the flat, and they sprinted, pushing against nothing, knowing that here, at least, there was no hill to beat, nothing except the limits they had to find inside themselves. They hardly talked in the evening. The morose pigeon-chested boy Mario shared a room with sometimes wandered into the bathroom and they talked about women, about cycling, about what they would do when all this was over, while Mario sat in the bath and shaved his legs into the muddy water. In a way, they all wanted to be alone; alone with the race, and they practised the usual rotation of leaders, the usual practice of overtaking each other and giving back the lead to the team sprinter at the crucial moments with an odd lack of sharing, an odd lack of a sense that they were all in this together.

'What do you want to do when we get to France?' the boy said, one night, watching Mario sit on the edge of his bed and examine his poor crippled feet, sole up, squashed and bound like the feet of Chinese empresses.

'I don't know,' Mario said. 'Win the race.'

'Come on,' the boy said. 'What do you really want to do?'

Mario considered. He wondered about this boy. There was always an informer in any sports team, he knew that, someone to keep an eye on any possible irregularities, any vague sense of disloyalty or unreliability. He would not say anything, not knowing, quite, what failure, what disloyalty, there was inside him, knowing, at the same time, that if anything would find out where his reliability ended, it would be this race itself, and not some pathetic Stasi informer, paid to ask dumb questions.

'Drink some French beer,' he said in the end. 'Eat some French food. Enjoy some French sunshine. Fuck some French girl. Win the race. Come home.'

'You don't stand a chance of fucking a French girl,' the boy said.

'Just watch me,' Mario said.

'It's too hard a race,' the boy said. 'You wait. You won't be able to get it up for a week after it's over.'

'You've got a point,' Mario said. It was true; cycling did make you impotent, as if you could only acquire the power to get you up hills by sacrificing any power to have sex. 'Well, enjoy the food and the sun and get home in one piece.'

'Right,' the boy said.

'And you?' Mario said.

'The same,' the boy said, dully.

It was as if a possibility had opened up before Mario; as if there had been nothing there, in front of him, but the race; and now, a new sense had opened up. What it was, he could not see, and would not see until it was there in front of him, in his face. He could not, quite, imagine it. He would not.

It came on the seventh day. The first days of the Tour were not testing. It seemed like another race; a big one, but another race, on the flat. He did respectably, towards the front of the middle of the field, with most of his team-mates. Sprinting, he knew, did not matter; it was the mountains that mattered, but he would not think, just yet, about that. Look at the road, he said to himself, not contemplating anything but the immediate future, not imagining or thinking of the mountains a couple of hundred miles, a hundred miles, fifty miles, ahead, not thinking of them even when they first came into view. He gave no thought to where he was, and talked to the rest of the team, the coaches, only about tactics. He gave no thought even to the boy he shared a room with, his probing to discover the intentions of Mario, who had no intentions.

On the sixth day, the mountains struck, and things started to change. The field, it seemed, began to fall away behind him; he and the bicycle pressed against the hill, and, one after another, he shed the riders he had gone along with, like a snake shedding its skin. Five hours up the hill, and he was almost alone; only three riders in front of him. At the end of the day, his team-mates looked at him, and said little; the bare congratulations coming with an air of surprise. They talked all evening about tactics, and it became clear to Mario that the whole thing was being rethought; reconsidered around him.

The next day was the seventh day. He made no plans; he just set off, and, again, he found himself at the front, within a couple of hours. This was bad, he knew; the intelligent thing was to allow some sucker to set the pace, to follow in the main body, and start to sprint at a point where you could maintain the pace. Well, today he would be the sucker. He just wanted to see where you could go. And the rest of the team he would leave behind.

But there are more roads than one; and it is not by the ordinary tarmacked paths, signalled and marked out by monitors, by people telling you where to turn, that all goals are reached. The seventh day was different, because it produced a new direction: the possibility not of winning the Tour de France, which had always been there and always would be there, but the possibility of not winning it; of leaving it; of continuing your life in a way not considered, not imagined, not thought of until it was suddenly real.

He was almost at the top of a mountain. And there it was, quite suddenly, just below the peak; nothing more remarkable than a police station, and that was all. It swam into his field of concentration, within his twenty metres of road, and he was looking, quite suddenly, at a road he had not seen before. And there it was to take. *Look at the road. Look at the road.* And it was a road he had never seen. And here it was, the beginnings of the road, and he would not look at what was at the end of it. He could not. He did not have the habit.

He was off his bike and running, out of the group he so easily headed, the magical bike wafted, as if from its own lightness, on to his shoulder, and up the steps, not looking to see what was behind him, whether the team sneak was chasing him, whether the team car was stopping, who was coming for him. And he was into the police station and safe. Not knowing, only, what was beyond that bit of road; not knowing, now, how to look beyond the next stretch, the next moments, not knowing how the road, the landscape, Europe, his own life would stretch before him newly as he left, with two bemused country policemen on either side of him, facing the flash-bulbs of a nine-days'-wonder, facing the terror of the newly revealed vast vistas of the future, and travel, and unconstrained choice with an equanimity only possible because the only choice was to contemplate the far-away sober face and mind of Hans-Christian, hearing the news, holding his head, and knowing, as if for the first time, the numb stupidity of loss. A man he would never see again.

* * *

'Don't you miss it?' Daphne said.

'You miss all sorts of things,' Mario said. 'Miss that? No; I still cycle.'

'I didn't know that.'

'You don't have to know everything.'

'I've never seen your bicycle.'

'No? I've got two; the one I came out on and another, not so good, I saved up and bought here. I keep them in a little garage I rent, fifty marks a month. I couldn't keep them here. I cycle every Saturday, you know.'

'Really?'

'Yes, of course, it's what I do.'

'Don't you ever think of trying out for the West German team? Could you get in?'

'Maybe then I could have. They certainly had a go at persuading me. Maybe even still now. I don't know if I still want to. I told them then I'd think about it. I like what I do now.'

'What do you do now? You put in a few hours a week at the library.'

'I do what you do,' he said. 'I study.'

'Well, what for?' Daphne said.

'Because what else is there to do?' Mario said. 'I want to do something with my life. Cycling up and down mountains, that's not doing something with your life.'

'It seemed like it at the time, though,' Daphne said. 'I bet it did.'

'Yes,' Mario admitted, at last. 'Yes, it did.'

'If I'd cycled at that level, ever,' Daphne said, 'I think it would be really difficult to settle down to being a weekend cyclist. I'd rather give it up completely.'

'You don't know about it,' Mario said. 'You get a sense of proportion about it.' Daphne drank her tea.

'Where do you go, then, on your Saturday rides?' she said, after a while.

'Where is there to go?' Mario said. 'I do the circuit.'

'What circuit?'

'I go round the Wall, in a day. It's about the right length. I have a route, I do the same route, every week.'

'No hills, though.'

'No,' Mario said. 'The only hill in Berlin is the Kreuzberg, and that's not worth crossing the road for.'

She looked at him. His training seemed so sad to her. What was he training for? Who was there to see his improvement? She contemplated the idea of Mario, every Saturday, setting off with his expensive bicycle, the property of the DDR, and sprinting off, banging at every corner into the restraining boundary of the Wall, buzzing round in his furious pace within the walled limits like a bluebottle in a jar, going nowhere, expending energy just for the sake of expending energy. She contemplated him, sitting naked at his kitchen table, the taut fibres of his legs, aching for a mountain to climb, and making do with what could be got, circling the flat city with furious impatience, wanting only what could not be had. She saw how his body must ache for the idea of setting off and riding, unimpeded, going as far as it could, testing his body against his capacities, hills, land, hurtling in a straight line, not sent back, disconsolate, by the imposed borders of states.

'Have you tried to go back, just for the day?' she said.

'No,' Mario said. 'I don't know what would happen. It might be all right. I just don't particularly want to. I haven't tried. I just have a bad feeling about it.'

'Tell me something else.'

'What would you like to hear?' Mario said. He took her

hand, and, kissing her fingertips, worked up her arm, nuzzling back the arm of the dressing-gown she wore, his dressing-gown. She watched him, amused, detached from his seducer's art.

'Anything,' she said, finally. 'Tell me something about when you were a child. Tell me something that happened to you before you went to the cycling school.'

Mario paused. He gave the inside of her elbow one last shivering lick.

'All right,' he said. 'I don't remember that much. I'll tell you a very small thing. Once we were all going out, my class at the first school, for a day in the country, and we all had to bring a packet of sandwiches for lunch, I can't remember where we were going, or why, or anything. I must have been pretty small, probably six or seven. Anyway, my mother packed my lunch, and, in with the sandwiches, she put in some fruit – some cherries, she'd been given or maybe managed to buy. But she didn't have anything to put them in, and she wasn't the sort of person who would just give you fruit in a paper bag. The only thing she had, which was what she eventually put them in, was an ashtray. Now, nobody in my family smoked, and nobody was ever allowed to smoke in the house, so I don't know why we had an ashtray in the first place. Maybe somebody gave it to us. Anyway, it was completely clean, never been used, and everything. It's just that I don't think I'll ever forget the horrible feeling, the humiliation, really, when the other children saw what I brought my fruit in, what sort of home they thought I came from.'

He paused. She believed him.

'What happened?'

'It's not much of a story, I know. All that happened was

that I threw the ashtray away. I don't know why. When my mother asked, I said it had broken in my bag. I don't know why she was annoyed. Well, she wasn't annoyed, just sad, which really seemed worse. I hated being told off. I always hated it. I always wanted to be liked and to join in and get my own back on anyone who ever had told me off. Maybe.'

'Did you eat the cherries?'

'Ha. Of course I ate the cherries.'

'What happened to your mother?'

'I don't know what to say about her.'

Daphne sat still, but that was it. She could not say what she thought; that her belief in Mario, her belief that he was telling her the whole truth, came and went unpredictably. She wondered what some casual research into Mario's stories of the cycling and the cherries and the Tour de France and the escape would come up with.

'What happened to Caspar?' she said.

'Caspar?' Mario said. 'Ha.'

He looked at her, almost affectionately; she almost broke the silence, and then she did not, but looked back levelly.

'You know,' Mario said in the end. 'I'm out of coffee. Do you mind going to get some more?'

'And Caspar?'

'Why don't you go and get some coffee?'

'I want to know about Caspar.'

'And I want some coffee. Why don't you go and –'

'I'll go if you tell me when I get back.'

He shrugged; it might have been agreement. She got up, thinking that Mario usually got his way. She was at the door when he said 'Daphne.' She paused, not turning round.

'Don't worry,' he said. 'It's just a bit of a complicated story.'

'With you,' she said, opening the door, 'everything always is. I won't be long.'

AT THE SOVIET MEMORIAL

IT WAS A Thursday. Friedrich saw Daphne; they were both in the supermarket.

'Herr Kaiser,' she said.

'Daphne,' he said, declining to join in with any jocundity. 'I thought you were going to call me to go out for a drink.'

'You never called me.'

'You never called me. We didn't make a date. It was just that I thought you might have wanted to.'

'Well, I did,' she said. 'Of course I did. If I ever get stuck on an East German motorway ever again and someone offers me the choice of who I want to get stuck with, you would be very near the top of the list.'

She smiled. He smiled back. There was nothing much to say to each other.

'Come for a drink, then,' he said. 'Soon.'

'I'd like to,' she said. 'Any time you like. Are you in the book?'

'My phone number? Of course. Come for a walk, now.'

'No, I can't,' she said. 'I've got too much to do.'

'Too much to do?'

'Yes,' Daphne said, laughing. 'I just came out to get

some stuff for my boyfriend. He lives round the corner. You sound as if you don't understand the concept of having too much to do.'

Friedrich hadn't meant to make a joke. 'So, what are you doing later?'

'Nothing,' she said. 'I had arranged to go out with Mario, my boyfriend, you know, but I really ought to go and see my aunt. What are you doing, then?'

'I'm just on my way to see Peter Picker, as it happens,' he said.

'That man?'

'Yes,' he said, not knowing how to deny it. 'What have you got in your basket?'

'Have a look, if you like,' Daphne said, amused. He looked. It was alarmingly full of delicatessen titbits; of small tubs of prepared dishes to which nothing could be added and nothing, except packaging, need be taken away; purchases which could constitute a small meal, but which, surely, could not be lived on for long. Ready-prepared carrot salads and bagged-up tomato-and-cheese dishes – a series of treats, Daphne's idea of what her boyfriend would like to eat, and not in any sense food, dinners, sustenance – what filled Daphne's basket was a diet which could only be kept up for a few days before succumbing to the feeling that some crucial mineral deficiency was about to set in. The femininity of Daphne's food purchases made him see himself in his own basket, filled with mud-caked vegetables and the raw material of bachelor survival – bread, milk, coffee – as if he had filled it on purpose to show a girl what honesty and plainness he was capable of. He was quite proud of his shopping, for once.

'You don't look like someone who really likes food,' he said, heartily.

'Oh, you're not one of those people who think they can interpret people's personality from what's in their shopping trolley, are you?' Daphne said. 'There's nothing more boring and smug, to be honest. And I'm not shopping for myself. I'm shopping for Mario.'

'No,' Friedrich said. 'I was just saying that the food you were buying looks like the food you'd buy if you didn't want to eat anything.'

'I don't see the difference,' Daphne said, apparently rather enjoying the acquisitive banter. 'And as it happens, I love stuffing my face with any old thing. Mario likes this stuff, but I'd rather – oh, I don't know why I'm bothering to defend myself from you.'

'It looks as if you might nibble it in front of the telly with your Mario for a while, but in the end you would probably just keep it in the fridge for a week and then throw it away.'

'Of course not,' Daphne said. 'Do I look like someone who's rich enough to be able to afford to throw food away?'

'Yes, you do.'

'Well, anyway, eating is almost my favourite thing in the world,' she said. 'I just don't much like –' she looked with momentary distaste at Friedrich's stout basket – 'all that *scrubbing*.'

'So do you want to go out or not, then?'

'Sure,' Daphne said. 'What did you have in mind?'

'Let's have that drink,' Friedrich said. 'We were supposed to go out after the New Year and we never did.'

'So long as we don't sit in bars all night. I can't stand that.'

Friedrich looked at Daphne moistly. There was something about her conversation he found impossible to understand.

'Do you dance?' he said eventually, with a sense of the slight absurdity of the two of them standing in the aisle in the supermarket, establishing through conversation just how far they could go with each other.

'Of course I dance,' she said. 'Don't you remember?'

'I remember,' he said. 'Do you go to S.O.36 ever?'

'I know where it is,' she said, and she seemed overcome with remembered naughtiness, as she looked, half-giggling, at the floor.

'Come on,' he said. 'Let's go and have a drink now.'

'No,' she said. 'Really, no, I can't. I've got to get back to Mario. He's sitting right now in his kitchen.'

'Oh, he won't miss you.'

'He will, he will. I said I'd be out for a moment. You know, the thing about men is –'

'Yes?'

She began, almost, to blush; he could see that it had occurred to her to drop it, but, instead, she went on. 'The thing about men is that they never think anyone else's concerns are of any significance.'

'No,' Friedrich said, pretending outrage. 'The thing about men is that they never think anything, in the end, is of much immediate significance. Stress on the word immediate.'

'That's right,' Daphne said, her attention wandering. 'Maybe you have a point. And the thing about women –'

'The thing about women?' Friedrich said. He fixed her eyes, there, under the strip-lighting, just by a display of fifteen sorts of no doubt more or less identical washing powders.

'Oh, nothing,' she said, and now she really was, surely, beginning to blush. 'Give me your phone number, and we'll go out.'

'I'm in the book,' he said.

'You're in the book,' she said turning away from him, and smiling, at no one, and for no reason.

In the air, as she went, the generalization about men, the unfinished generalization about women hung beautifully, like perfume, like an achieved intimacy. How odd it was, Friedrich thought, standing there as if struck on the back of the head, as if about to drop his basket of muddy vegetables and bread, the bare means of physical support, as if about to fall, face-first, to the floor, that an absurd generalization about all men, about all women had the power that no personal comment, however frank, could have; the power to break through the politeness and banter through which most relations are conducted, the power to produce a sudden bare intimacy, like the power of a woman, raising her head, and looking directly into your eyes, and seeing you, and letting you, for the first time, see her. He stood there, and the shoppers in the supermarket negotiated him, awkwardly.

Picker was already waiting for him. Not inside the café, but on the street, impatiently looking at his watch, although Friedrich was pretty well on time.

'If I were you,' Friedrich said, 'I wouldn't stand on the Oranienstrasse with fifty thousand marks in my pocket.'

'It's not funny,' Picker said. 'You're ten minutes late.'

'Only ten? I thought it was fifteen.'

'Never mind that,' Picker said. 'Have you got the stuff?'

'No, of course not,' Friedrich said. 'I need the money first. You don't just get given fifty thousand marks worth of drugs on credit, you know. Not even me.'

'You never said that,' Picker said in an agony of panic. 'You never said that. You've got to get the stuff.'

'I can't,' Friedrich said. 'They need the money first.'

'And if I give you the money,' Picker said, 'what guarantee do I have that you won't just waltz off with it?'

'None,' Friedrich said. 'But what else are you going to do? And look at it this way. What guarantee does my dealer have that I won't just waltz off with his drugs and not pay him?'

'Why shouldn't he trust you? He knows you, doesn't he?'

'These guys,' Friedrich said impressively, 'aren't in the business of trusting anyone. And who's that?'

Picker's little boy was standing there, his legs half giving way, looking up at Picker and Friedrich, with a long-suffering mid-afternoon expression.

'I know,' Picker said. 'I'm sorry, I had to bring him, there was no one to look after him. Let's go in.'

They sat down and ordered some coffee. There was an array of fly-blown cakes on the counter.

'Shall I?' Picker said. 'No, I'll be good.'

'Does Tom want something?' Friedrich said. 'Tom?'

The child gazed at Friedrich.

'Do you want a cake?'

He looked blank. Picker said something to him in English. The child shook his head, exaggeratedly.

'He never wants to eat in places he doesn't know. Don't worry, he'll be good. So, look, I have *fifty thousand marks*,' whispering, 'here in my wallet. What I need to know before I tell you the rest of the deal is, have you set up the stuff already?'

'Yes, yes,' Friedrich said. 'All waiting, tip-top stuff, direct from some drop-out chemistry student's bedroom in Neukölln, or so I imagine. It's best not to know too much of where this stuff comes from, to tell you the truth.'

'And the guy you're dealing with –'

'Martin,' Friedrich said in a moment of inspiration. Martin, his drinking friend.

'He's reliable, right?'

'Very reliable,' Friedrich said. 'Safe as houses. Reliable as an ostrich. Whatever. I've been dealing with him for years. He's not the sort to fuck us around.'

'And respectable?'

'Very much so.'

'And not dangerous or violent?'

'Not at all.'

'When are you seeing him?'

'Well, straight away,' Friedrich said. 'You said you wanted me to get the stuff over to the East this afternoon?'

'Excellent,' Picker said, relaxing. 'I have the solution. You and I will go to your dealer's, and I will pay him directly, then *you* can take the drugs and go to East Berlin with them and hand them over. How about that?'

'Well, I don't know,' Friedrich said. 'The thing is, he knows me, but he doesn't know you. And he doesn't know anything about you. All he knows is I've got a commission from some bigshot. It's really much better if he doesn't know anything about you at all. And you don't want to take your child to these places.'

'I don't know,' Picker said. 'I thought you said he was respectable.'

'Look, don't you trust me?'

'It's always better not to trust anyone,' Picker said sententiously. 'I trust you about as much as I trust anyone. Which is not very much. And I wouldn't go anywhere where I wouldn't take Tom. It's not a bad rule in life.'

'You'd better start thinking about trusting me, chum,' Friedrich said. He was good at rage, when he made the effort. He swore to himself. The whole thing was definitely going horribly wrong. 'Because I don't know if you've realized, but sooner or later, whatever happens, you're going to have to trust me with something, either the money or the drugs. You're going to have to trust me at some point.'

Picker obviously thought, and thought hard.

'Yes,' he said finally. 'That's all right. But I still think I'd like to come with you to the dealer's. I think I'd like to see what sort of people I'm mixing with. And at some point things might change. I might well need to know where you're getting it from.'

'Okay,' Friedrich said. 'I'll need to phone him to set a time and to make sure that's all right.'

'Fine,' Picker said. 'It's quite nice, isn't it?'

'Sorry?'

'The weather,' Picker said. 'It's quite nice today, isn't it?'

'Sorry, I don't know what you're talking about.'

'I was just saying, it seems a bit warmer today than it has been.'

'Yes, I suppose it has.'

'And the spring can't be long now,' Picker said, laboriously.

'No, indeed.'

'I always look forward to the spring,' Picker said.

'Right,' Friedrich said. 'I've just got to make a phone call.'

'Of course,' Picker said. Friedrich went to the back of the café and called up Martin. It couldn't be helped; he had to be brought in on it, up to a point.

'Look,' he said when Martin picked up the phone. 'What are you doing right now?'

'Sleeping, you cunt,' Martin said.

'Well, wake up,' Friedrich said. 'This is important. Go to

the chemist, right now, the chemist's at the corner of your street, and buy one thousand, that's one thousand, small white tablets. I don't care what they are. Nothing with any kind of imprint on it. Got it?'

'No what?'

'No imprint, no mark, no company name, no logo. Okay?'

'Sorry, one thousand small white pills, did you say? What pills?'

'Small white pills. Go to the chemist's and buy one thousand small white pills. They'll give them to you if you give them some money in exchange.'

A long moaning wail came from the end of the telephone.

'A thousand small white pills. What pills? What sort of pills? What are you talking about? Who is this?'

'It's me, it's Friedrich. Look. I just need you to do something very very important for me. Please get up and go to the chemist at the end of your street, and buy one thousand small white pills. It doesn't matter what sort of pills you buy. Don't buy anything poisonous, or dangerous, or anything which means you have to start negotiating with the chemist. I'll give you the money for them when I get there. Paracetamol are good. Now, do you understand?'

'A thousand? A thousand small white tablets?'

'A thousand. Paracetamol are good. Can you do it now? Within three quarters of an hour.'

'If I must. Do I have to? Is it really important? I was asleep. Do I really have to?'

'Yup.'

There was another wail which might generously have been construed as agreement.

'I'll be round to pick them up with a fat man and a small

child. I'll give you the money for them then. Don't leave
them in their packages; empty them out into a plain plastic
bag. Do you understand what I am saying to you, Martin?
I know it sounds very strange indeed, but it's a good plan.
I'll tell you the whole thing later. Just do what I tell you.'

'No.'

'Will you do what I say?'

'I think so.'

'I'll explain why later.'

'Will you tell me why?'

'Yes, I just said, I'll tell you later. Just do it.'

He hung up and went back to Picker.

'That's okay,' he said. 'He'll be home at one o'clock. It's,
what, twenty past twelve now.'

'Fine,' Picker said. He was incredibly nervous, Friedrich
realized; his hand kept running down to pat his trouser
pocket where his wallet bulged; his eyes ran ceaselessly
over the whole empty café. He held Tom's hand, who was
the calmest, apparently, of the three of them. As Friedrich
had half-seen, Picker had not been difficult to persuade. A
walk in the Tiergarten; Friedrich had raised the subject
again, and they had run through the subject of how to
bring down the DDR with much the same enthusiasm
from Picker as before. Picker's sense of wrong against the
DDR was almost personal, Friedrich was coming to see,
and it took not much more than Friedrich saying, Well,
why not? Picker had looked at him with a strange admiring intensity, and laughed. Then Friedrich had said, once
more, Well, why not? And Picker had looked, and not
laughed.

And that was it; Picker ran through the idea again, on his
own, Friedrich listening, and all the time Picker punctuat-
ing the plan with 'It's not so mad, is it?' and 'Well, just

think of the *result*,' and hardly noticing anything around him. In his absorption and his appearance of fierce growing rightness, it was much more as if he were trying to convince Friedrich. They were an hour in the Tiergarten, and at the end the whole thing was agreed, was half-arranged, and Picker had promised to give Friedrich fifty thousand marks in cash.

Friedrich's plan had been to take Picker's money and do nothing else, but it became clear that Picker wanted some kind of demonstration that drugs had, in fact, been bought and taken to East Berlin. That would have been all right; there was no problem in showing a bag of innocuous pills to Picker and even offering to go with him to East Berlin. The problem arose with persuading Picker that there was, in fact, some kind of distribution system in the East which Friedrich could use. Friedrich's general idea was to go up to someone at random in the Alexanderplatz, drop the pills into their shopping bag in front of Picker and get the hell out of it; deftly done, it could easily look to Picker like a clandestine swap. And, with a bit of luck, he wouldn't even want to come to East Berlin, meaning that Friedrich could just take the painkillers from Martin and go nowhere near the East, not even across the Wall. It was all working out beautifully.

It would be understandable, Friedrich supposed, that Picker wanted to keep an eye on him. If what it meant was that he'd actually have to go to the trouble of taking a bag of pills to East Berlin, dropping the pills into a stranger's bag and running for it, that would be quite possible. And he might not want to come. There was always that strong hope to keep in mind. Even if Picker smelt a rat and refused to fund an on-going business, fifty thousand marks for this one-off operation was better than nothing. All in all, it was much better not to manufacture some kind of bogus contact in the East; it was bad enough having to bring Martin in on it, who could never be relied upon not to make a terrible mess of things. Friedrich was quite pleased with the smoothness of the operation, and wondered whether, in fact, he wouldn't be much better off giving up the bookshop (two days a week) and taking to the confidence trickster business full-time. They made a date, for the week after.

Martin lived on the fourth floor of a building on the Erkelenzdamm; Picker, carrying Tom, had to stop twice before they reached the top. Despite himself, Friedrich was impressed; if he had wanted to find a flat unmistakably lived in by a small-time seedy crook, he could not have done better than Martin's. Nothing in Martin's life was as criminal as all that, in fact; he worked behind the bar at a dancing school, and lived an impeccably respectable Kreuzberg life of paying his rent and drinking in the Oranienbar. But the atmosphere he lived in was somehow seriously dodgy – he was always being stopped by the police, skulking in the side streets – and anything left of Picker's self-confidence visibly diminished as they climbed, as his panting increased.

'Are you sure this is all right?' Picker said.

'I don't mind if you want to wait outside,' Friedrich said.

'No,' Picker managed to get out. 'That's quite all right.' Perhaps he was reflecting that whatever was at the top of the stairs would be an improvement, as far as reliability went, on Friedrich.

'What's all this then?' Martin said, opening the door.

'Have you got the stuff?' Friedrich said.

'Yes, no trouble,' Martin said. 'I wish I knew –'

'The less you know, the better,' Friedrich said. 'This is a friend of mine. He's called Christoph. And this is –'

Picker took his cue, shooting Friedrich a grateful look. 'Hi,' he said.

'All right,' Friedrich said, 'we haven't much time. Let's have the stuff.'

Martin picked up a large plastic bag full of pills from the table and handed it to Picker. Picker took a pill out and inspected it.

'There's no logo on it,' he said.

'Yes,' Martin said, puzzled. 'I thought you said you didn't want a logo on it.'

'I thought they normally had a logo,' Picker said. 'Mickey Mouse or something. That's what I always thought.'

'This is commissioned work,' Friedrich said. 'You didn't say. Less conspicuous. That's what we asked for.'

'Ah,' Picker said, knowingly.

'Mickey Mouse?' Martin said.

'Just an example,' Picker said.

'There you go,' Martin said, still obviously bewildered. 'A thousand painkillers, exactly.'

Friedrich shut his eyes.

'Painkillers?' Picker said.

'Yes, a thousand of them,' Martin said.

Picker effortfully put the boy down, and rustled about in his pocket. Producing his little notebook and pencil, he made a note.

'Painkillers,' he said. 'I'd never heard that before. I'm English. I like to keep up with these things, keep track of it. It's difficult sometimes to follow German slang. Painkillers. Yes, I like that. Great.'

Friedrich gave Martin a quick apologizing look, as if to

say that there was no limit to what these Englishmen might say and do.

'Give the man your money, *Christoph*,' he said.

Picker carried on writing.

'Christoph,' Friedrich said.

'Oh yes, quite so, quite so.' He pulled out his wallet and a fat wad of 100-mark notes. Reverently, he passed them to Friedrich who passed them to Martin, who just held the wodge, goggling.

'But –'

'No need to count it,' Friedrich said smoothly. 'It's what we agreed. We'll be off.'

Picker took a second to shake Martin's left hand – the other was too tightly gripped round the money to let go – and they were through the door. Friedrich took the precaution of swiping Martin's keys from the hook by the door and – by now Picker and Tom were halfway down the stairs – locking Martin in his flat. Just for five minutes.

Picker followed Friedrich to the underground station. He looked quite as terrified as he had when he still had the money.

'It's all right,' Friedrich said. 'It's working like clockwork.'

'So far,' Picker said. 'The next bit –'

'The next bit is something you don't need to worry about.'

'No, I'll come with you. Are you going to Friedrichstrasse?'

'Yes,' Friedrich said. 'Are you coming over with me? It might be a problem.'

'I don't know,' Picker said. 'I haven't thought. Maybe I should.'

'I might need to make a run for it,' Friedrich said. 'It

would be better if I didn't have to wait for you and the boy. And have you got your passport?'

'Well, that solves that,' Picker said ruefully, as they stepped on to the train. The carriage was almost empty, in the middle of the weekday afternoon. 'No, I forgot my passport. But we'll come with you as far as the Friedrichstrasse crossing, and meet you back here afterwards, at five, the same place, just to make sure everything went well.'

'Fine,' Friedrich said. 'Now, one more thing. The money. You promised me ten thousand marks for this.'

'Ten thousand marks? When did I say ten thousand marks?'

'In the park. Don't you remember?'

'Frankly, no. If you want to know the truth, I assumed you were taking a direct cut out of the fifty thousand.'

Friedrich did injured innocence, or tried to. This was really pushing his luck. 'No,' he said. 'I bought fifty thousand marks' worth. You saw me give the fifty thousand to Martin, didn't you?'

'I see,' Picker said. 'I'll think about it.'

'No,' Friedrich said. 'It's not really fair to ask me to smuggle drugs over the border without the promise of any money at all. I mean, would you prefer me to rip you off? Shall I rip you off next time?'

Picker weighed the whole thing up. 'No,' he said in the end. 'It's a bit of a mess, all round, isn't it. All right, I'll give you ten thousand when you get back.'

'Fine,' Friedrich said, and settled back. There was always a reward to be had from the underground trip to the Friedrichstrasse station. The doors closing for the last time in the West, and then watching the train proceed in its stately manner past a slew of closed stations in the East;

well-guarded, not disused but somehow preserved in its grey half-lit atmosphere, each successive station was like an old watch, encased in felt, whose continuing tick, if it were ever unwrapped, would be cause for astonishment. The whole line of such stations, the arrival at Friedrichstrasse, with its bright lights and brisk, decrepit atmosphere, was every time alarming, every time precisely resembling what it was, an arrival in a foreign country.

Friedrich stood up, and nodded goodbye to Picker. He ruffled the little boy's hair and, just as he did so, the boy spoke. He seemed to speak in German.

'Be kind to your future,' the boy said, or seemed to say, as he fixed his gaze on Friedrich's face, a sorrowful, soothing gaze, as he turned his head away and looked at his father.

'Sorry?' Friedrich said. 'What did he say?'

'Nothing,' Picker said.

'I thought he said *Be kind to your future*,' Friedrich said.

'No,' Picker said. 'He was saying something to me. Off you go, now.'

Friedrich stood for a second, then stepped off the train, feeling the mid-afternoon quiet of Friedrichstrasse as palpable as the concrete dust which filled the air. He was someone who thought of the universe as proffering, at necessary moments, odd messages from unexpected places, unpredictable people; in the past he had been told by car number plates to be brave, understood from beer advertisements that if he worked harder, he would be happier. It never occurred to him that anyone else might draw the same message from the same random collection of letters; for Friedrich these messages, which always appeared, he always knew, when he absolutely needed them, were moments when a gap of need had opened up, and the random universe was there with an instruction, rarely lucid, usually cryptic, but always true. *Be kind to your future*; that, surely, was the universe speaking through somebody's stumbling learning tongue, his mishearing over the train's hissing noises, and not a calm small boy. The child had not meant to say it, had said, in fact, something else entirely, but through him the universe had strangely spoken, had said, strangely, *be kind to your future*, and once again was silent, blank, inscrutable. He stored it up, preparing to rid himself of all evidence of guilt in this inbetween, this nervous waiting place, and rid himself perhaps not only of the evidence of guilt, but of guilt itself.

The obvious thing to do now was to wait for the next train and not go through into the DDR. It was not clear to Friedrich why, now he was here, he felt that he might as well take the painkillers through and throw them away in the DDR, but it was a feeling there was no arguing with, and he joined the small queue without demure. He carried the drugs in his rucksack. He had thought, vaguely, of hiding them, before reflecting that, after all, there was probably no law even in the Democratic Republic against importing paracetamol, even a thousand paracetamol. In any case, even if there were – even, to be honest, if what he was carrying was what it was supposed to be – the guards at Friedrichstrasse were fantastically slack. Deprived of anything as sophisticated or effective as an X-ray machine, their security was limited to requiring everyone to walk through a hardboard arch, impressively decked out with a pair of fairy lights, which couldn't have detected a Sherman tank, and the bored guards' usual resort of, once a day, requiring some berk in a new suit to remove it in a side room before fist-fucking the poor sod in the name of the search for contraband.

Anyway, that was the word. Nothing worse had ever happened to Friedrich than having a truly awesome female guard in a shade of blue eyeshadow formally approved by the People's Parliament wink at him, but he had heard that such things happened. Not today, however; this was the last trainload, evidently, before the guard knocked off, and he was rushing through them, barely glancing up before waving each of them through. And then Friedrich was on the streets of East Berlin; of Berlin.

It was true that each half of Berlin thought of itself as being Berlin and accorded a geographical description only to the other half. But always, emerging into Friedrich-strasse, it was impossible to understand how such a city could maintain any illusion that this was where things really happened, where excitement was perpetually in the air. Nothing was in the air here except the surprisingly sudden smell of brown coal, mysteriously ubiquitous in East Berlin, mysteriously imperceptible even two metres from the Wall on the other side, and the constant sound and smell of building works, the floating damp smell of concrete dust. Astonishing how much time was spent in building work in East Berlin; astonishing how the building, once finished, immediately had the tired and crumpled look of everything else in this half-town, the look of a decade-old pair of underpants.

Everything seemed to move in a denser atmosphere here, more slowly. Friedrichstrasse was, in theory, the tip-top shopping and business street of East Berlin, but, emerging from the train station, all one saw was a very old lady in a moth-eaten coat and a very old man with a vulgarly chirpy little dog, each with two blue-and-white checked woven plastic bags, approaching each other mas-sively, like a slow-motion film of two trains about to collide. God knew what the rest of the country was like; for himself, Friedrich found himself thinking, on his occasional trips to the East, that the whole place had had a collective lobotomy in 1964, after which nobody had felt any urge to behave in any way distinguishable from their parents. Mostly this seemed rather creepy, though Friedrich always had to admit, when proposing this view to a scoffing friend, full of tales of riotous clubs in Prenzlauer Berg, saucy bars wedged between civil-servant apartment blocks in Pankow, that actually, he almost never stayed long enough even to speak to anyone. What he never admitted was that once in a while it seemed not lobotomized but peaceful, innocent, correct, not wrecked like Kreuzberg, but rational, as if it had seen what the future would hold, and turned away, collectively, from the exhausted delights of the Oranienstrasse, seen that there was nothing much to be got in the way of pleasure or goodness or satisfaction out of a neon sign for Mercedes-Benz, and decided, all in all, not to bother. If Friedrich had ever said any of this he, no doubt, would have added that, of course, he didn't have to live there, and settled back on his stool to ignore the arguments of others.

It was always striking how the rambling anecdotal grey of most of East Berlin's streets was occasionally felt to be in need of some kind of spectacular punchline; so, every so often, the long rows of sober palaces and heavy blocks, many still alarmingly marked, forty years on, with the bullet marks of the advancing Russian army, gave way to some inept piazza, lined with buildings constructed out of plastic and pre-stained concrete, some moon-lovely windswept motorway, lined with the colossal brick-glazed palaces of correctitude. But more impressive were the periodic statements of unimaginable expense and grandeur; all memorials of some imagined glorious past, all looking forward, unavoidably, towards the tawdry present. It was to one of these memorials that Friedrich now felt like going. He wanted, somehow, to go further into the East, to a famous blank space, to the Soviet Memorial; and not, just yet, to wonder or inquire into or understand quite why.

The Soviet Memorial was set down with brutal massiveness in the Treptower Park. The perfect immaculate blankness of the space, set around with thirty great thick blank sheets of white stone, recording the triumph of the Soviet armies, had its own beauty; the double fold of stone opening, like a vast voluptuous hard velvet curtain, before the theatre of the space, had its own pressing overpowering beauty; and the two kneeling heavily cloaked steel soldiers, the colossal steel blond striding forward from his pedestal into his colossal blond future had a loveliness it was hard, quite, to look at. The glittering confidence of the place made you quail. Only the real, unsatisfactory boys in their neat grey felt uniforms, trembling slightly, as if with nerves, at the weight of the weapons they held before them, not quite letting themselves look at anything, just stomping rhythmically, under the base of their fifteen-metre comrade betrayed the excess of the claims being made in this quiet wooded place. The memorial had the sober glittering beauty of Berlin; not a picturesque beauty, not a yellow perfumed Tuscan town, sinking into a lavender hill, not the bulging sunset behind a palm-tree, and some double-starred tourist attraction, and a half-smiling blonde bikini'd girl with an umbrella-shaded drink; not a *postcard* in short, but an adult sober city, with solid surfaces and handsome great enduring spaces, grey and brown and white, not seeking to entertain or flirt, but only to stamp its weight and sorrow, its past, its knowledge, on the patient waiting unmarked crust of the earth. There was no one there except the Russian soldiers; the sun was beginning to set.

He started to make his way around the Busby Berkeley marble slabs, each with its high-kicking rabble-rousing paragraph by J. Stalin. On each was an elegantly stylized representation of some episode in the war, done with such refinement that you liked the slightly camp café decoration of a chorus line in its twinkling apotheosis before realizing that it represented, in fact, a battalion of soldiers. There seemed to be no one else there, and he almost leapt backwards when a small man popped out from behind the ninth stone. He stood there, grinning in a way almost terrifying, almost the poisoned dwarf in the fairy tale. He was nearly familiar in his scrawny eager cheer; Friedrich thought for a moment that he had seen him before until the realization came that he was only familiar because he was so much a type, so perfectly what one expected to see. Friedrich, having stepped back, stepped forward, his expression assembling itself.

'Hello,' the man said.

'Hello,' Friedrich said.

'What are you doing here?'

'Nothing,' Friedrich said. 'I was just looking.'

'Me too,' the man said. 'You're a Westerner, aren't you?' He had an odd trick of nodding his head while he spoke, providing his own agreeing audience to his words.

'I suppose so,' Friedrich said.

The man laughed delightedly. 'You suppose so? Aren't you sure?'

'I came here, really, to be alone,' Friedrich said.

'A very good place,' the man said sagely, 'to be on your own. I often come here to be on my own. No one comes here, only me, and the soldiers. Shall I join you? We'll simply walk around here for a while.'

'I wanted to be on my own,' Friedrich said.

'And soon you will be,' the man said. 'They are interesting, these murals, aren't they?'

'I'd only got up to the fifth one,' Friedrich said. 'They seem very bloodthirsty.'

The man stopped, and looked at one. 'Yes,' he agreed. 'I suppose they are. I hadn't really looked at them. So, do you often come to the East?'

'Not often,' Friedrich said. He tried a little joke. 'I don't like to travel.'

'I see,' the man agreed seriously. 'I don't know if I like to travel, or not. I never have.'

Friedrich forced a laugh, then saw that the man wasn't joking. 'No,' he said. 'I suppose not.'

'My life is in ruins,' the man continued conversationally. 'My wife needs an operation. My son is in prison. My daughter is getting married next month and I have no money to buy her a present, even, or to give her a party.'

'I'm sorry,' Friedrich said.

'And I have no means of earning money,' the man said. 'Do you have money?'

'No,' Friedrich said. 'I'm sorry.'

'I'm not begging,' the man said. He raised his head, and, looking round, sniffed the air like a dog, cautiously emerging. 'I'm just offering you some Ostmarks. If you wanted to change some of your Western marks into Eastern marks I could give you a very good rate. I need to make some money, for my daughter, and my wife's operation. It would be good for you, too.'

'I'm sure,' Friedrich said. 'But I don't have any money.'

'I don't have any money,' the man said, as if Friedrich had said nothing. 'You must have money.'

'I don't,' Friedrich said. 'I've got to go.'

'I too,' the man said, now quickly recovered from his disappointment. 'What is your name?'

'Peter Picker,' Friedrich said.

'And do you often come to this side of the Wall?'

'From time to time,' Friedrich said. 'As little as possible.'

'If you come again,' the man said. 'And you have some money. And you want to change some money, we could arrange a place to meet. My wife needs an operation. My son is in prison. My daughter is getting married, and I need some money to buy her a present.'

'I'm sure,' Friedrich said, breaking into the man's recitation. 'But now I really have to –'

But the man was gone, having seen, perhaps, something; turning quickly aside, disappearing behind the nearest flat marble episode, he was immediately gone, dissolved in the late-afternoon aqueous light; and as he went, something broke, the right shoulder strap on Friedrich's rucksack. It fell to the ground behind him, and as it hit the ground, the bag of pills poured out. In the quiet park they made, it seemed, a terrifyingly conspicuous noise. Friedrich gazed into space; it was only as the seemingly immense rattle died away into the somehow comforting faint clop of the soldiers stomping that he understood that he, now, was quite alone, quite unobserved, and, for once, quite safe. *Be kind to your future*, he said to himself, reciting, as it were, a mantra, and, leaving the pills where they lay, took the rucksack and walked quickly into the thick woods.

It was just beginning to rain, but that was not why Friedrich, now, began stumblingly to run through the unkempt park, the immaculately kept and clean memorial surrounded by an uncared-for wilderness. He could hear nobody following him, or calling after him, but still he ran, and soon he came to a road. It was not a road he recognized, and certainly not the direction he had come in; he could not, while running, work out exactly where he was, and soon he slowed to a walk. An unsignposted crossroads offered no help, and he stood there for a moment, still listening for any noise of following People's Policemen; he could not understand how he had escaped their notice, but in this wooded suburb, he could hear nothing.

He could turn left or right; there was no bus-stop, even, to signpost him, nor could he see, above the trees, any landmark, any tower to give him a sense where he should go. And for a moment, temptation came to him, a strange, solid, huge temptation. It didn't seem to matter where he went; whether he went home, where there was nothing much for him, or deeper into the East, where he could perhaps sink, perhaps disappear, perhaps find something new. What, after all, was he going back for? Just because it was home, just because it was where he customarily lived. This empty place, where people's lives were planned for them, seemed, just there, at this quiet clean crossroads, a place of happiness and content. He could walk up to the nearest police station, and announce his intention to emigrate to the East; it had been done, and he too could do it. They would find him a job; they would find him a flat; he would live peacefully, and that would be that; his life would be taken out of his hands. Would that be so bad? He turned, for no good reason, left.

The road was empty, and Friedrich, with his now empty rucksack, felt his heart slow, and his mind become calm. One decision, and that would be it; he would leave the fifty thousand Deutschmarks with Martin, who was, he supposed, still locked in his own flat, and just begin a new life here, mending cars, or, like his father, a carpenter. The temptation of usefulness, how strong it was, and how much happiness there was in the recognition that he, too, could have a useful life. He continued to walk; a small cream hardboard car came towards him. That could be his, after he had saved up for it; and a small one-bedroom flat; and a wife; and a child. The State would look after it. The temptations of it. The rightness of walking away from all that, all that unbounded, all that illusory freedom, and never walking back – never being able to walk back – into responsibility, or memory, or misery. Just now, he wanted exactly that.

It was not long before Friedrich, with his mind full, saw coming into view a neat square brick building, heard a rumbling train and realized he had, somehow, walked right round the Treptower Park and come to the S-Bahn station; and then, of course, he knew his decision was made for him. He bought a ticket, and worked out his route back to Friedrichstrasse; it seemed to him an unnecessarily complicated route, full of changes at awkward junctures, and then he saw how much the network had been constructed with an eye on the ease of managing it, and not on the convenience of its passengers. He deplored this weakness in his mind, while accepting that he would never get rid of this way of seeing things, this Western way of imagining things only from his angle, of imagining that the world should be run only for his convenience. Thoughts of defection, he saw, as the polished pale wood train arrived, with its doors already hanging open, dangerously, were like thoughts of suicide; they were consolations, they were a comfort when you saw the possibility, the last possibility of all. But they were not real thoughts; neither suicide nor defection was there for you. They could not be done; they could not be run to; they would, in the end, only turn to you, and take you, when there was nothing else, when they decided that you were the one for them. And the moment had not come; not the moment for suicide, not the moment for defection, not the moment for disappearance. They had all come for Friedrich's father, but, as he passed the Friedrichstrasse crossing he found, with a kind of rapture, an intense and sorrowful knowledge of his own unworthiness, he found that he was obliged to say to himself that he was, now, not worthy of suicide. Nor had he earned defection to the East; and he could only use the idea of disappearance as a quiet consolation, as a thought in bad times, as a kind thought, a thought of one of the few ways in which the world could be kind, and, in the end, would be.

It was almost five o'clock when he finally got back to Kreuzberg, and reached the café where he was to meet Picker. He had planned to go back to Martin's flat, to unlock him and claim – by force if necessary – the fifty thousand marks, but Martin would just have to be patient a while longer. Poor Martin, he thought, with amusement. And as he turned the corner into the street where the café was, he saw an unexpected sight of magic; he saw Picker, smiling at nothing, approaching in the other direction, and his son, dancing backwards in front of him, and looking up at the sight of his father. Picker saw Friedrich, a hundred metres away, with the café between them, and Friedrich saw him say to Tom, *Look who it is*. Nothing more. And Tom, as Picker spoke, turned, and saw Friedrich, and recognized him, and began to wave, and to run in front, towards him, smiling harmlessly, unharmed; and Friedrich, for the first time, with an ache of pain and happiness and innocent flattery, saw that he had been included in someone else's world, without ever asking for it; had never bargained for it, had never thought of it, and looked at the child running towards him to say hello, just that, with a flutter of undeserved and unmixed pleasure, of sudden new gratitude.

THAT'S HIS STORY

MARIO WAS STILL sitting at the kitchen table when she got back from the supermarket.

'Where have you been?' he said.

'Just to get the food,' she said. 'I bumped into someone. You know that boy I was stuck in the car with at New Year?'

'No,' Mario said. 'I never met him. You've been ages.'

'I'm sorry,' she said. 'Does it matter?'

'It's not important,' he said; there was a sulkiness about him, an unwillingness to let her apologize, preferring to go on with her in the wrong. She went into his kitchen, leaving him at the table; he was still naked, wrapped only in the blanket he used as a throw over his one armchair, and rubbed his sides from time to time. She took out the food which Friedrich had found so unsatisfactory, and for a moment she saw it as he had seen it. He was a nice boy. She took the stuff out slowly, placing each thing with glazed eyes on the table, and, in Mario's temporary kitchen, she forgot so much where she was and what she was doing that it was a surprise when Mario's voice and not Friedrich's called out to her.

'Are you making some coffee?'

'Sure,' she said, and came out into the main room. 'You were going to tell me what happened to Caspar.'

'Caspar?' Mario looked surprised, as if he had not been asked this once already.

'Yes,' Daphne said. 'I was wondering before what had happened to him, and you said you'd tell me when I got back from the shops.'

'Well,' Mario said. He rubbed his hands together; he looked, not at Daphne, but out of the window. His air was the air of somebody about to embark on a long and complicated journey, one with no assurance of success or completion. 'Oh, he went over.'

It was his usual facetious manner; for a moment Daphne thought she could not have understood what he meant. It was as if he had meant that Caspar had gone to the East. 'Over where?'

'Over there,' Mario said. 'Over the fence. To East Berlin.'

'How long for?' she said, not understanding.

'For good,' he said, apparently surprised that she didn't know.

'For good?' she said. 'Are you saying he's gone to East Berlin permanently?'

'I don't know that he's still in Berlin,' Mario said. 'I know where he was crossing, but that's it. I have an idea where he might have been settled, but that's just my guess. I don't think he had any idea where he was going.'

She looked out of the window. From here, the city just looked like one city; the glimpse of distance, at the end of the street, was a glimpse over an undivided landscape, the eye leaping across Berlin. She felt as if a new life had been called into being, and not as if an old one had continued, strangely, in a strange and unknowable new place. There was an uncrossable bridge of air, which, Mario seemed to be saying, he had crossed in one direction, and Caspar had now crossed in another. She stood in her old floral dress and picked at an unravelling seam, and in her head came the beginnings of an impossible imagined life. There he was, over there, in a grey and secret place, like a man who had swum away from their small island, and with gratitude let the ocean, quietly, profoundly, swallow him. On the other side of the bridge of air, somehow, Caspar now was, living the beginnings of his unknowable pseudonymous life.

'Where was he from?'

'The Ruhrgebiet, I said.'

'You knew a lot more than you were saying, though,' Daphne said. She remembered the curious benediction of Mario's kiss, its farewell and blessing and elective beauty in one.

'Of course,' Mario said. 'It wasn't sensible to tell any-one.'

'Even me?' Daphne said, with a stab at flirtatiousness which, she could immediately feel with the wave of cold air which seemed to greet her, was the wrong note to strike.

'Even you,' Mario seriously agreed. He looked at her wryly. She was going to have to do all the work, ask the right questions.

'Who was he?'

'He needed help, and he needed to get out fast,' Mario said. 'We were just in a useful place and were the best people to help him, that particular Sunday.'

'Was he in trouble, or something?'

'Oh yes,' Mario said, delighted. 'Very very big trouble indeed. Great steaming piles of trouble. You don't run away to hide in the DDR for forgetting to pay your parking fines.'

'Go on.'

'Go on with what? He was in some sort of big trouble. That's all I know.'

'You know.'

'No, honestly. I'm telling you the truth. I don't. Nobody told me anything. I don't know his name, or what he had done, or –'

'But you can guess.'

Mario sat for a moment, his patient thoughts like a great weighted book between his thin hands.

'Yes,' he said eventually. 'I suppose I can.'

'Well,' Daphne said. She felt she had manoeuvred him into a position of her choosing; it was not until later that she wondered how much of this Mario had always planned to tell her. 'Tell me what you guess.'

Mario seemed to consider, rolling his tongue around his cheek. 'All right,' he said. 'Well, my guess is it's some kind of political thing. I have a fair idea of what it is. I think he was RAF.'

'Fuck,' Daphne said. 'Fuck. Who is he?'

'I don't know,' Mario said. 'Honestly not. I mean, if you're saying, is he Raspe risen from the grave, I don't think so. I don't think he's some famous RAF name. He's probably some quite small-fry second- or third-generation RAF. Still, if he's on the run, and he's worried enough to disappear permanently into the DDR, he must have done something pretty terrible. My guess is – you know that Friedemann boss?'

'Yes,' Daphne said. 'Of course. That's not small-fry stuff.' She had the unoxygenated feel of going underwater, as if her hands, twitching, were reaching out for something, anything, and finding only new water, new nothing, giving way under her hand as she flailed, falling where she had thought herself supported. The Friedemann murders had been in the newspapers for weeks at one time; it had fallen so far out of Daphne's idea of what she and the other Class War guys were doing that she could not remember even having talked about it with anyone.

A board member of Friedemann, living in his elegant tightly walled villa outside Frankfurt, had been telephoned by his god-daughter, a young woman of twenty-one or so. He was fond of her; she had been away for a couple of years, and he had not seen her since she was in high school. She was in the area; could she drop in for lunch, perhaps, on Sunday, if he was not busy. Of course, he said. Unfortunately, there were some colleagues of his, also from Friedemann, also on the board, coming for lunch on Sunday. Bores, of course, no use denying that, but if she could bear it? Perhaps she would like to come early, so they could have a nice chat, like old times? It really would be nice. She seemed to pause; it might have been as if a hand had been placed over the mouthpiece. Yes, she said, returning to the telephone, that would be very agreeable. But it might prove difficult for her to come very much earlier; there was an old boyfriend she had promised to go for a walk with that morning. She would see what she could do. It was so kind of her second family, she said, so kind. She was exactly the same as ever; the same sweet, charming, nice-mannered girl they had always liked to have around.

They did not come early; they came late. The man's wife was just saying that this was unlike her, that it was almost worrying, and the man was just about to tell her, with his usual bluffness, that she had surely got herself lost with her old flame, there was nothing yet, surely, Dorothea, to get worked up about, when the bell at the outer gate rang. All the other guests – bores, stuffed shirts, undeniably, who it was periodically necessary, the man occasionally confided to his wife, to be civil to on a Sunday to compensate for the beastliness he had shown to them all week – were there. The maid buzzed them through the outer gate, and opened the door to the car, a surprisingly respectable saloon for a student. She let the smiling girl and the small, dark man in. What did she know? She only knew that the god-daughter was expected, and if she came with a friend, perhaps the Frau Gräfin had not remembered to tell her, not considered it worth telling her, and who was she to refuse the entry of a guest to the house? Who indeed?

He left the small group he was talking to and walked towards his god-daughter. Perhaps, now, only she, on whom all his expression was bent, could now say whether he looked at her with all the fondness and warmth he had always had for her, or if, at this last, there was some tinge of surprise, of alarm even, at this unsmiling companion of hers, an expression which perhaps only slowly turned to terror as the man standing behind the still smiling god-daughter drew his gun and shot the man in the head with expert swiftness. The body was still falling as the god-daughter, in turn, got out her somehow characteristically neat and small pistol, as they began to shoot on the other guests, as the guests went where they could, turning and finding themselves against a corner, a walled-in neat target. Five dead; three crumpled, moaning and shot, but breathing. The wife of the godfather, one senior executive, all but one of the staff were somehow unhurt, having found their way quickly enough to the door of the kitchen, spared by luck and the mysterious charities of time and chance.

Perhaps no more than twelve seconds. The two turned and went, and as the front door slammed, as the engine revved, the wife of the godfather, slumped heavily against the kitchen door with the crying white-faced survivors, found herself thinking, with conscious calm incongruity, only 'So soon? Must you dash off? You've hardly got here!' thinking, grotesquely, that it was hardly worth their while to come and, so swiftly, to go, having no more than gone round the room and greeted, in their way, each guest.

They were RAF. The great days of the Red Army Faction were, it had been hoped, over. It was now twenty years since Andreas Baader and Ulrike Meinhof and Raspe and Ensslin and the rest had disappeared from their own lives, reappearing only on the doorsteps of left-leaning sympathizers to ask for shelter and secrecy, surfacing only with guns and stolen cars and the ordinary black carnival masks of terror to carry out their necessary deeds in the name of who knew what; fifteen years since their capture, a dozen since they were found, most of them, dead in their prison cells. And still it went on, every year or two a new generation, calling themselves RAF, appearing for a moment with a calm hi-there expression, breaking through the calm surface of the well-ordered German streets before sinking again, leaving the flotsam of their deeds, the terminal moraine of their black acts abandoned on the great icy movements of history, their history, bodies in a Frankfurt drawing room, to be regarded with as much thought and collection as the stains on the carpet when the bodies were gone.

'That was him?' Daphne said.

'I suppose it was,' Mario said.

'He's got a nerve,' she said. 'I mean –'

'I know,' Mario said.

'I mean –' she pressed on – 'every policeman in the country must know what he and his friend look like. The identikit's been on every lamp-post from here to Munich.'

'It doesn't look much like him, though, you must admit.'

'No, true,' she said. 'But he must have been off his head to have done something like that. I mean, what would have happened if we'd run into policemen straight afterwards? Did he really think throwing shit at Turks was worth the risk?'

'It's crazy,' Mario said. 'I told him not to.'

'You told him not to,' Daphne said.

'Yes,' Mario said, apparently not caring much what Daphne thought about how much he knew, or had known, or had guessed. 'I think he was just bored, wanted to have one more bit of fun before he went over. There's a lot of bravado in those guys, you know, all that stealing cars out-side police stations, and, poor sod, he was climbing up the walls.'

'He was staying with you.'

'For a few days, until the action. He went off after that. I didn't see him again.'

'He was staying with you.'

'Until the action.'

'I don't believe it. I just don't believe I'm hearing this. I mean. Taking him out for a drink, taking him to the flicks, that would have done if he was that bored,' Daphne said. 'I mean, what about *us*? Class war is one thing, but trashing a place with a known RAF murderer – I mean, my god, what does that make us look like? What do you think the police would have done with us?'

'What do you think he cared about us?'

'And you, what do *you* care about us?' Daphne said. 'You knew pretty much what was going on. What do you care about us? What, come to that, do you care about me?'

'Come on,' Mario said. 'I didn't know. Not for certain. And it's not certain. And it's not something you just ask someone.'

'And you had instructions from very high up,' Daphne said, 'to take him along.'

'To look after him, anyway,' Mario said. 'Coming along was his idea.'

They sat there for a moment. It was clear from the tinge of suppressed panic in Mario's eyes, the look of half-closed confidence, that he knew what she was going to ask next; she was going to ask who the very high-up people were. And after that, the question she always should have asked Mario, always from the beginning; who was *he*?

'You know,' she said, instead. 'What I don't understand is why someone like you would have anything to do with the RAF.'

'Come on,' Mario said. 'I don't have anything to do with them.'

'You did. So did I, though the difference is I didn't know it at the time. But what do you think the RAF want? They want something like the DDR – I mean, something like what you've escaped from. I mean, what do you want with them?'

'Maybe,' Mario said slowly. 'Or maybe they don't want the DDR either. Maybe they want what we want.'

'And what are they doing dealing with someone like you?'

'That,' Mario said, 'I can't answer. I mean, I don't know. I don't know. I think we were just convenient. As far as they were concerned, we were in the right place at the right time.'

'So what do you want?'

Mario sat, his hands between his bare knees, for some time.

'It's freezing,' he said eventually. 'I want the heater on.'

She ignored this. She had got beyond anything she might recognize as Mario's charm. And it wasn't that cold, not really cold at all. She wouldn't fall for this; she saw, all at once, that she was beyond ever falling for Mario ever again. 'What do you want?' she said again.

'I suppose I want what you want,' he said. He looked her in the eye; he shone, happily, confidently. 'I want a just society. Isn't that –'

'It just seems to me – I don't know why, but I've never thought this before – it just seems odd to feel strongly enough to escape from a socialist country and then carry on working for the socialist utopia you've just left.'

'Oh, come on,' Mario said. 'Maybe I didn't know what the West was like. Maybe I want a society that's nothing like the West or the East. Isn't that possible?'

'Possible,' Daphne said. She resolved not to go on letting Mario explore the various possibilities before him in the hope of hitting on something she might believe, and, after a while in which sincerity radiated from his eyes, his every seriousness was bent forcibly on her, he sank to her feet. Kneeling, his head in her lap, he stayed like that, letting her stroke his head, letting her observe his degree of baldness, surprising but not important or significant or even interesting in someone as young as Mario, and she stared, not at him but at the wall. After a time, she let him pull at her knickers, parting the dressing-gown, his, she wore, and let him bury his face in her crotch, thinking all the time, her twisted underwear still pulling her calves, unwilling to be parted, together, before the familiar loosening surges of Mario's tongue made her forget to think at all, that this was really it between them. He was bad news.

THREE

REICHSKRISTALLNACHT

DO YOU WANT

THOSE BERLIN WINTERS; how they went on, light-lessly. In November, the clouds rolled over, hanging low above the divided city, sheltering, oppressive, blanketing; there was a palpable proximity to them, a sense that the thick layer of cloud would reach down at any time and envelop the city. From November onwards, that was how the winter days were; the narrow strip of hours filtered through the thick cloud, a weak grey day extending from mid-morning to mid-afternoon, and the rest was darkness and night.

The winter seemed so lightless and heartless only afterwards in Berlin. Only, really, when the clouds broke in March – April – or even, that year, in May – and the sun was quite abruptly there did anyone think that they had been living under zinc-black skies with no sign of any break, any sun, for months. The fretted city, snapping at itself in queues, in trains, put up with the dark days without knowing, entirely, the simple thing they were putting up with; finding causes for rage in ticket machines, in telephone bills, in anything except the sky, because against the skies, there was no point, none at all, in raging.

By May there was a sense of layer upon layer, thick cloud upon thick cloud, built up slowly and impermeably over the months. If you flew out of Berlin, it was almost a surprise how quickly the machine broke through the thudding grey, broke through into something which was as one imagined, the vast plains, valleys and rearing hills of cloud below, and, above, the clear winter's blue, sunlit, unbounded, unbordered. There was something wrong about the skies over Berlin; they took no account of Berlin's borders, took no interest in where lines on earth were drawn. No circular ray of sunshine pierced the clouds to outline the circular walled city in the West, no beneficent parting of the clouds conferred any blessing on one system or another, and West Berlin – deprived of the saccharine benediction which the sun, like a torch held steady and pointing into unfathomable black waters, would, surely, if it had only known, conferred on it – made up for its deprivation with electricity and neon and the constant roaring generators. It was a diamond on black velvet; a colossal beautiful cheap artificial jewel. And every year with the spring breaking of the clouds it was as if a great blank wall had been punched, and shown to be only great grey paper. And quite abruptly, people found they could breathe, without knowing they hadn't been able to; they only knew that, now, they could begin.

Things were changing. Things were changing in the world. But it felt as though nothing had ever changed, and it felt as though nothing would ever change. News from the East; news always came from the East, as long as there had been an East to send news and a West to listen. Something was breaking in the East, something which had held for so long it looked, from a distance, an edifice of perfect rock-hard smoothness. It was only close to – it would only be afterwards – that the cracks would appear, its tinny, patched-up surface making it only astonishing it had held so long.

Something was breaking in the East, and the creaks and groans of its giving way could be heard even in Berlin. In the news, crowds could be read about, movements of peoples, quantified in numbers; in Berlin, it seemed only a question of individuals, refugees turning up as, for decades, no refugee had turned up. The population was changing; it was a city where, for years, only the young and the old had lived; those who remembered the old days, and those who were running from something. And now, these days, families were appearing; not just draft-dodgers and the seedy old ladies, but forty-year-old married couples and their ten-year-old daughters, gazing about them in curiosity, hardly noticing that the city, in turn, gazed at them, and was astonished. Berlin had always treated the East as a single unremarkable fact, unresponsive and uninteresting, like a caged sleeping pet, and now it was as if the sleeping pet had sat up and drawn attention to itself not with a bark or an animal shrug, but by opening its own cage door and uttering a whole rational sentence. In the city, within its walls, people called Tucholski or Kapossy – people who never for a moment had thought of themselves as anything but Germans, coming from anywhere but where they lived – had their doorbells rung by complete strangers. The Berlin Tucholskis looked at these grubby families on their doorstep, heard them proclaiming themselves distant cousins, listened to their dramatic stories – as week succeeded week, these stories became decreasingly dramatic, increasingly a saga beginning with a fib and proceeding through an incredible amount of form-filling – and wondered what on earth the world was coming to. What the world was coming to was, perhaps, not a great change, not a remarkable shift in human nature, and after a few weeks the Berlin Kapossys could observe the Budapest Kapossys, selling their Hungarian underwear outside the U-bahn at the Zoo, with not much more than the usual pang of conscience, not much more than the usual resistible temptations of kindness.

There were probably not many more than two thousand people in Kreuzberg who went up and down the Oranienstrasse and drank in the bars and listened to gossip and retold what they heard, and most of them had fairly defective memories, or a vigorous spirit of invention, as if to make up for the undeniable fact that nothing much ever happened around here.

So pretty soon it was universally known that Daphne had been fucking Mario and was no longer, that Mario was heartbroken and Daphne was fine, and vice versa, that Friedrich had been seeing a girl who he'd danced with on an East German motorway, that he was seeing a fat man a great deal, who he had visited Martin with after having asked him to go out and buy a thousand paracetamol, and had then given him fifty thousand marks in cash, locked Martin in his own flat and then returned, hours later, without his fat boyfriend and would you believe it some little boy and had broken Martin's little finger in getting it back, and frankly the whole place was going to the dogs if the neo-Nazis were going to start attacking Turks who were just trying to make a living, and someone said that RAF boy had gone to East Berlin and what did anyone think about that, and, really, there had always been something a bit peculiar about Friedrich when one came to think about it.

Not all of this formed part of the same story; nor did

everybody who told any of it quite know the names of any of the participants, or believe anything in the whole story. But part of it, at least, was pretty well-known to all of Kreuzberg, and certainly to Daphne, if not to Friedrich – she judiciously closed her eyes at some of the more horrific parts of the recitation – by the evening they had finally managed to agree to go out together.

The first person Friedrich saw when he entered Rose's bar that summer night was not Daphne. There was a boy at the bar who he recognized without being able to place immediately. Blond-haired and pink-cheeked, his eyes blue in his bony face, he looked altogether too healthy, too eager to be a regular at Rose's. He was resting on a pile of fur, a pert odalisque. If he hadn't been leaning back with his mouth open in laughter at a doubtless obscene remark the barman had just made to a nearly empty front bar, one might have thought he had wandered into the wrong place, and had decided, strangely, to hang around.

'You fuck off,' the barman said, switching his tone of voice effortlessly as Friedrich came in. 'Yes, I'm talking to you.'

'Who,' Friedrich said, neatly turning and performing an exaggerated double-take for the benefit of the bar. 'Who, me?'

'Yes,' he said. 'I'm not joking. Fuck off. After the last time.'

'What last time?'

'You know,' he said. 'Or if you don't it's because you were too drunk to remember. So –'

'It's all right,' the boy said, turning round to Friedrich and smiling. 'I know him. He's a reformed character.'

'Thanks,' Friedrich said, when he had ordered – out of bravado – a beer. 'That was nice of you.'

'Well,' the boy said, ruminatively, 'you might be a reformed character, for all I know. I just hope you do the same for me one day.'

'You don't know how bad I am, or used to be,' Friedrich said.

'I've seen you fairly unforgivable,' he said. 'To be honest.'

'Do I know you?' Friedrich said, not rudely, but genuinely curious.

The boy gave another peal of laughter, almost falling off his chair. 'Do you know me?' he said. 'Do you know me? I'll say you do. Do you not remember the Polke *vernissage* – weeks ago now? And your Mr Picker?'

'I remember,' Friedrich said, not admitting anything resembling embarrassment. 'I can't remember your name, I'm sorry.'

'Pierre Stifter,' he said. 'You were terribly drunk and, you know, every time I spoke to you, you just said the same thing. You just kept saying –'

'I don't want to know,' Friedrich said. Too much of his life, he always thought, was spent listening to people telling him about himself.

'Well, I don't mind telling you,' Pierre said. 'Call me Pierre. Everyone does.'

'I'd rather not hear,' Friedrich said. 'I'm waiting for someone. And I wasn't going to call you anything else.'

'Not for Peter Picker?' Pierre said, making a pantomime dame's pout and offensively rolling eyes. 'I thought someone was taking care of him recently.'

'They might be,' Friedrich said. 'Not me, though. No, I'm waiting for a girl.'

'A girl?' Pierre said, but before he could start the stream of innuendo poised on his tongue, Daphne came in. It was a warm evening, and she was wearing only a slightly grubby T-shirt and a black mini-skirt; the heavy black boots, however, were, as usual, there. She came over, not having learnt to mask her enjoyment at the mere idea of spending an evening with another human being, her smile seeming to cover her face. Friedrich simply looked at her; his feelings towards her blank, even to himself.

'Hi, how are you,' she said, apparently to both of them.

'Hi, fine,' Pierre said, nodding at her in a conspicuously cool way. Friedrich decided to be cool too, and not to ask, as he burningly wanted to, how they knew each other.

'Have you been abroad recently?' Pierre said to Daphne when they were all settled, opening his eyes wide and sparkling with all his social charm, or, more likely, all the social charm of his mother or his sister or his aunt.

'Sorry, why do you think I've been abroad?'

'I don't. I was just asking if you had been abroad recently.'

'Why?'

'Because the alternative to making conversation is to sit here like stuffed animals in silence. Now, shall we start again? Have you been abroad recently?'

'No.'

'Shall we go abroad together, you and me and him?'

'I don't think so,' Daphne said.

'Yes, why not,' Friedrich said. 'Where?'

'Let's go –' Pierre said – 'to the DDR! Let's go to Marzahn, where the setting sun glints off the evening cocktail on the concrete balconies; let's journey to faraway Friedrichshain, where dusky maidens recline to the relaxing sound of surf beating on sand, or at any rate the soft plop of some organic object dropping into the Spree. Well, in any case, let's go to East Berlin –'

He pushed his face up against Daphne's, leering enthusiastically at her.

'– and get really, really drunk.'

'Yup,' Friedrich said.

'Let's see,' Daphne said. 'Anyway, that's not abroad.'

'Well, you're no fun,' Pierre said. 'Is it a different country? I think *so*. What is the definition of abroad? I think it means a different country. Is the DDR abroad? I think, therefore I'm an old nun's favourite banana. Tell us the last time you had some fun, sweetheart.'

Daphne looked quite shocked.

'Go on,' he said. 'I can't wait.'

'I have fun all the time,' she said. 'Don't be ridiculous.'

'What do you do?' Pierre said.

'I'm a student,' she said.

'Oh, that sounds great,' Pierre said. 'Tell us about the fun you have in class.'

'No,' she said. 'I go out, and I see films, and have a laugh with friends, and all in all I have as much fun as anyone I know. I think you must be the rudest person I've ever met.'

'I bet you don't have as much fun as me,' Pierre said.

'What have you seen recently?' Friedrich said. 'Go on, tell us.'

'Yes, do,' Pierre said.

'Don't be so rude,' Friedrich said to Pierre. 'She's right, you really are the rudest person I've ever met. No, really, tell us.'

'I saw a film,' Daphne said, 'called *Out of Rosenheim*. It's an English film. No, American, but it's about Germans. It's got a fat German actress in it. It's about this German couple who are travelling in America and they have an argument and he throws her out and she is left on her own in this place in Arizona. And all she has is a suitcase full of men's clothes because she took her husband's clothes by mistake and a box of magic tricks. And she winds up at this café in the middle of the desert.'

'Does this get any more interesting?' Pierre said.

'And she takes a job there,' Daphne said. 'And she sort of gets accepted. It's really nice.'

'Is that it?' Pierre said.

'No, there's lots more,' Daphne said. 'There's this scene where the daughter of the black woman who runs the café –'

'Is it important that she's black?' Friedrich said with a straight face.

'Not really,' Daphne said. 'But the daughter –'

'So why mention it?'

'I don't know,' Daphne said. 'I'm sorry, I didn't mean to be offensive or anything.'

'Me,' Pierre said, 'I can't stand black people. Can't bear them. Can't bear the cooking smells they make or the languages they talk or the way they are always going on about being black, all day long, Yak yak yak. And so loud. Don't you agree?'

'Yes,' Friedrich said, appallingly amused, against his will.

'No,' Daphne said. 'I don't think that's funny at all. Do you want to hear this or not?'

'Let's take a vote,' Pierre said.

'And the daughter is coming back –' Daphne said.

She broke off, less through the double gaze of polite interest on either face of Friedrich and Pierre, rather the approach of a wandering salesman of cigarette lighters. The hawkers of lighters were one group of people, one of many, who went from bar to bar, all night long, selling or attempting to sell roses, sandwiches, novelty items, photographs of their victims, each other. The lighter hawker, perceiving a tiny gap, like inattention, in the studied and customary blankness towards him, homed in on them, reached into his pocket to begin the display.

'Oh dear,' Pierre remarked.

'Have you ever noticed,' Friedrich said, 'that these people always have exactly the same lighters to sell?'

'Well, of course,' Daphne said. 'I suppose they all get them from the same source.'

'Some sort of darling little sweat-shop, do you think,' Pierre said. 'With sweet clever little men thinking up new ideas for novelty cigarette lighters and nimble-fingered little eight-year-old boys shackled to their machines and singing "Whistle While You Work" for fifteen hours a day? What a charming idea, I can see it now. Oh, *look* –'

The smiling man, his mobile, angled, almost pentagonal Calcutta face alive with his own pleasure, whipped out a brass German shepherd dog, ears pricked and tail flagged upwards for the pursuit. Only the attendant policeman seemed missing. He flicked backwards at one of the ears, and the eyes lit up with a Baskerville green; an unconvincing, electronic dog-noise accompanied the alarming dragon-bark of flame from the dog's mouth, a sudden nightmare blast.

'Seen it before,' Friedrich said, lighting a cigarette from the flame.

Undaunted, the hawker reached in his pocket and produced a model showerhead. He clicked at something, and, instead of water, what came out of the showerhead was gas, and flame. He grinned, the salesman, as if it were nothing to do with him.

'Seen it before,' Daphne said, lighting a cigarette in her turn.

He delved deeper in his pockets, and what came out next was, shockingly, a heavy brass phallus, veined and modelled with unnecessary enthusiasm. A little naughty silent moue he made at them, displaying such a thing in front of the lady, and quickly squeezed the testicles. A metal flag shot out of the scrupulously formed urethra, a German flag, followed by a jet of flame, and, tinnily, a tune began. Involuntarily, they all bent their heads down to listen.

'The Emperor's Hymn?' Daphne suggested.

'Something like that,' Friedrich agreed, not quite knowing what he had heard or seen.

'And in any case,' Pierre said, 'I've seen it before, and I've seen bigger on statues.'

The man seemed delighted at the refusal, and delved again; producing, now, what seemed to balance the last monstrosity. A naked woman, ironically topped with the famous face of Rosa Luxemburg, an ironic wound in her side out of which – you pressed the left breast – the flame emerged.

'Seen it before,' Friedrich said.

The double-headed Hohenzollern eagle was next, an unlikely double flame from the mouths of the bird, and with a deft twist – it could not be seen quite how – the hawker turned the thing inside out to reveal a gaudy pet, a budgerigar, and if the eagle had been diminished, pathetically, in scale, the badly painted budgerigar seemed grotesquely enlarged, ridiculing both what it had been and what it had become.

'Seen it,' Daphne said.

'Seen it,' Friedrich said.

'Seen it,' Pierre said, and now, at last, the man seemed somewhat dismayed that they were not tempted, that he could show them only the familiar, and, at last, dipping as deep as he could in his pockets, from the back end of German history, with an air of the *pièce de resistance* he whipped out, unfolding, a flat square sheet of metal, tiny squares of tiny painted figures in three formations. They could not immediately recognize or name what was clearly meant as a battle, but there was no doubt that, as the man pressed the button beneath the model and the three armies advanced and retreated jerkily for their entertainment, one last time, that the flame would jut out from the little cannon at the head of the blocks of blue soldiers, the great Prussian army, in this Prussian bar, become a toy, become something to light a cigarette which would not last five minutes.

'I've seen it before,' Pierre said. He was suddenly and inexplicably irate, as if responding to the salesman's change of mood. 'We've seen it all before. You can't show us anything we haven't seen a hundred times before; there is no price low enough to tempt us with any of this. And in any case –' he reached, in his turn, into his pocket and produced a plain blue plastic lighter, the size of his thumb – 'I've got a light.'

The Indian gathered his novelty objects together, placing them with surprising care in the pockets of his coat, muttering slightly as he swiftly vanished, disappearing off to another bar.

'And now,' Pierre said. 'Let's get out of this place and go to S.O.36.'

'S.O.36?' Friedrich said.

'Yes,' Pierre said. 'Any objection?'

'No,' Friedrich said. 'It's just that I remember once – well, months ago now – I said to Daphne that if we got back to Berlin in one piece, because we were stranded, shipwrecked almost, in some place, on a motorway, that we'd go together and dance at S.O.36. And I'd forgotten. And you remembered, without even knowing it. And Daphne had remembered too, and wasn't saying anything, because she's so polite. That's so sad. That makes me feel so sad.'

'Don't worry,' Daphne said. 'I hadn't remembered, to be honest. It's nice that you remembered at all, and it's nice that we're going to go.' She smiled at him, a smile kept carefully from Pierre, and it was a moment of kindness, of forgiveness, between them, when there was nothing to forgive.

'I see,' Pierre said. 'Do say if I'm not wanted, won't you.' He gathered his coat up behind him. Friedrich had vaguely thought the thing he was sitting on was part of the furniture; it now revealed itself as a grand floor-length mink, which Pierre swathed himself in as if it were the most ordinary thing in the world. The bar fell silent as he left, followed by Friedrich and Daphne. 'There must exist a small amount of fun,' the terrible old song on the weary cassette announced with an energetic bouncing beat as the three of them left. They stood on the street for a second. 'S.O.36, then?' Pierre asked, or rather announced.

S.O.36 was a nightclub, of sorts; it resembled a large village hall, with a cloakroom at the entrance and a record player with a ferocious amplification system at the other end. Each night there had a different name. There was a night for ageing punks to jump up and down to their music, called Hot Soup. There was a night for lesbians, which Friedrich had once got into by smoothing his hair down and gluing a monocle into his eyesocket (using hair-gel for both purposes). In white tie and borrowed tails, he made, it was true, a credible lesbian. This night was called

Rosa Klebb. The Friday night, which they were heading for, was loosely supposed to be fancy dress. They pushed Pierre Stifter, in his fur coat, forward. It had no specific limitations in clientele, no habit of exclusion, and one of the most inexhaustible of Kreuzberg's street proverbs was that sooner or later you saw everyone you knew, even your mother, leaning against the wall at S.O.36 on a Friday night. For this reason, the Friday night dance at S.O.36 was called The Inexorable Pleasures of Polymorphous Perversity, and was packed.

For none of these nights was much of an effort made in the way of changing the appearance of the club, except the punk nights, when all furniture not actually bolted to the floor was removed to a storeroom. The rest of the time, it was a long room, its floor, halls and ceiling painted a dull black; a colour which somehow amplified the always deafening music, which ricocheted in the space as if it were empty. It worked hard at an atmosphere of exhausted dreariness, and, to its appreciative customers, it achieved it.

The point about the night – the joke about the night, one might almost say, given the straight-faced solemnity with which its slight absurdity was executed by everyone there – was that it was a night for ballroom dancing. Like concentrating pranksters, the two hundred waltzing couples frowned in each other's faces, bending all their will, it seemed, on preserving a front to fool the innocent dupe. By a quick-growing convention, unspoken, the various armoured social groups which, each Friday, met in the grotty provincial arena of S.O.36, did not preserve their customary cool aloofness, their pose of not even noticing those who did not dress and stand like themselves, who did not resemble themselves, but, like jolly colliding circus limousines, discharged the bright clowns who rode in each car, each group, who mingled, fumbled, remounted their now tattered engine in an entourage not their own with only the faintest twinge of not quite belonging, of accepting someone surprisingly different to themselves. A pretty Turkish boy, his first moustache just beginning – you saw the unfamiliar prickle, how he reached up, as if in shame, to his upper lip – had come in with his usual cronies, their faces a dark olive oil on which rose petals floated, suggesting, illusorily, fatally, a quiet embarrassment, an innocence with a need to be taken in hand. Now he danced, one arm self-consciously dangling as he let his partner glintingly lead – a hard-edged spinster who even in daylight would admit only to thirty-five. A leathery queen, whose voluminous moustache aimed, inadequately, at the specific suggestion of his recondite sexual practices but succeeded, in the end, only in recalling Bismarck, mildly smirked at his hunting pack at the bar over the shoulder of a big-handed tranny, sinking demonstratively into his arms as if this was all she ever wanted or desired. Only sometimes – two clean-cut tall boys, one dark, one blond, facing each other, advancing, crab-wise, in a ferocious tango like drama students practising the mirror-imitation game – did the participants in the S.O.36 Friday night dance with their own kind, and never, in fear of gaucheness, did they do so for the whole evening. That was the thing; a spectacle which to find its audience turned inwards, performed for the benefit of its performers only, applauding because they applauded themselves, and because admiration is always good to receive, even from oneself.

'Do you want a dance?' Friedrich said.

'Oh, yes,' Pierre said.

'Not you,' Friedrich said. 'Daphne.'

'Of course,' Daphne said. 'I remember dancing with

you. Do you think I'd forget that, or pass up the chance again? And you – can you get me a drink?'

Pierre went off to talk to some friends, not discarding his fur, and Friedrich and Daphne went to the dance floor.

'Is this going to go on all night?' Daphne said. 'Have you brought him for any particular reason?'

'I didn't bring him,' Friedrich said, taking Daphne in his arms. 'He was in Rose's when I went in. I've only met him once. All right?'

'Yes,' she said, and then they were off, an odd, eccentric vision of orthodoxy, a man in a dark suit leading a woman in a skirt, and gazing into each other's faces. And those who saw them saw a strange tenderness, a bright care in the way they looked at each other, and talked while they danced. 'Where do you live?' Friedrich said, and Daphne answered that she lived with her aunt, and had since she moved to Berlin. They went on, with the tango they both half-remembered from school, and remembered, so well, so clearly, from the midnight motorway, and making mistakes all the time, and laughing at their own lack of technique as they trod on each other's toes, or miscounted, or bumped into other couples, and carried on telling each other stories. Or Daphne told; because it was enough that Friedrich listened, his face clear and excited with this woman talking, and knowing, quite consciously, that the evening was going in the right direction, that what he had imagined as he stood and watched her leave the supermarket was going to happen, was going to happen to him.

A generalization had begun it; the generalization that Friedrich had made in the supermarket, a week or two before, and listened to the generalization Daphne had made in return. A sense that when you said to a girl, oh, women are like this, or she said to you, men are all the same, what resulted was not a more generalized, a less personal relationship but a greater intimacy, as if by talking in such terms a man and a woman could arm themselves against the mass of humanity, could retreat into some new privacy. And gazing at her, and listening to her, talking now about her past, telling him something or other about her childhood, he had the sense that there was nothing they could not talk about now, that intimacy and public display were now perfectly balanced, that in her bright face, in which he saw only his own reflected, there was no shadow of anything but pleasure to come, the pleasure she would create for him, whether he resisted it or not. He gazed at her, but he did not see what was there; he felt, overwhelmingly, a physical sensation, a physical pleasure which balanced the pleasures of now and the pleasures of remembrances; a single thing, her familiar and yet unencountered scent. He remembered the scent of her in his arms, that night, months before, though he had not thought of it for months, and, as he gazed at her, the scent came back, and with it, the night, and the pleasure, and the whole forgetting and newness and sense of no past and no future, with a woman, this woman, this scented beautiful woman, yielding, and allowing herself to yield, in his arms. Right now, he would not care what sentences she said to him; he would not care if she said to him *no man's ever made me feel like this before*; it would, almost, be good. And his pleasure was in her hands; she stepped backwards in the dance, allowing him to master her, allowing him to strike the powered pose he always wished for, never, quite, knew how to attain. She had helped him, shown him how, and it was by her control that he found himself in a position of strength, as if she had got there first, and abdicated it, left it empty, just for him. He closed his eyes; her scent was so much there, so much there for him, and bringing with it the night, the New Year's Eve, so long remembered, so much, so fully there. The dance was over.

'What about that drink?' Daphne said to Pierre.

'Oh, sorry,' Pierre said. 'I got caught up with these very naughty boys.'

He gestured at the small group of moustached middle-aged men, who smirked, closing their eyes in unison, in shyness or (they obviously wished) superior superciliousness at Daphne and Friedrich.

'And you didn't say what you wanted.'

'A dark beer,' Daphne said.

'And me,' Friedrich said. 'We'll go and have another dance while you get it.'

It is sometimes a mistake, the second dance, like the last beer of the evening; and there was an unmistakable sense of tightening that Friedrich could feel about the smile on his face. It was hard to know what it was, but that sense of the six a.m. last beer pervaded the mere midnight of their dance. Perhaps the music was different; perhaps the light fell a little differently on Daphne's face, or on his; but they moved each other more stiffly round the floor, and their conversation was only polite. That pause, the fermata between one dance and the next had chilled them, and they both tried, keenly, to stir up the sense of ecstatic gaze. But there was a sense of artificiality about Daphne's sinking face, a sense of wrongness in the manly expression Friedrich tried so hard to assume as he squared his jaw at her, and, all in all, it was as well when the dance came to an end and she said to him (or, perhaps, he said to her), 'I could do with that drink.'

'Here's your beer,' Pierre said.

'Gorgeous,' Daphne said.

'And now,' Pierre said, 'let's go to the East.'

How and why they joined in with Pierre's suggestion to go over the Wall Friedrich could never afterwards understand. He and Daphne found themselves, as it were, taken along in Pierre's imperious wake, as, not waiting for their assent or refusal, he got up and put on his coat. They tagged along, hardly exchanging a rational word until they reached the queue to the Friedrichstrasse crossing.

'Incidentally,' Pierre said. 'What's your name?'

'Friedrich,' Friedrich said stupidly.

'Not you,' Pierre said. 'I remember *your* name. I've got it written on a piece of paper inside my pillow, as I cry myself to sleep every night at your failure to give me a ring. I meant *her*.'

'Daphne,' Daphne said.

'You'd wait for half your fucking lifetime before this one would introduce you,' Pierre said. 'You really would. Honestly, where were you brought up?'

'The Ruhrgebiet,' Friedrich said, and started laughing, right there in the Friedrichstrasse queue.

'Well, that excuses everything,' Pierre said. 'I am called Stifter, although my very dear friends are so kind as to call me Pierre. I don't encourage that immediately, not for another hour or two, perhaps.'

'Do you mean,' Friedrich said, 'you don't actually know each other?'

'No,' Daphne said. 'Why did you think –'

'No reason,' Friedrich said, unable to remember what had started any of this. 'What would the Museums' Director of all Prussia say, you with your fur coat on.'

'Nothing, I dare say, you with holes in your elbows,' Pierre said grandly. 'Everybody wears fur coats in Berlin. It's a well-known fact.'

'Look around you,' Friedrich said.

'It would be rude,' Pierre said. 'We haven't been introduced, so I can't stare at them. And it's not for you to insult me –'

'I wasn't insulting you –'

'Because at least *I* don't fuck fat old wankers.'

'He's not a fat old wanker,' Friedrich said.

'Yes, he is,' Pierre said.

'Well, he's fat,' Friedrich conceded. 'But he's all right.'

'Who?' Daphne said.

'No one you know,' Friedrich said. 'And I'm not fucking him, in any case.'

'You're not fucking anyone?' Daphne said.

'I'm not fucking *him*.'

'You can fuck me,' Daphne said.

'Fuck off.'

'And *me*,' Pierre said. 'Yum yum.'

'I wouldn't fuck you with a fucking *bargepole*,' Friedrich said, emphatically prodding Pierre in the chest, turning, extravagantly, to include Daphne and, stumbling slightly as he gestured, the whole queue in his vaunted celibacy.

'Oh dear,' Pierre said meditatively, and quite unconcerned. The queue fell momentarily silent, before a rash of half-giggling broke out. 'That's what they all say, until they do. And in any case I wouldn't expect that you would admit that you're fucking him to me and in front of her –'

'Who?' Daphne said.

'The fat wanker,' Pierre said, extending his hands and observing his very clean fingernails. 'Naturally.'

'Oh, I want to know, I want to know,' Daphne said.

'And what if I wasn't fucking him,' Friedrich said, triumphant at having found a gap in the argument. 'What would I say then?'

'Oh,' Pierre said, 'I expect you'd probably claim you were sleeping with him anyway, just to make yourself seem a tad more interesting than you actually are. There's no point in admitting it if it's true.'

'All right,' Friedrich said. 'I am sleeping with Peter Picker.'

'You're sleeping with Peter Picker?' Daphne said.

'There you are,' Pierre said. 'Now, don't you feel better, now that you've owned up to it?'

'They'll have that fur coat off your back, soon as you get out on the street,' Friedrich said, irrelevantly.

'Nonsense,' Pierre said. 'They love a bit of glamour over there. They'll stare, but one doesn't mind that. Here we are. Well, cherie, hello.'

The neat customs guard looked bemused, whether at Pierre's unconventional greeting, his luxuriant apparel, or his ability to render the word *hello* as a five-syllable ascending scale of lewd suggestiveness was not clear.

'I do love doing this run,' Pierre continued over his shoulder. 'Amazing, you know, what you can get in these pockets –'

'Passport, please,' the guard, blushing furiously, said.

'Once managed to get through with a video recorder, strapped to my back –' Pierre continued, handing over his compulsory twenty-five marks and taking the twenty-five Ostmarks in exchange.

'Here you are, *sir*,' the guard went on, scribbling his initials on the single sheet visa and slotting it into Pierre's passport.

'And thank *you*,' Pierre said. 'See you in a mo, darlings.'

He whisked through, leaving Friedrich and Daphne to the pink-faced guard.

'There you go,' he said on the Friedrichstrasse, when

Daphne and Friedrich were through. 'You know, I live in hope one day that one of these boys will *really thoroughly* search me, if you see what I mean, and, I'll tell you now, the sight of me, trouserless, is not one anyone with a pulse could resist, but *that* was a very nice second-best.'

'What?'

'This,' Pierre said, smirking. He got out the slip of paper from the passport. Where the guard was supposed to initial it, he had written Juan Richter, a telephone number, and a kiss. 'Terribly boring for them, out there all day, of course. He's given me a proper visa as well as this, so that I don't hand back his phone number on the way back and get him into trouble.'

'Are you going to ring him?' Friedrich said incredulously.

'No, of course not,' Pierre said. 'Still, it's nice to know that, even at one's hideously advanced age, one can still pull a piece of *boy*. And it's always useful to have some friend in the East to whom one can give all one's spare Ostmarks. Honestly, twenty-five marks, every time you cross, what a scandal it is, sheer extortion. Now, where shall we go?'

The bar they ended up at was one of those bars always said to exist in East Berlin, but which few people could find, or wished to find. It was a gay bar of sorts; it proclaimed its nature, nervously, through its décor and a single, fidgeting middle-aged man in a dress sitting near the back exit. The eight or nine customers smiled at each other, as if out of gratitude, and carried on drinking; there was the man in a frock, a few heavy, middle-aged, already rather drunk men, and the principal object of their attention, a skinny, big-nosed, spotty boy, barely out of his teens, drinking at the bar and smoothing his greasy yellow hair back every minute. In odd ways, it was not unlike Rose's in the West; it was hung, this summer night, with gold tinsel over vivid red velvet walls, and lit with lurid red lights. Unspeakable music played.

'God, what an awful hole,' Pierre said in his precise and carrying voice. They stood in the door of the bar, and watched as every single customer turned towards them with some expression between alarm and distaste, and, when it was apparent that this was not a raid by the police or the local thugs, turned back to their beer.

'You suggested it,' Daphne said.

'So I did,' Pierre said. 'Do you know somewhere else to go? This is the only place I ever come to in East Berlin. They always pretend they don't know you, but I'm practically a regular. I must come here once a month at least. God knows why.'

'Probably because it's so cheap,' Friedrich said. 'We certainly won't get through all those Ostmarks.'

'Actually, I always think it's rather easier to pull a boy in the East,' Pierre said. 'That must be it. But they never ever have anywhere to go; they always live with their mothers or their wives and you end up having a shag over the back of a dustbin behind a bar and them looking over their shoulder the whole time for the People's Police to arrest them for public acts of sodomy, not that there's anything else to do in this godforsaken hole. I wonder whether the penalties are worse for the boy doing the sodomy or the one being done. No, I don't know why I come here. And look at what's on offer. Nothing much at all.'

'Oh, I don't know about that,' Daphne said. 'What about this gorgeous number, here, at the bar?'

'The one who hasn't washed his hair since Tuesday? He'd certainly agree with you,' Pierre said. 'Once I'd got him out the back I'm sure I'd find I'd rather shag the dustbin, to be honest.'

'You don't stand a chance,' Friedrich said. 'He's completely out of your league.'

'Out of my league? Watch me,' Pierre said.

He walked up to the boy, his legs squarely apart like John Wayne's. 'So,' Friedrich heard him say. 'Do you come here often?'

'No,' the boy said.

'Can I buy you a drink?' Pierre said.

'No,' the boy said.

Pierre beat a retreat.

'Out of your league?' Friedrich said.

'I don't think so,' Pierre said.

'I think he thinks so,' Friedrich said.

'Come with me,' Pierre said, pocketing a book of the bar's matches. Friedrich followed him to the back, leaving Daphne where she was, next to the skinny nervous boy, still looking around every thirty seconds as if his parents were about to come into the tinsel-hung bar. Pierre leant on the telephone by the lavatories and drew Friedrich conspiratorially close.

'What are we going to do?' Friedrich said.

'We're going to have some fun with the twat,' Pierre said, gleefully.

'Oh, fun,' Friedrich said. 'I remember fun.' He was quite exhausted by Pierre's desire for hilarity, quite crushed and depressed by his appetite for merriment.

'Now,' Pierre said, 'this boy, the thin one with the bad hair and bad skin and bad clothes –'

'The one who's just told you to bugger off?'

'– you think he's out of my league?'

'Oh yes,' Friedrich said. 'And so does he.'

'We're going to telephone him,' Pierre said. 'Out of my league. You must be joking.'

'How?'

'With a telephone,' Pierre said. He picked up the receiver, and, looking at the number on the bar's book of matches, dialled. The telephone behind the bar rang, ten metres away. The barman finished pouring a glass of beer, then wiped his hands on his apron and turned to answer the telephone.

'Oh, good evening,' Pierre said in his best polite voice, his voice immediately falling an octave. 'I was looking for my friend, and I wondered if he was in the bar.'

'No, I was just about to tell you what he looks like.'

'No, I'm his –' exaggerated tone – '*friend*.'

'Well, he's twenty, and he's quite tall, and pale, with floppy hair, blond, and quite a big nose, though I shouldn't say, and quite bad skin. And he's wearing, or he was when he went out, a sort of pale blue plastic anorak, you know the sort. Can you see anyone like that in here – in there?'

'What happens if he asks you what his name is?' Friedrich hissed when the barman had turned away from the telephone to look.

'Don't worry,' Pierre said. The barman came back. 'Is he not? Are you sure? Is he really not there? Only he promised me he would be. Couldn't you just have a tiny look for me, just for me, darling?'

'Oh, that is nice of you, thank you. Is he really there? Can I have a tiny word with the sweety?'

Pierre juggled with his loosened jaw, preparing himself for a conversation, like an opera singer before curtain up.

'Ah-*hum*,' he said. The boy, his eyebrows rising into his hairline, beginning a violent blush, seemed to be denying that anyone knew he was here to the barman. Finally, the barman shrugged, and handed him the receiver.

'Hull-o,' Pierre said. 'You don't know me, but I know you.'

'No,' he went on. 'This isn't Christian. No, I said, you don't know me. But I've been admiring you for a while. I saw you going into the bar and I thought I'd telephone you. Tell me, what sort of men do you like?

'Big dark ones? Do you like them firm and muscular? Because that's what I'm like. I'm very muscular and dark. Some people think I'm too muscular, but I hope you won't mind that. Do you mind if a man's got a really big cock? I hope not. Some men say that my cock's just too big, but if you don't like big cocks, then just say, and I'll stop bothering you. You don't mind me talking to you like this? Tell me, what do you like to do in bed? Will you tell me, now, what you'd like me to do to you? I'd love to hear.'

Pierre fell silent. The boy was muttering into the telephone, his hand clamped to his other ear against the bar music. Daphne, sitting next to the boy, began to pay attention to him.

'Can you speak up a bit?' Pierre said. 'I want to hear everything you say.'

The boy carried on talking, his face bent slightly. Daphne exchanged a look with the increasingly curious barman.

'Oh, yes,' Pierre said, eventually. 'Oh, that'd be great. Will you come to me? Will you? But we've got to meet somewhere first. Where shall we meet? Somewhere convenient.' He clamped his hand over the telephone.

'Fuck it,' he said to Friedrich. 'I can't think of anywhere to meet him.'

'The Victory Column,' Friedrich said stupidly.

'In East Berlin, you fool,' Pierre said.

'The Soviet Memorial in Treptower Park,' Friedrich said.

Pierre took his hand off the telephone. 'Sorry, I lost you

for a moment there. This stupid telephone. I was just saying we could meet in the Treptower Park. How about that.
I live quite near there. At the Soviet Memorial. Yes,
tonight. I want you tonight. I want you, I want to lick you
all over. You want it, I know you do. I can be there as soon
as you can. How soon can you come to me?'

The boy paused; he looked up. The barman and Daphne
and the other customers around the bar looked back at him
with undisguised interest. He muttered something quickly
into the telephone, and quickly put it down.

'Perfect,' Pierre said, putting the telephone down.

'You are a bastard,' Friedrich said.

'Oh, I know,' Pierre said. 'But I don't suppose anyone
round here voluntarily goes to the Soviet Memorial, and
it's simply gorgeous, even at this time of night. He'll have
a lovely time. He might even meet someone. Perhaps we
could telephone somebody else and tell them to go there as
well. Except that if we claimed to look like that, we'd never
get anyone in their right mind to cross the road. No, we'd
better stand here for a moment or he'll hear my voice and
realize he's been set up.'

The boy paid for his drink, and then, picking up his coat,
left the bar, still looking round him.

The barman said something to Daphne, and then,
following her gaze, saw Friedrich and Pierre by the telephone.

'But why?' Friedrich said.

'Oh, come on,' Pierre said. 'Didn't you think that was
funny?'

'Well, no,' Friedrich said. 'I can't imagine anything
much amusing about making someone stand in the Soviet
Memorial and wait for a man who isn't going to come.'

'Not amusing for him, of course,' Pierre said. 'It'll just

teach him not to be so German Democratic Republic. It's just so *passé.*'

'Well, that's where he lives, of course.'

'But can you imagine anything more frightful than choosing to be a frightful spotty homosexual and wear horrible plastic clothes and live in the German Democratic Republic?'

'Of course,' Friedrich said, 'he hasn't actually chosen all those things. Or any of them, actually.'

'He's chosen his clothes,' Pierre said.

'Not necessarily,' Friedrich said. 'Have you ever bought anything in East Berlin? There's no choice at all.'

'But what I can't understand is why they don't run up their own outfits. Or wear those nice navy blue party uniforms, terribly elegant, really, and so flattering. But they all wear these revolting stonewashed jeans, all of them with the same sort of bagginess around the hips, as if they had nappies on underneath. And some of them even wear stonewashed denim jackets with their stonewashed denim trousers. Horrible, horrible, horrible. It really is baffling. And the tops – oh, don't get me on to the *tops* they wear – all that detailing, all that padding, and more stonewashing. I don't know why nobody ever says to them all that there's only one way to dress well. If I ran the German Democratic Republic, I'd have a television programme which went out every night, at the same time, and of course, they all have to watch the same television programmes, and there's nothing else to do here, so they all stay in and they'd watch my programme. And this programme I'd make and show them –'

'Some of them get West German television as well, you know,' Friedrich said.

'Really? Are you sure? They just seem to have so little

idea about fashion, you'd think they'd pick something up, some clever little ideas about what to wear, even from West German television, even from West German fashion, which, as you know, almost entirely consists of persuading overweight old ladies to wear a lot of military paraphernalia and gold braid, and all that obsession with building out the shoulders the whole time, like *admirals* or something. No, I'd make a fashion programme, but it would be completely *revolutionary*. A revolutionary programme for the darling revolutionary *Volk*. Because it wouldn't show a choice of outfits, or anything like that, it would just have, for half an hour, a single voice, saying, over and over, *Remember, keep it simple. A simple line, a plain colour, keep it fitted, and keep the trimmings to a minimum*. Really, what they need to wear, what would be really wonderfully elegant would be those little blue suits Chairman Mao designed for the Cultural Revolution. So lovely, so plain, and so understated, and if you can only solve the problem of what shoes to wear with it and whether you can get away with a bag, there would be nothing nicer. Do you suppose one could buy a suit like that in Germany? No matter – you could probably run one up yourself.'

'I like your coat,' the barman said. He had come up from behind without them noticing, and now stood there, smiling in a manner which suggested that he knew more than they did; not knowing more about anything in particular, just more knowledgeable, in possession of more secrets, and understanding them better, perhaps than they did themselves. 'Nice and warm.'

'Lovely and warm,' Pierre said briskly. 'You need a nice warm coat for the winter here.'

'But it isn't winter,' the barman said. 'Aren't you hot in it?'

'No,' Pierre said. 'I have very bad circulation, unfortunately.'

'Ohhhhh,' the barman sighed. 'Bad circulation. That can be awful. Chilblains in winter.'

'And low blood pressure.'

'Which means you can't fall asleep,' the barman said. 'Or does it mean you fall asleep all the time?'

'One of the two, anyway,' Pierre said.

'So, tell me,' the barman said. 'Was it you two telephoning that boy at the bar?'

'Well,' Friedrich said. 'Yes, it was.'

'I thought so,' the barman said. 'And you don't come from round here, do you?'

'No,' Pierre said, and Friedrich noticed that there was some nervousness in the way he stood and spoke. 'No, we come from over the Wall.'

'So you've come and you're looking for some fun,' the barman said. 'It's a shame we can't do the same thing, go over to you, go over and visit one of those white spaces on the maps, see what's there, and then come back and say, like you're going to say when you get back to your place, well, we have more fun over here, anyway.'

'Yes,' Pierre said. 'Yes, it is, an awful shame, isn't it.'

'But the thing is,' the barman said. 'I wondered what sort of fun you were looking for. Because I might have some fun here which you don't expect to find over this side of the Wall.'

'Oh?' Pierre said. 'What sort of fun is that, then?'

'You'll need to prove to me first,' the barman said, 'that I can trust you. So how can you do that?'

'I've no idea,' Pierre said. 'You'll just have to trust us or piss off back to the bar.'

'Well,' the barman said. 'I don't suppose that many of

the People's Policemen dress like that. I've got some stuff, some nice stuff. Some fun in a pill. You'll love it.'

'Oh, how gorgeous,' Pierre said. 'DDR drugs. Whoever heard of such a thing?'

'Are you in business?' the barman said. 'I'm not interested if you're going to mess me about.'

'Yes, of course,' Pierre said. 'We'll have two, one for me and one for him. One for the lady, do you think? No, maybe not. Yes, just two. Show us them.'

The barman, with a single swift gesture, reached into his jacket pocket and produced, what Friedrich knew he was going to produce, two of the unmarked painkillers he had made Martin buy, the painkillers he had thrown away in the Treptower Park at the Soviet Memorial. He made himself go blank; the world did these things to him, and it was not often wise to inquire, immediately, into their meaning.

'Sixty marks,' the barman said. 'Westmarks.'

'You're selling them to us?' Friedrich said.

'Well, I'm not giving them away,' the barman said. 'Sixty marks.'

'Gorgeous,' Pierre said, reaching for his wallet. 'What are they?'

'Good stuff,' the barman said, laconically.

'Are you sure?' Friedrich said. 'I mean –'

'If you don't want to,' Pierre said, 'I've had it before. Well, not these, but probably something quite like them. It's nice. Have you had it?'

'No,' Friedrich said. It was, after all, Pierre's money he was throwing away; and, even if he spent the money in his pocket, he would be spending Picker's money and not his own. He wondered what had happened; he wondered how these pointless pills had been picked up, had found their way to some kind of distribution network, had been sold, and then reminded himself not to think about it. He watched Pierre hand over the sixty marks, oddly disconsolate.

'Great,' the barman said. 'Have fun. It's good stuff. I've got customers to see to.'

'No,' Friedrich said, as the barman left them. 'I just thought it's not such a great idea buying drugs from someone you don't know anything about. And it's not likely to be brilliant quality over here. He could be selling you anything.'

'Oh,' Pierre said. 'You don't get ripped off in East Berlin. The police would be down on you like a ton of bricks.'

'You think they exercise much in the way of quality control over drug dealers?' Friedrich said. 'I'm amazed anyone risks it over here.'

'Well, me too,' Pierre said. 'I've never heard of such a thing. That's why I'm curious. Do you want one, or shall I have two?'

'No,' Friedrich said. 'I'll give it a go.'

'Come with me,' Pierre said. 'I'm not going to take it in front of the whole bar. I have terrible problems taking pills, I always have to stand and gulp like a camel or a llama or something, far too conspicuous.'

Friedrich followed Pierre into the lavatory.

'Here you go,' Pierre said, turning and with his palm flat, pressing his hand against Friedrich's face. There was suddenly a pill in Friedrich's mouth; a strange and immediately bitter taste. He swallowed, Pierre's flat hand covering his mouth. 'Might be nice,' Pierre said. 'You never know.' He took the second pill, delicately, between thumb and third finger and, head back, dropped it into his own mouth. 'Yum yum,' he said.

A man came into the lavatory. He was one of the fat lorry drivers. Seeing Friedrich and Pierre standing there, he immediately grabbed his own crotch and shook it up and down with what seemed an impressive lack of a sense of his own hideousness. Pierre and Friedrich gazed at him with equal degrees of distaste; he gave his groin a final readjustment and went over to the urinal. Friedrich went out, only noticing when he held the door behind him that Pierre wasn't following.

'You were gone some time,' Daphne said.

'Oh,' Friedrich said. 'We were just having a bit of fun.'

'A bit of fun?'

'Yes,' Friedrich said. 'You know that boy – the one sitting just there – you know?'

'Yes,' Daphne said. 'Someone phoned him up, and then he started to say some really filthy things into the telephone, and then he put the phone down and dashed out.'

'Yes,' Friedrich said. 'It was us phoning him up.'

'Sorry?'

'We went to the phone and called him up.'

'Why?'

'We thought it would be funny.'

'Well, it was funny, but what did you say to him?'

'We told him to go and stand in some incredibly cold and distant park and then some gorgeous dark man would come and fuck him up the bum.'

'And he believed it?'

'Wouldn't you?'

'Nope.'

'What are you two talking about?' Pierre said, returning from what must have been quite a brief interlude in the latrines. The lorry driver, following close behind, waggled past, but, knowing the limits of his own luck, went back to his beer rather than try to join them.

'Oh, about that poor, poor boy,' Daphne said, 'standing freezing in some horrible park waiting for someone to come and fuck him.'

'He won't freeze,' Pierre said, heartlessly, 'it's quite a warm night.'

'A fat lot you care,' Daphne said. 'No, I think it's funny. I wondered who had phoned him.'

'You know,' Friedrich said. 'You know, I think –' But then. But then, a wave of nausea had, he found, come over him. 'I think,' he said, but already his voice seemed very very far away, already seemed a single strand in the complex and yet comprehensible texture of sound in the bar. What had been a vague babble, a murmur of conversation mingled with two partly-compatible backing tapes now abruptly resolved itself into a terrible clarity of vowels and consonants, an echo chamber of individual voices, all of which were laid out for him, in which he found his own voice, and listened to it, like a treasure-hunter coming across some lost jewel of his own former possession. It felt like falling backwards, but blissfully, into the arms of another, into some soft and scented world, and the warmth of the bar and the tingling delicious scalp reassured him, made his limbs want to stretch, as if with a gorgeous luscious ache and energy and restlessness. He could feel his mouth stretching into a grin, wide as a house, being pulled back by some pleasure outside himself, some pleasure he could not quite understand and did not quite want to. He shut his eyes, and the falling backwards rushed in on him. The sick feeling was appalling; he opened his eyes. They were looking at him.

'Good?' Pierre said. 'That was pretty quick.'

'What is it?' Daphne said. 'Are you all right?'

'We bought –' Pierre said, and he was off on an explanation, telling Daphne about Friedrich with a lucidity, just now, beyond Friedrich. It was so funny that everybody knew so much more about Friedrich than Friedrich did, that was so funny. He moved, experimentally. That felt worse. 'Do you want to dance?' Pierre said, cutting short the explanation. Friedrich shook his head. 'Do you feel quite tickety-boo?' Pierre said. 'Sometimes – you know – sometimes it's a bit strange first thing. Do you want to go out for some air or something?'

Friedrich made some kind of gesture with his head, and then Pierre was leading him out of the bar, with everybody staring at him, but somehow staring at him *warmly, kindly*; how nice it was to come to this place and be wished well by everyone, be found not wanting, to be regarded as someone who could so easily be accepted. 'It's taking its time for me, this fucking pill,' someone – Pierre? – was saying, and there he was, in some kind of back courtyard, among the bins. The dark was bliss, soothing cool dark bliss on his blazing eyes. He stayed with it, shutting his eyes against the dark, leaning back with the cool dark bliss of the damp wall through his shirt, the bliss of the sense of fur, not his, but Pierre's mink against his bare skin, his chest, as a pair of hands unbuttoned his shirt and he, unresisting, pleasured, let them. He had never so had the sense of his own skin as it was touched; it was more like touching someone than being touched. He felt as the fur brushed so shiveringly against it, as he felt some dry mouth lick at his chest, as he felt the first gentle flick of the teeth against the tender edge of his pink ridged nipple, that he was feeling himself, his pale soft skin and drawing pleasure from himself as he allowed himself to be pleasured. And on it went, and there was nothing he had to do; just letting the good blankness work down, letting his clothes be removed, his trousers unbuttoned and, unprotesting, let fall with his nice shabby old underwear to the ground, and thinking only with strange clarity *I am now naked* as this sensation, this blind fur with a long and tenderly toothed tongue worked its way over him; as this stranger, this – that strange clarity again – this *man* took his cock in his mouth, and pulled with his tender inside part at the tender soft flesh. For a moment it seemed unrousable, soft and pale like the rest of him, and he hardly knew where the moaning he heard was coming from, from where this noise of pleasure, whose, what, why, how; and then, as Pierre tipped back his head and moved underneath and up into, something never felt or known before, into something so terrifying, so new, the feeling and sure knowledge of a scratchy unshaven chin rubbing against the soft pink flesh of his arse, and then, as he felt, like a spectacular revelation at the centre of the whole drugs and skin and fur and dark cool bliss of it, the soft pink flesh of Pierre's tongue pressing against and into the secret soft flesh, he found he hardly knew whether he was aroused or not, and hardly knew, any longer, how to tell.

Sensation was beyond him and yet it was the whole of him. He observed the sensations on his skin and inside him with an absolute clarity and knowledge; observed it, too, with a perfect lack of control as his legs were seized and wrenched, amazingly, upwards, as he was suddenly on his back, the squared-off sky of the back courtyard stabbingly diamond-brilliant with the DDR stars, and against his face was another face. 'Do you want?' the mouth said, wet with saliva, the eyes bright-black with happiness, and, not knowing what he wanted or what he was asked, Friedrich nodded.

Afterwards; afterwards; he was alone, and lying there with the sky and the clear small noises of the bar and the street and the houses around, lying there naked and pleasured and cool against the cool dark stones of the floor. He did not know how long he was there; he did not know how much time had passed while he lay there, and only the occasional distant change of a song alerted him to the fact that he was alone, and there, and quietly half-thinking. He got up. Pierre was gone. He gathered, slightly shaking, his trousers, and pulled them up, buttoning with his other hand his shirt, walking all the time into the bar. There was no one there, or rather, all those people, all those strange people; only Daphne and the East Germans and the barman. He stood and let them all look at him; let Daphne stand up and come towards him, gather him up and brush at him, and take him, her arm behind him, pushing him out of the bar quite softly, and towards the underground station. There was a journey; one punctuated by Daphne holding his hands in both of hers and asking him, all the time, if he was all right, and around him no familiar place, none at all, just new faces, new voices, and Daphne there. He turned to her, perhaps once, perhaps twice, perhaps all the time, and each time, there she was, stroking him, stroking his face, his hands, with her big-eyed look of love and concern; her look of knowing everything, and forgiving everything. And quite suddenly, without him knowing how or why or when they got there, they found themselves in his flat, and it was as if a heavy cloud had parted and left him under clear and startling and clean sunlight. He sat down on the bed, for fear of wobbling.

'You're all right,' she said.

'I'm fine,' he said. 'I'm fine now.'

'What was it?'

'I don't know. I thought it was nothing at all.'

'It had no effect on that man. He went saying that he'd bought a dud, he didn't know what had happened to you. Who was he?'

'I don't know,' Friedrich said. 'I've met him before, I know. I can't remember his name.'

'He said his name was Pierre.'

'Yes, that's right,' Friedrich said. Then he changed his mind. 'No, I mean the pill. I know it was nothing at all. I recognized it. Oh. No, it shouldn't have done that. I don't know how.'

'It's okay,' Daphne said. 'Are you all right? Shall I stay?'

'Yes,' Friedrich said. 'Please stay.'

They were quiet for a time. Friedrich got up and went into the kitchen.

'I'm going to make a cup of coffee,' he said, effortfully. 'Do you want one?'

'I'll make it,' Daphne said. 'I don't mind. What happened to that man? Pierre?'

'I don't know,' Friedrich said. 'He just went.'

'What were you two doing out the back?'

'Nothing,' Friedrich said. 'Nothing much. Just talking.'

'Stop it,' Daphne said. 'I said, I'll make the coffee. I don't mind.'

'No,' Friedrich said. 'I'd rather.'

'Okay. Do you want to hear some music?' Daphne said. 'I'm not tired at all.'

'Yes,' Friedrich said, in the kitchen. 'Yes, I think I do. There's some cassettes there. See if you can find one, and then put it in the machine and press the button which says PLAY on it.'

Somehow the making of a cup of coffee seemed, right now, terribly hard. As he unscrewed the cap of the coffee jar, the kitchen retreated from him, and, wavering, held him at arm's length. He stopped, the jar in one hand, the lid in the other, and listened to the noises around him. Everything, again, was shockingly disparate. He felt as if he could determine every single sound. There was the hiss of the kettle, which was not one noise, but several, its over-tones, its bass tones whispering in his ear; the crisp shuffle as he moved his feet on the slightly sticky floor; the cars – how many? Six? – on the streets around, the wind in the trees, and a quiet ambient roar which he could only think of as the noise of sunlight. He stood, and waited, and con-centrated on the sound, the clatter, of Daphne sorting through the cassettes.

'I can't find anything,' she said.

'No,' he said, focusing as much as he could on the warmly shifting colours of the kitchen.

'Half of these aren't labelled.'

'No,' he said. 'They're old, most of them. From home.'

'Do you know what they are?'

'No,' he said. 'I never listen to music.'

'I can't find anything,' she said. 'There's nothing very exciting. Shall I put one on anyway?'

'Yes,' he said.

'I'm going to live dangerously and put an unlabelled one on.'

'Yes,' he said. 'It might be anything at all. It might be stuff I liked when I was twelve years old.'

'Let's see what it is,' he could hear her muttering. 'That would be nice.'

He stood there in the kitchen. He watched the shapes around him hold, glowing, each with its small aura, its small sense of existence in the world, existence quite sepa-rate from everything about it, like a painting by some inept painter, a work in which each object is radiantly isolated with its black outline. Light was made stuff, here in this room; that was good and interesting. He closed his eyes, and before his closed eyes came a vision of the intensity of shape, how everything was conditioned by the shape it had. He had never seen it so clearly before. He concentrated on his brilliant and true and inconceivable thought. He waited, as if for the world to settle down, to return to what it was. He stood, a spoon in his hand, an open jar of instant coffee next to two empty mugs, and, listening, he paused for some time. He had no idea how long for. He heard her finger, against the careful strands of multitudinous sounds, press against the PLAY button. He stood there. And then his life changed.

A VOICE

'So I'll be off,' the voice said. It sounded harsh, stiff, stagey, the voice of somebody unaccustomed to reading something out loud; it was clearly reading from a piece of paper. 'Things have been getting bad here. You don't need me to tell you that. I haven't been much good in the last few months and you'll be better off without me. I don't want you to worry about me. I'm going to try and make a new start somewhere else. And if that doesn't work out then I'll call it a day. But I don't think you ought to worry about me any more. I've been getting too much in the way and the best thing I can do is just to go.'

Friedrich came out from the kitchen. There must have been something in his face which frightened Daphne; perhaps it was a fear in his features which Daphne's features so clearly reflected. She stabbed at the machine, stopping the tape.

'What is it?' she said.

'It's my father,' he said. He hardly knew where to stand, what to look at, how to hold himself upright. The voice, so long unheard, had never gone from his mind; always, there, in the back of it, a quiet Westphalian accent, rippling on in

269

its complaint, and now, it was as if something so long known about, so long held down had surfaced one last time into the air. He stood and looked out of the window.

'I'm really sorry,' Daphne said. 'I wouldn't have –'

'That's all right,' Friedrich said. 'I've got to tell you something strange. I've never heard this before. I didn't know it was there. I didn't know my father recorded it. He must have left it for us before he went, and nobody found it.'

'It just got into the pile?'

'I suppose so,' Friedrich said.

'Before he went?'

'Yes,' Friedrich said. 'He went.'

'I'm so sorry,' Daphne said. 'I don't know how to say –'

'Please,' Friedrich said. 'I think I want to hear it. I never knew what happened to my father. He just went away one day and nobody ever found out what happened to him. He just disappeared.'

'I'm really sorry.'

'It was years ago now. It was like someone dying but with no body there to bury. Sometimes every day it seems as if he might just turn up.'

'But he doesn't.'

'No, he doesn't.'

He sat down on the bed.

'He didn't leave anything. Just went. Just this. I really want to listen to this.'

'I'm sorry,' Daphne said. 'I'll go.'

'No, please. Can you not go? Please. I think maybe this is a time when –'

He could hear himself; the hard way it was to speak. He did not know what it was; the drugs, his exhaustion, the voice he had kept so long in his head.

'Do you want me to stay?' Daphne said. 'I don't mind sitting with you while you listen. But will you tell me when you want to be on your own?'

He nodded. She patted the bed she sat on. He turned from the window and sat down, as she leant forward and pressed the rewind button. It fizzingly went back. He found he could not look at her, as she pressed the play button. And there it was again, like a conjuring trick which, so surprisingly, could be repeated, could be recreated; his father's voice, filling a room his father would never see.

'So I'll be off. Things have been getting bad here. You don't need me to tell you that. I haven't been much good in the last few months and you'll be better off without me. I don't want you to worry about me. I'm going to try and make a new start somewhere else. And if that doesn't work out then I'll call it a day. But I don't think you ought to worry about me any more. I've been getting too much in the way and the best thing I can do is just to go.

'I've tried never to worry you,' the voice went on. 'But I can't hide how bad things are at the moment. You've probably guessed that everything is going wrong, and that there's a real problem with the business. I've got to go because I can't carry on, I can't change the way things are. I'm sorry. I'm sorry that you're going to find out once I've gone exactly how serious things are. But things will be better for you without me. Try not to hate me for doing this, just running away. You can't think any worse of me than I think of myself.

'I've left you in a mess, but I can't see any other way out. If I could take you with me I would. But I can't and I hope one day you'll understand why, and after that I hope you might be able to start to think about maybe forgiving me. But that's a lot to hope. Too much. I don't know what else to say. I never said I love you. I never knew how to. I've been thinking about what to say for weeks and now I can't say anything. There's only one thing I have to say to you, Friedrich. I just want to promise you one thing. I promise you that I will be back for you. When you need me I will be back for you. You have a life you need to live but I will be there for you. I will be back. I promise.'

The tape ran on. There was something which was not exactly silence and not exactly noise. It was the sound of the room in which Franz had lain as he made his recording, and, beyond that, Friedrich thought he could hear the frail sounds of the distant and blanked-out Cologne street. It went on; neither of them knew quite how to lean forward and stop the tape. There was a clatter on the tape, the noise of someone fumbling with the recording apparatus, and quite abruptly it dropped into the middle of an old American pop song. It was a cassette of Friedrich's; perhaps all Franz had been able to find. Perhaps he had thought that his son, constantly playing music too loudly, would come across the message almost immediately; perhaps he had not considered, with an absence of vanity Friedrich found almost touching, that the only reason his son listened to music was to irritate his father, and with his father gone, there was no reason ever again to put the music on.

'Are you all right?' Daphne said.

'It's a shock,' Friedrich said. Who was this man? He was not his father; the message, the feelings his father had put on tape were not feelings he had ever envisaged his father having. He thought with an awful sense of clarity that this tape was, after all, not his father, was someone else, leaving it, talking with his father's voice; and then, like a card flipping over, the certain truth came to him that he had never known his father, never understood what he was capable of and never speculated, never thought with any kind of accuracy about his father's feelings; seen only a pointless rage, a pointless frightened disappearance, and never known or imagined what his father had wanted and thought and cared about.

'Did you –' she said. 'Is it important?'

'I don't know,' he said. He would have told Daphne what he thought; he did not know, quite, how to say it, even how to say it to himself. 'No. I don't think so. It doesn't say anything we didn't know. Only that he didn't go with the intention of killing himself straight away, and we knew that, or we assumed that they'd have found a body.'

'You talk about it –'

'Yes?'

'I don't know. You talk about it in a strange way. It's like it's nothing to do with you.'

'It's difficult to talk about it at all,' Friedrich said. 'I talk about it in the only way I can. I don't avoid the subject.'

'How do you feel?'

Friedrich stopped and concentrated on what he felt. It was hard to say. His jaw would not stop moving.

'Now? Not much. Disorientated maybe. I'm not sure. I haven't heard his voice since he left. It's strange. It's like hearing a recording of Napoleon's voice, or Julius Caesar. It's sort of what you expect and what you always knew it would be like, and you don't know whether it's momentous or trivial or somewhere in between. You have photographs of people who leave your life, or who die, but you don't usually have recordings of them. It's like he's fulfilled his promise now.'

'What promise?'

'The promise on the tape, that he'd be back when I needed him. It feels like he is back. I don't know why he only said that to me. It's like he knew the tape would end up with me, that I'd be the only one who heard it.'

'Aren't you going to send it to your mother?'

'What's the point? It's too long ago. She's better off without it. The only reason would be if I thought she'd find out I kept it from her. But that won't happen.'

'Perhaps,' Daphne said, 'you want to be on your own.'

'I think so,' Friedrich said. 'We never had our shag.'

'Were we going to have a shag?'

'I thought we were,' Friedrich said. 'I thought I asked you and you said yes. Maybe I just thought it. But now we've not had our shag and now we're not going to have our shag. And that's terribly sad. That's the saddest thing in the world. That's so sad.'

Daphne smiled at him. There was something new in her smile, something uncommitted, something not quite fully there. 'No,' she said. 'We never did have our shag. You didn't ask me. And I don't know what I'd have said if you'd asked me. But it doesn't matter any more. I'd better go.'

'Don't go,' he said, but he knew, and she could tell that he was just saying it out of some strange convention, that what he most wanted now was for her to go, for him to be alone with the voice of his father in the small black un-labelled tape. She shook her head, and, taking his bowed head between her hands, raised it an inch or two before kissing him, putting her dry mouth against his closed eye-lids, first one then the other, a tiny pock in the air each time. He raised his head, and looked at her, as she shook her head, smiling a little, and left his flat.

When she had gone, he went to the cassette player, but, instead of playing the tape again, he pressed the eject button, and took it out of the machine. He held the small thing, and went to the window. He stood there, watching Daphne go down the street, and slowly, clumsily, undressed to go to bed. It was getting light outside already; he did not, for some reason, feel he wanted to look at his watch. He opened the double doors and went out on to the balcony. She was almost turning round the corner into the Oranienstrasse, when he saw the strangest thing. Down there, in the empty street, she fell to the ground. At first, he thought that she had dropped her bag, and then he saw that she had no bag; that she had just fallen, let herself drop to the floor, and knelt there, her arms around herself, pulling herself into a tight comforting ball. He realized, slowly, that she was weeping. He stayed there, for as long as it took, watching her. After a time, she raised her head, down there, and got up slowly, and carried on walking away. He stood there, and watched her turn the corner into the Oranienstrasse. He was alone. In his hand was his father's voice, and, as the first beginnings of an ache came into his body, he straightened his arms backwards, tipped his head upwards to look at the sky. There was only one thing to do, and he did it, hurling the small black cassette as far as he could. He closed his eyes, and felt, rather than saw, the arc of the thing through the air, falling who knew where, falling who cared where. And then something he had never known he possessed was gone, and gone for good.

The air fell on his bare chest, a cool sweetness as the day began. Outside and beneath Friedrich's high balcony, there were birds in the trees, yawking; a couple of cars somewhere close; and otherwise it was silent, Kreuzberg not even offering the usual solitary drunk, dragging his feet down there on the street. As he shut his eyes and tipped back his head, and yawned, it was like a deep drink of something once tasted, years before, never again experienced. He stood there, waiting for a memory to come to him. It would not come to him; it was no specific moment, but the whole of his past he seemed to be drinking down as he stood there in the end of the long night, the beginning of a long day. Today would be a good day to go and see Peter Picker. Yes it would. He turned round, rubbing his arms, and went inside to try to sleep, with the overwhelming sensation, inside his skin, against the sheets, of something, some fragile surface on liquid, some crust, cracking and dividing and splitting. And as he fell asleep, he felt that the world was being silenced as he fell into oblivion, and knowing, all the time, that the world was continuing, continuing with its usual uproar, and it was only him who, for a brief time, was leaving it.

The birds outside stopped their noise, and flapped off, lazily. They settled in trees they had no business to be sitting in, but from which nobody thought to trouble them. They flew, if they knew, eastwards; and as they crossed the barrier, somewhere beneath them on the earth, of the Wall, they seemed to applaud with their heavy wings, a noise unheard, except by them. They flew on.

The earth, the sky, took no notice of the barriers put up by men in this city, in this country, on this earth. Everything was temporary; the birds, with their short lives, the insects, their lives still shorter, existed without reference to it, as if knowing that not just this wall, but all walls, all the works of men were temporary; temporary not because they were wrong but because the works of men, whether right or wrong, did not last. And the birds flew over the Wall, without benefit of passport, and flew back again, without thinking of the journey. The Wall had been constructed with a broad curving top on which no bird would perch; they flew over it, perching on gutters, on watchtowers, on either side of the Wall, as if they were observed, as if they performed their to and fro for the benefit, only, of their human observers. Pigeons born on one side of the Wall mated with pigeons born on the other; insects tunnelled, indifferently, into the no-man's-land. They knew that men had gone from the earth, leaving only their curious monuments; their lives continued around what men had left, and left to decay.

When Friedrich woke, his idea, or resolution, that this was the right day to go to Picker's flat was still in his mind. It was dusk outside. He thought about telephoning first; he set off before coming to any kind of conclusion. When he left his flat, the landlord Helmut Meier was standing, as usual, on the stairs. Friedrich paused for a second, and then his resolution was firm. He would not stand Meier one more minute.

'Herr Meier,' he said. 'Do you have a moment?'

Meier turned, morosely. 'If it's not too long,' he said. 'I'm busy.'

'I simply wanted to say,' Friedrich said, 'that I will be moving out at the end of the year. I wanted to give you plenty of warning.'

Meier's face was one of those reversible portraits; his sour expression gave way, as if inverted, to one of delighted horrible pleasure. 'At the end of the year?' he said. 'Not sooner?'

'No,' Friedrich said. 'On the first of January. Is that quite acceptable?'

'Oh,' Meier said, hissing between his loose teeth. 'Oh, quite acceptable. May I ask –'

'No,' Friedrich said. He did not quite know what had persuaded him to be so firm; he only knew that there was a tremendous relief in the idea of never again having to speak or deal with Meier's stairwell bullying, and left the building with a sense of everything having changed, everything become quite new. There was no need, either, even to think of beginning to look for a new flat; the first of January was months away.

He began his journey without a clear idea of his destination, just heading westwards; it wasn't until the train reached Gleisdreieck that it occurred to him that he could not, after all, remember exactly where he was going, or how, exactly to get there. He got off and bought a map of Berlin, and stood for a time on the platform like a tourist, half-noting the trains pulling in and out.

After all, there was a bus which went from outside the Wittenbergplatz station to the end of Picker's street. He left the station and stood at the bus-stop, still quaking slightly at the vicious intensity of the street lights. The bus was due in a couple of minutes, but it did not come; neither the eight minutes to the hour nor the two minutes past. The queue began to talk to each other, and Friedrich could never remember such a thing happening. The first bus came at twelve minutes past, unapologetically; a couple of old ladies who, like Friedrich, had been waiting for twenty minutes, gave the driver a hard time. To them it seemed like a nuisance, and no more; to Friedrich it seemed, this unexpected collapse of the most secure of Berlin's clock-like mechanisms, like an omen; things not working; things waiting to fall apart. He sat and waited for the right place to arrive outside, like a scrolling tapestry.

Picker's street was entirely silent of traffic and people. Friedrich got off the bus and stood for a moment, watching it draw away. He buzzed Picker's bell. There was a short wait, and then, instead of a voice inquiring, the door was abruptly opened. He wondered if Picker had seen him approach, and went in. Picker's flat was on the top floor, and as he climbed the stairs, he looked up, partly expecting him to be hanging over the banister, suspiciously watching his approach. But the well of the stairs was empty, blank and white, and, though he could hear a door on the top floor opening, no fat face appeared.

The door was open, and Friedrich went in, calling Picker's name. The flat was, as he had not noticed before, surprisingly elegant, white and cream and beige, and the hallway quite lined with books in English and German. He never usually noticed other people's flats; it was as if his decision to leave his own flat had sharpened his appreciation. A door to the left opened, and Picker came out. He looked at Friedrich in surprise.

'How did you get in?'

'The door was open.' Friedrich gestured behind him.

'Tom must have opened it,' Picker said. 'I didn't hear the bell go. Did you ring the bell?'

'Yes,' Friedrich said. 'Someone opened the door.'

'I had the television on,' Picker said. 'I must be going deaf or something. Tom must have buzzed you in. He's supposed to be in bed. He's not very well.'

'What's wrong with him?' Friedrich asked, but just then the kitchen door was pushed gently open, and there, standing in a pair of blue and white striped pyjamas, a tiny camel-coloured dressing-gown tied roughly round the middle and slippers an awkward size or two too big for him, was the child. His hair sticking up, his big eyes solemnly looking at Friedrich as if nothing so interesting had ever come through the front door, he held a big glass of bright orange squash in both his small hands. His face was flushed; the glass shook slightly, as if too big for him to hold.

'He's not well,' Picker said. Then he said something in English. The child stood there for a moment, before turning round and leaving the hallway in his half-run, his toppling gait. 'Come in. That's a good sign. He's been crying a lot and hasn't felt like getting up for hours. He likes company, you know.'

'What's wrong with him?' Friedrich asked, following him into the drawing room.

'He's got some kind of temperature, like a fever, and some kind of rash – a rash?' Picker asked. 'I don't know these medical terms at all.'

'Have you had the doctor out?'

'I'll get him tomorrow, if he's no better. These things come and go with small children.'

'No,' Friedrich said. 'Get him now.' He sat. He could not quite tell whether he wanted to say this because of concern, or because of his continuing chemical derangement.

'What are you talking about?'

'I don't know,' Friedrich said. 'I've come a long way.'

'Why have you come?' Picker said. 'It's not serious, you know, a child with a temperature. I don't know what you're talking about.'

Friedrich thought. 'I don't quite know. I just wanted to come.'

'And now you've come.'

'Yes,' Friedrich said. They sat there for a moment. There was something so important that Friedrich had to say to Picker; there was something so important he had to get Picker to tell him. He looked round the walls, their bareness, their calm quiet soothing blank good on his eyes, and wanting only to stay there, in this quiet, and not to think, and not to talk, for the moment. 'Tell me something.'

'Tell you what? What do you want? You're being very peculiar.'

'Tell me –' Friedrich reached for something – 'tell me about who you are.' There was something wrong with his phrase; he could not do any better.

'You know who I am,' Picker said.

'I don't,' Friedrich said. 'I don't know anything about you. You told me once where you came from, though I can't remember the name of the place –'

'Palmers Green,' Picker said.

'I want to know about you.'

Picker stood up, and walked, in a leisurely way, to the bookcase. He pushed back one paperback, which stood out from the shelf a couple of centimetres.

'It's nice, your flat,' Friedrich said. 'It really is.'

'Thanks,' Picker said. 'You can get something nice in Berlin for no rent at all, really.'

'How much do you pay?'

'I can't remember. A thousand marks? Something like that. Look, I don't mean to be mysterious. It's not that I'm hiding from you. I just have a thing about people telling each other stories about their childhood. It just seems false and boring, it just ends up being a way of disguising or excusing or telling people lies about yourself.'

'What do you mean?'

'Maybe it's just this town, I don't know. Everyone you ever meet is incredibly keen to tell you all about their past, tell you all these stories about how they got here. All that history. I can't stand it.'

'I don't think it's just Berlin,' Friedrich said.

'Maybe not,' Picker said. 'The thing is, I don't want to join in with it. That's a choice I've made. The way people sit you down and tell you about their past, the way some awful thing has happened to them in the past, it's as if they're saying, well, it's not *my* fault things are like this.'

'Sometimes it isn't,' Friedrich said.

Picker turned round. He could move surprisingly quickly when he wanted to and, for a second, it occurred to Friedrich to wonder whether he had lost some weight. Just for a second, Friedrich thought that he had hardly noticed Picker's physical condition for some weeks, as if, in his substantial bulk and pale face, he had made himself invisible through nothing more than being unattractive. But he was not unattractive, quite suddenly he was not; not an unattractive man like thousands of other unattractive men, all quite unlike each other, but just Peter Picker, who had grown invisible just because that was what Peter Picker looked like. His hair was trimmed back, neatly; his stomach, surely, was less enormous than it had been.

'Not your fault?' Picker said.

'Sometimes things aren't your fault,' Friedrich said. 'They just happen.'

'Things never just happen,' Picker said. 'That's the sort of thing people are always saying. But your actions always have consequences, and there's no point in saying, Oh, I couldn't have done anything other than that because that's what people like me do. You have to take responsibility for what you do. It's not true that your past makes you act in a certain way. You always have a choice.'

'Not always,' Friedrich said.

'Yes, always,' Picker said. 'You always have a choice, and every minute you have to choose what to do next. When someone says to me, Let me tell you about my childhood, it always seems to me that in ten minutes I'll be listening to them telling me why they couldn't help crash-ing my car, or stealing my wallet, or hitting me in the face, because that's just the sort of person their childhood made them into. But they've let their childhood turn them into that sort of person. They have.'

'You had the right sort of childhood, that's all.'

'You don't know anything about my childhood. And do you think I'm a happy person, overall?'

'I've never thought about it.'

'Nonsense, of course you have. That's something you can't help thinking about every single person you ever meet, even girls in shops. But I won't tell you about my childhood, or about my past, because I know what it's like when a German starts telling you about his past. It sounds like someone hiding, someone saying, Let me tell you all my secrets, and just hiding all his secrets much more effectively, much more efficiently. Everything is so much on display, when someone tells you about their childhood, about their past, that it doesn't occur to anyone to say, but what about you, now? I don't do it for one reason. I don't want to have any secrets. I want to be open to everyone. I want everyone to judge me on what I'm like now and not on the various excuses I make for myself.'

'But the end result,' Friedrich said, 'is that when someone says to you, tell me about yourself, you say, I don't want to talk about it. Which seems fairly secretive to me.'

'It shouldn't,' Picker said.

'But it does,' Friedrich said. His neck ached; he twisted his head from side to side, lolling backwards. There was something inside him, something making him move like this. It hurt. He wanted to know what it was. Picker was staring at him.

'Are you all right?' Picker said. 'That's exactly the way Tom keeps moving his head. You might have picked up the same bug.'

'I think I'm all right,' Friedrich said. 'You know those drugs I took over the border.'

Picker nodded. 'I've been thinking –' he said.

'I took one of them.'

'When?'

'Last night. I was in East Berlin and someone offered me one. So I bought it.'

'You bought it?'

'Yes. I thought I'd try one. I thought it was nice being offered one of your own pills.'

'How did you know they were yours?'

'I recognized them.'

'Unless there's someone else using the same source. And you bought it?'

'Yes.'

'They didn't offer it to you for nothing? I thought the idea was that they were going to give them away.'

'I thought they were going to give them away but I said to the man will you give me a pill for nothing and he looked at me as if I had said something very strange so I bought it.'

'You bought it.'

'Yes.'

'Where?'

'In a bar in Prenzlauerberg. A gay bar. I can't remember what it was called.'

'Try. This is important.'

'I can't remember.'

'And you bought it.'

'Yes.'

'So it didn't work. They started selling them as soon as they got over the border. They started making a profit. And they started selling them back to Westerners anyway. I knew it wasn't going to work.'

Friedrich concentrated.

'There's something else,' Friedrich said. 'I've got to tell you. I don't know why but I know I've got to tell you. They're not the real thing. They're fake.'

'What do you mean?'

'I mean they're fake. I bought them and they're fake.'

'You mean that man – that dealer – that friend of yours – he ripped you off? Is that what happened?'

'No,' Friedrich said. 'That's not it at all.'

He got up and went into the kitchen. He opened every cupboard door until he found a large glass, then poured himself a glass of water. In the hall, the small boy was watching him, big and flushed and sore with his big eyes. There was fear and suspicion there, and pain and terror; too much for a child so small. Friedrich drank the water in one go, gulping ferociously at it. He stood for a while, gasping like a seal.

'Come back in here,' Picker called.

Friedrich went.

'So you're telling me that the stuff isn't real,' Picker said. He was reclining on the sofa; he seemed quite unperturbed. For a moment Friedrich thought about not going on with what he had to say.

'No,' he said. 'It isn't.'

'And yet,' Picker said, 'you say you took some, last night, in East Berlin, definitely the drugs you bought, and it had some effect on you.'

'Yes,' Friedrich said. 'I can't explain that. Something strange happened. It had an effect on me. But it was fake. I know it was fake.'

'Why are you so sure?'

'Because I told my friend to buy some fake stuff. He wasn't ripping us off. I was ripping you off. And the other thing is I took them to East Berlin but I threw them away. I didn't have a contact. I just threw them away. I binned them. And the next thing I know I'm being offered them in a club.'

'I see,' Picker said. He lay back; he seemed to be observing the ceiling. 'All in all, it seems to me that the pill you took last night can't have been one of the pills you took to East Berlin, since they were fake to your certain knowledge, and you threw them away in any case.'

'Yes,' Friedrich said. He was being offered the explanation, now, and everything was becoming clear to him. Yes, it wasn't the same pills that he had bought, but a completely different pill, a pill of Ecstasy. It made him so happy to know that the world was starting to make sense again that he punched the air in a small way and almost smiled. 'Yes, that must be right.'

'And why, may I ask,' Picker said, not seeing Friedrich's cheerfulness, or the reason for it, 'have you decided to tell me this now?'

'I don't know,' Friedrich said. 'I just didn't want to go on with it.'

'You just didn't want to go on with it.'

'No,' Friedrich said. The calm of Picker's recitation, his acceptance of this news, was diminishing his excitement at having understood the truth of the matter by the second. Friedrich remembered something; something to make it all better. 'But look, I'll give you your money back. I didn't want to keep it. I don't want to keep it. I've spent a bit, not much, not so much as five hundred marks. I'll give you that back, as well, if you want that. Look, it was a mistake, I thought I wanted to make some money, and now I know I don't. And it didn't work anyway.'

'It worked for you,' Picker said levelly.

'Yes,' Friedrich said. 'The pill, you mean? It worked for me. I don't see why or how. They were only paracetamol. No, that's right. They weren't the pills I bought. They were completely different pills someone else bought. Yes, that must be right.'

'Why are you telling me this?'

'I told you, I just wanted to stop the whole thing and make it all right. It's all right, isn't it? I mean –'

'I think I'd like you to go,' Picker said.

'I mean with the money and everything?'

'There's more to it than just the money,' Picker said. 'It was a question of trusting someone. It's hard to understand what has happened. I think I'd like you to go.'

'Please, Peter,' Friedrich said. 'I've had a terrible time. I just wanted to come and sort something out.'

'And you have.'

'And everything's all right, now, isn't it?'

'Yes, quite all right, if you don't mind –'

'Let me tell you about it,' Friedrich said. He felt wild-haired; he felt as if things were sliding from beneath him. Picker levered himself into an upright position, stood up and walked into the kitchen. He would not look at Friedrich. The world had gone wrong and it was going to stay wrong. 'Do you know the sort of things that have been happening to me? Please, you've got to listen to this. I can't believe you won't listen. Please listen.' He was following Picker, talking all the time, and, as he looked down, he saw his hands, freed from his own will, pulling and tugging at each other with some untellable anguish and dread, dread of something.

'I can guess,' Picker said.

'You can't guess,' Friedrich said. 'How can you guess? The things that happened to me?'

'Not precisely,' Picker said. 'But in general I can guess. I can guess that it's history, or, in other words, excuses. I'm not interested. I'm mainly worried about my son, who has a slight temperature, who I want to see get well, and not, to be honest, to listen to what you have to say.'

'You have to be interested,' Friedrich said. 'There's no one else I can talk to.'

'That's not true,' Picker said, cutting a slice of bread. 'There are plenty of people you can talk to. I'm the person you can't talk to, because I won't listen, and I'm not interested.'

'You're interested,' Friedrich said. 'I know you're interested. You were always interested. You want to know about me. I know you do.'

'Not any more,' Picker said. 'And I never wanted to know about your past, I never wanted to hear you make excuses for how you are now. There's only one person in the world who I want to know everything about, about who I want to know the whole of their life, from day one.'

'Not me,' Friedrich said.

'Not you,' Picker agreed. Then he saw that Friedrich was at a loss, and, impatiently jerking his head towards the child's room, he said, 'Him.'

Friedrich stood for a minute, watching Picker spread the slice of bread with butter and jam. He felt so shaky; he wondered if it was with a hunger he could not detect.

'I'm sorry,' he said in the end. 'I didn't want to tell you. Or I did want to tell you. But I wanted it to be all right. I didn't want to tell you and make everything go wrong.'

'Too late,' Picker said, his mouth full.

'But sometimes you have to talk. To relieve some kind of pressure. I had to tell you.'

'I'm not here as a safety valve,' Picker said. 'I'm not here as someone for your convenience. Do you understand?

People don't exist where you want them to exist. They don't disappear, they don't turn up when and where you want them to. You don't need to have a child to understand that, but by God it helps. I will listen to you, but when I want to. Not just when you want to talk.'

'Peter –'

'Don't keep saying my name.'

'Peter –'

Picker stared at him. 'All right,' he said. 'Are you quite all right?'

Friedrich shut his eyes. In the doorway, his hands on either jamb, he swayed backwards like a sail in the breeze. There seemed no end to this long intoxication, this hiss in his ears, this unbalancing pressure inside him that took the earth from beneath his feet and made every movement of his knees a crucial and strange one.

'I don't know,' he said. 'I took this drug. I think I'm all right now. But this thing happened to me. This boy I met. You remember that boy, the boy you know, from the museum, the one when we got drunk. I met him in a bar, and he took me to East Berlin.'

'I know,' Picker said.

'You said you knew what had happened to me,' Friedrich said. 'But you don't. This boy, he took me to this bar, and he bought me the drugs, the drugs I bought for you, the ones which wouldn't work. But they worked. They worked for me. They didn't work for him. And then he fucked me.'

'I see,' Picker said, quite calmly.

'No,' Friedrich said. 'Don't say that. How can you see? I haven't said anything. I took this pill and straight away I felt really strange. And he took me out behind this bar and before I could say anything he had taken my clothes off and he had sex with me. He fucked me. He did. He really did. And then he went.'

'I see,' Picker said. 'Is that it?'

'That's it,' Friedrich said. He felt as if there ought to have been more, to match the hesitation and fear in him. Picker carried on eating, turned to the sink and poured himself a glass of water. Friedrich held his glass out, and Picker, taking it from him, poured him another glass. He took his time, and when he turned back, Friedrich had both his hands out to accept it. His eyes were on Picker's face, but Picker would not meet his gaze, and passed him the glass almost roughly, before turning away from him.

'Oh,' Picker said, his voice roughened by some sort of thought, some burden of caring or contemplation. 'Friedrich, you're such an awful little tease.'

It took Friedrich a moment to understand what Picker had said. 'An awful –'

'You know,' Picker said. 'I think it would really be best if you went back to Kreuzberg and slept it off. It was quite nice knowing you, but, really, we both lost, didn't we? And I don't know what we would quite think of each other if we met again. No, it was nice. I enjoyed, almost, being teased by you. It was almost better than if it had really worked out. Anticipation, they always say, is better than fulfilment. Travelling hopefully is better than arriving. Planting the seed is a better feeling than plucking the fruit. Whatever. There are a million proverbs, aren't there, to get you to accept that things aren't going to work out for you? Yes, all in all, I really almost enjoyed having my prick teased by you, you wanker.'

Friedrich stood there, his mind going through the motions of thought like an empty mill, and all the time producing nothing. He could feel his head slowly nodding; he was incredibly tired. After some time, he walked forward in Picker's rented kitchen, while Picker was here, and did what, at some moment in his life. Picker had wanted him to do; he placed his arms round Picker, and rested his head in exhaustion, or pleasure, or acceptance, for a second, on the back of Picker's neck. There was no response; only in the way the skin tautened against his cheek was there any sign that Picker even noticed or cared that a man, voluntarily, had come to him. There was a moment of indefinite time, and Friedrich, his eyes closed, knew that Picker too had closed his eyes, in pleasure, as they both allowed the other's presence to comfort them, not caring what the cause and need of comfort in the other was, simply accepting the need for consolation, the need for the good quiet embrace.

Friedrich began to talk. He did not quite know why. 'Do you know something?' he said. 'Something about Kreuzberg. You know, the place I live. Do you know it never existed? You know, it's somewhere they invented, quite recently, when Berlin stopped having any kind of history, after the Wall. It was just a district they needed to find a name for, somewhere that had been lots of different places, lots of different names, and they carved it up, and gave it this name, and now it's a proper place, with a proper character, and no history, and nothing to blame it for, and nothing to remember, and nothing to forget, just the bars and the Turks and the filth and the poor, and oblivion, and the forgetting of nothing. And that's where I live. And that's where you've never been.'

He could hear his voice vibrating in Picker's body, the silent rumbling thrill in his ribs, the tense thrum of Picker's skin against his embracing arms. Picker took his hands and, turning round, disentangled himself from Friedrich's grip.

'I think it would be best,' he said carefully, 'if you went.'

'Are you sure?' Friedrich said.

'I've never been so fucking sure of anything in my life,' Picker said, not raising his voice. 'I never want to see you again as long as I live. And keep the fucking money. I'm not interested. Now fuck off.'

'I think,' Friedrich said, but Picker had left the kitchen, and walked into the sitting room, slamming the door behind him. Friedrich gathered his coat and his bag, and, trembling a little, left the flat, closing the door discreetly, not to wake the child.

The bus was coming down the street, and Friedrich had to run for it. Only two stops after the terminus, it was almost empty, only four old people and a tough-looking man on the edge of middle age. He looked out of the window at the blackness, the thick woods lining the road, and tried to think. He had been thrown out of other people's flats before, of course he had, and afterwards it had been all right after a telephone call or two. He would leave it a week or two. Perhaps more; perhaps this would take, he thought with an unaccustomed weight of dread and pain, a few months before Picker would be prepared to say that Friedrich was forgiven for everything he had ever done. He wondered why he was so certain that he would bother. He dwelt on his own certainty.

The bulky man, almost a thug, was standing by him, and holding something out. Friedrich turned slowly and looked first at it, then at him. It seemed hard to understand what he wanted, and at first Friedrich thought him one of the monoglot Polish or Hungarian beggars who were appearing in such numbers, each with their own placard asking for food. But then he focused, and saw the man's photograph on the little card, and he understood what he wanted.

'Your ticket or pass, if you please,' the man said civilly. Friedrich sat for a moment, trying to work out what day of the month it was, and, as he fumbled in what he knew was an empty pocket, realizing that this was not one of the days for the inspectors, nor one of the hours at which they always operated, but some new freakish test for him, an inspector turning up when they were not expected and catching him out.

'I don't have a ticket,' he said.

'Why not?' the inspector said.

'Does it matter?' Friedrich said. 'Fine me.'

'Your name, please,' the inspector said, taking out his pad.

Friedrich gave his details, and all the time thinking of someone else. The bus was driving with teeth-grinding slowness into town. Everything was falling apart for him. The world was not behaving as it always did; it felt as if he were losing his grip on it, losing his control. And all the time, while the patient big man wrote his name and his address and his date of birth and his place of birth, a voice inside him was talking to him, at the end of a long and difficult and angry day and night and day and night. It was an old and a familiar voice, and it went on talking to him from where it lay, somewhere in the mud and dust of the Oranienplatz where Friedrich had hurled it, and thought, somehow, to lose it forever. Call it a day, the voice was saying. Call it a day. Call it a day.

THE IMPERIAL CRYSTAL NIGHT

A ND ONCE UPON a time the SED let go of power, and on the other side the SEW, which saw its sister, its parent on the other side transform itself like a pale clever prestidigitary witch into the PDS, chose to wither rather than change; and every IM and FDJ saw what was happening, and, like them, the RAF watched what was so quickly breaking in a moment of panic and pleasure and choice, and observed the change with unmixed feelings; and the FDGB and the DGB watched and thought, each of them, a different thing, and the VoPos and the GrePos and the whole box of tricks all watching what was happening to the BRD and the DDR and, over the whole thing, the whole steaming matted jungle of public life, its initialled secretive institutions, blank behind every blank name, every blank pair of thick heavy doors, the CDU, brooding in its quiet moment of rightness, of knowing that everything had conspired to prove it correct, and it sat and waited with the appearance, only, of deep thought. And then . . .

And then, and then. One more time, from the top, with feeling.

The telephone rang. It was Martin.

'Haven't seen you about for a bit,' he said. It was as near as it came to offering Friedrich forgiveness for breaking his finger.

'No,' Friedrich said cautiously. 'I've been busy.' It was as near as it came to an apology.

'What are you doing tonight?'

'Nothing. Any suggestions?'

'We thought we might get up a poker game.'

'Sure. Where?'

'You know that bar by the Wall, end of Kochstrasse, old place, always empty?'

'Sure,' Friedrich said. 'What time?'

'Eight?'

'Fine, see you there,' Friedrich said, putting the telephone down. And then everything was all right between them. This was the way it always went; some terrible act, some unforgivable vileness committed by one of them, a satisfying assault by the victim, a period of cooling off, of licking of wounds and then, just as if nothing had ever happened, a telephone call, a poker game, and back to normal relations. Friedrich looked at the wall. Six hours to kill; six hours, an afternoon, November the ninth, nineteen hundred and eighty nine.

It was an anniversary which neither of the two Germanys felt on the whole much like celebrating. It was the night when, fifty years before, the State had unleashed its full right to lawlessness on some of its citizens, and the Jews had cowered while bricks were heaved through their windows, and indignities heaped upon them. Germans, assaulting Germans, and permitted by the German State; a night never to be forgotten, and never to be remembered. The Imperial Crystal Night. It was not an anniversary which anyone cared to mark, and, in general, the city preferred to mark it by staying in and watching rubbish on the television, and not mentioning the destruction of the property of the city's Jews, the beginnings of murder which many of them still recalled with ease. Whether they did this because they thought about such things, or because they did not think about them, was just one more thing which nobody cared to discuss.

But it was an anniversary, and it was about to become an anniversary all over again. A curious trick of history, to ensure that the shattering of the crystal barriers of two empires occurred on a day which afterwards could never be celebrated, could never be thought of calmly, without embarrassment, without a momentary twinge of doubt.

Does history repeat itself? Do events recur? The feelings of the participants in both of these nights, both Imperial Crystal Nights were, after all, not so different; the fierce exhilaration of smashing and running away, of a violent destruction, the sure knowledge that the destroyers, as their arms swung with a great arc, a brick in hand, towards Jews' windows, as their grandchildren found, from who knew where, a sledgehammer and brought it down on the Wall, again and again, making it waver, making it topple, that these destroyers had the unarguable right of the State behind them; this is a special and a specific emotion; one seldom to be encountered in everyday life. The emotion is the same, although it is in poor taste to point it out. Even an informal and a disorganized historian must sometimes wonder whether the acts, too, in some sense, were the same act. Whether history, here, repeated itself; whether the ways in which the first Imperial Crystal Night succeeded were not the same ways in which the second Imperial Crystal Night failed. The first wanted to make others suffer, and succeeded; the second wanted to make the suffering of others end, and failed. And the lesson they teach, in their strange repetition, is the same. That suffering cannot be ended; that suffering is necessary; and for suffering to end, it is always necessary, in the fine exuberant *Schadenfreude* which is what constitutes the political consciousness of almost everyone, that other people's suffering should begin.

And that was right, really. Because the Imperial Crystal Night demonstrated, in the end, only one thing. It proved how much the life of the German nations depends on a German word, a quality the Germans identified and named and gave to the world; how much life rests on *Schadenfreude*. Because in the end happiness cannot be universal; freedom cannot be everywhere; goodness and riches and pleasure cannot be everyone's. Because in the end, it is not enough that *he* should succeed; it is necessary that *she* should fail. It is not enough, for freedom to flourish, that *they* should be free; it is necessary that *we* should be enslaved.

For a moment, history appeared to disprove its usual lesson, demonstrate the falsity of the banal truth. It was as if the first Imperial Crystal Night, when the liberties of the good and the blond and the straight and the tall were so wonderfully exercised, when the liberty of the righteous had, it seemed, no end as they found themselves permitted to smash and burn and loot, had always existed in order, fifty years later, for its lessons to be disproved in a second Imperial Crystal Night. It was as if the second great universal – or almost universal – feast of smashing and destruction demonstrated that, after all, liberty was not limited; that freedom and goodness and riches could be everybody's; could belong to the West, the East, the rich, the poor, the enlightened and the benighted. A moment opened up, seeming, illusorily, to demonstrate that *Schadenfreude*, the single biggest lesson of history, was, after all that, mistaken, was not universal, could be abandoned and resisted, before, once again, it wearily resumed its accustomed place, showing how little, really, anything had changed; how the liberty and goodness and blond righteousness still needed the poor, the mistaken, the deprived, the enslaved. *Wrongs*, in short; it needed them so much it would go as far as creating them.

Once more, once more from the top . . .

News from the East; news always from the East; and now, a Russian came from the East, as Russians had come before, and stood in the city, and spoke. What was he there for? Well, another anniversary, of course. All these anniversaries, all that counting back, all that burden of dates, all that memory of wrong. He was there to celebrate the fortieth birthday of the State, of this Germany, of the DDR. It had been celebrated before, the State's birthday, and it would be celebrated again.

(In Prague, not so far, an embassy garden was filling with tents, with new arrivals, with – they said with a straight face back in Berlin, not quite understanding how they had got there – filling with *traitors*. In Prague, in the West German embassy, the staff looked out of the windows, looking at the tented families – and who had ever thought to see Germans, in tents, squatting in mud, as *refugees* – all filling the immaculate garden. And they seemed, for a moment, to see the future of Germany.)

He spoke cryptically, the Russian; he spoke, not quite in public, not quite in private, to reporters. What he said was not quite clear, not quite baffling. He spoke to reporters, and for one moment, a mysterious sentence was understood by everyone who listened; by everyone. *He who detects the signs of life within society and whose politics are shaped by his instincts need not fear difficulty.* That is what he said, and around their televisions, they hunched, and listened, and tried to unravel, to listen to what they for so long had ignored, the abstract speech of politicians.

And the police came running, running to those who heard what he said, and to those who went out, filling the quiet streets of the East with noise. And the jails filled. And that night people stood in cells, and were beaten, and stripped and beaten again, on their faces, on their limbs, on their backs, on their soft parts, as they shrunk away from what they had always expected. And the police, beating them; what did they think? Did they, the bored thugs at the Friedrichstrasse, the shy boy who had passed, risking who knew what, his telephone number to Pierre, did they too hear the Russian say *you need not fear difficulty*, and did they reflect on the beatings they were inflicting on Germans, and reflect how many times Germans had beaten Germans, and ask how long this would go on, the weary beatings, and think what they said, as they shouted, weary for confession, at those they beat, *ach was, sag einfach ja*; oh, just say yes, give in and say yes.

And the Russian went, and people began to talk. For the first time it seemed, people talked as if they expected to be listened to, and to be understood, and agreed with. A politician spoke, and he found a phrase in his mouth; *the imagination of history*. People found the phrase in their mouths, as if they had thought it up, and as if history had not thought them up. Again, history had an imagination, and it dreamt what it had forgotten; it dreamt its ninth of November, every one, one after another. It dreamt its Imperial Crystal Night, the night in 1918 when the emperor fell, when, once before, a man said just that, *ach was, sag einfach ja*; when a reluctant chancellor listened to his deputy proclaim a republic; when the republic, twenty years later, organized spontaneous demonstrations, Germans assaulting Germans, and making them pay. The imagination of history, dreaming of new nights, new empires, empires of glass to smash, waiting for the signs from the East.

What does this mean, this vast uproar? Is it the East, bringing me fresh news? The heart's sore wounds, there they were; there they had always been, soothed, fanned, by the winds of speech, and speech, borne by breath, was passed on, and spoke, magically, unsuspected, like a charm for locked doors. What does it mean, except the capacity of news to bear itself, to be itself, to be speech, talking about speech, signifying only the unarguable truth that speech was only there to be passed on, that its meaning lay not in its content, but in its nature. For once, speech was not a vessel, but itself alone; it is enough that the millions opened their mouth and made, from the deep wounds of years, a noise, and heard those they spoke to, speaking back.

It is a Thursday. Outside, it is raining and dark. The overcoats of the journalists are uncomfortably damp when they lean back in their chairs. Schabowski is giving a press conference. He is a dull fellow, sitting in this brown-tinged light in the International Press Centre; none of the Politburo is especially rich in charisma, and he is no better than any of them. Still these days, the hacks never know when this ramshackle crew running the DDR are going to use the International Press Centre to announce something interesting; Schabowski is getting not just a substantial audience, but an attentive one. He blinks, as if nervous. Most of the press corps are privately assuming the declaration, pretty soon, of a state of emergency; not today, but perhaps next week, or the week after. And you never know when it might be worth turning up.

He has said nothing much. It is five to seven.

A journalist asks a question about permission to travel. He is fishing, and the catch is spectacular.

Schabowski gets out a piece of paper from his inside jacket pocket. With an air of boredom rather than the twinkling sensation people will afterwards try to discover, he begins to read.

'Personal trips,' he reads, awkwardly, 'to foreign countries may be applied for without preconditions, reasons, or family relationships.' He stops; there are the beginnings of a rustle. 'Yes,' he says, indicating a journalist. He asks a question, an obvious one. 'Yes,' Schabowski says. 'This applies to all border crossings from the Democratic Republic to the Federal Republic and to West Berlin.'

He goes. That is all. But that is enough.

'What are you doing tonight?' Daphne's aunt asks her.

'I thought I might go out,' Daphne says. She hadn't really thought. She hasn't made any plans, and is at a bit of a loose end. It occurs to her to go to Kreuzberg. She might bump into Friedrich. She might, on the other hand, also bump into Mario. She wonders about her feelings about these two possibilities; what she can't stop herself feeling seems strange in both cases.

'Yes,' Daphne's aunt says vaguely. 'Yes, why don't you. I worry about you. You work too hard.'

'I don't work hard enough,' Daphne says. 'I'm going to be in trouble.'

'You'll work yourself to a frazzle if you carry on like this. I don't know. I thought students were never supposed to be out of bars, having fun, but you're always hunched over your books.'

This is so much not the case that Daphne says nothing in reply.

'And that boy you were seeing –' her aunt goes on.

'I wasn't seeing a boy,' Daphne says quickly. She never told her aunt about Mario.

'That boy you were seeing, what happened to him?'

'I wasn't seeing a boy.'

'Well, go and have some fun, anyway.'

A woman, somewhere in East Berlin (perhaps – it hardly matters where – perhaps in Marzahn, on the ninth floor, in a grubby brown apartment just off the Schönhauserallee, or not in Berlin at all, perhaps in Potsdam, where the crumbling palaces, encrusted with gargoyles, crumbling with the ancient bullet marks of the Russians or British or Americans, face each other as if nothing new could ever happen to them, perhaps in a town where every third building has been painstakingly re-façaded with its fine gold baroque, every first and second building – and the interiors of all of them, to be honest – constructed out of the plastic asbestos horror the DDR could usually afford), has been listening to the radio. She is peeling a small pile of carrots, and as she listens, she turns a carrot slowly round in her hand, thinking about what she has heard. She carries on shaving the carrot as the voice continues, not hinting by its change of manner that it is saying anything interesting. The carrot's skin is off, nothing but clean bright flesh beneath the knife, and she does not see it; she carries on turning, and peeling, and listening. Only when it breaks in her hand, and she looks down and sees that there is nothing left of the carrot, that, unthinking, she has trimmed it to nothing while listening to the voice, does she put down the knife in a pile of orange shavings and let her eyes refocus on what is around her, the kitchen, the table, the walls. She gets up, with an odd and inexplicable sense of weariness, and switches the radio off. She goes to the window. Out of it, there is the same view. She has the sense that only she has heard this, only she quite understands. The news is for her, and for her alone. She knows that now she can get up, and walk, and no one will stop her, and no wall will stop her. She looks into the black, and enjoys the pleasure of knowing, just for now, that she could stay here, and go nowhere, and for the first time she can choose to go nowhere. She looks out into the night, and considers what to do next. She is twenty-four. A life is before her. It is her life which is before her. Her name is Sandra Bonheim.

Schabowski is travelling home. He has an official driver. He seems, to the driver, not quite interested in anything he, the driver, has to say. He looks out of the window, although the streets are quite as they were. There is nobody about yet. He looks like a man gritting his teeth against a violent impact. The driver concentrates on the road, the few cars in it identical, travelling in the same direction at nearly identical speeds, since the car manufactured by the State permits small variations in tempo. Schabowski's car is a different car; dark blue, and shiny, and long, and he tips back in it and waits for the streets outside to change. He knows what he has said.

The streets everywhere are empty, or, better, emptied, rather like – it will seem in retrospect – rather like a city waiting for something to happen. That hush, that Berlin quiet, it is not, tonight, the quiet of a city where nothing much ever happens; tonight it seems like the silence Daphne heard, pausing before carrying out violence. It is the silence you hear from an audience waiting for a performance, a crowd waiting for display. And tonight's silence, as the weeks and months and years go on, will start to seem like the way the silence had always been. Always the silence of Berlin's streets had seemed like the quiet of a vacuum, and now, remembering that silence, the people of both Berlins, of both Germanys, of both worlds, will throw a thought back, and consider how much the silence of a vacuum is the silence of a space waiting to be filled; how the quiet of Berlin was always the stillness of an audience waiting for the performance to begin; and in almost every case they will think, and think wrongly, that the performance which was about to begin, that November night, was always scripted, was always destined to happen in exactly this way. Here they come, rushing towards the vacuum, the huge waves of history, rushing, as they have so often rushed before, towards this grey city. And nobody, just yet, quite hears them; not even Mario.

Not even Mario, who right now is walking, in the dark, in the Tiergarten. It is something he likes to do, though he has never mentioned it to anyone. He stalks the park, in the dark, moving through the unlit paths, never far from a road, walking through the black evening silence, alone with his thoughts. No one walks in the Tiergarten at night; no one without good reason to. As Mario walks through the paths, he sometimes walks past a man, standing against a tree, sheltering against the rain, still hoping for another man to come along. If a shaft of light catches Mario's face, or if a waiting man, lighting a cigarette, happens with the light to throw a flame's illumination across a path, four men will suck in their breath at the sight of such walking loveliness, such sex on legs, and, not unusually, they will abandon their watchposts and follow what they have seen, walking in the rain like entranced victims. Mario pays no attention. He has seen it before; he secretly thinks that, in fact, this is the sort of thing which happens to almost everybody, that everybody is always followed. That human beings, on the whole, admire each other. This is the sort of thing he thinks. He is not, in fact, vain; the world is vain on his behalf. He walks, expending no thought, except an approximate amusement, a faint sense of being bothered, on his bride's train of suitors, of pageboys following, lifting the graceful intangible stuff of his flame-lit loveliness behind him. He is on his own, with his thoughts. They are not our business.

The door falls shut behind Sandra Bonheim; she does nothing about it, feeling that she hardly cares, for once, whether the flat is ransacked, abandoned, whether it will still be there when, if she returns. There is a glorious sense in her that she no longer cares if the whole of the East goes up in one great blaze, a looting inferno. Because she will not be back. She knows it. There is a wonderful submission in her to the spirit of the Imperial Crystal Night; the spirit of the Imperial Crystal Night is in her, and is her. She knows that possessions are wicked; that everything she has always been told about private ownership is right, and she does not care whether the things among which, the places in which her life has been spent are destroyed. She knows they will be.

For the moment, in her utter certainty, she is like a snake shedding its skin, a woman, who having come into a legacy, a lottery win, lets her old shabby coat fall to the floor as she steps into the warm, dream-bright lights of a shop she can barely imagine. This is the strange fact; she has always been told not to be materialistic, and only now, with the fall of every one of her teachers, the discrediting of their every lesson, she has learnt to stop caring about the things she has amassed, learnt to leave it all behind. Freedom is in letting go, and as Sandra lets the door to the flat fall back behind her, hardly knowing if she has her keys on her, if her husband will be able to get in if she is out, she steps forward, entranced, agape, on the edge of something she feels must be happiness.

There is so far to go. She has left her apartment on the Kopenhagenerstrasse, just off the Schönhauserallee. The Wall is near, about five hundred metres or less, but she will not go there. Some sense of history, some possession of history's dreaming pulls her in a different direction, and, entranced, bright in the eyes with the certainty she now begins to trust, she starts to walk, a tightrope walker, progressing with no possibility of failure or falling, no possibility of turning back, just an enchanted forward path, surrounded and supported by air, and rope, and who knew who, for just one moment, held it up. There is so far to go. The full length of the Schönhauserallee, the huge blank length of the palaces and embassies of the imperial boulevard, and who knows, just for the moment, what is at the end of it? But she will not run; she has the sense of walking, rather, more slowly than the others, placing one foot gracefully, peacefully in front of the other as the scattered beginnings of a crowd starts to run past her. It will wait for her; she has waited for it for long enough, never knowing that this was what she waited for, and now, as she walks with her queenly catwalk tread in this great street, it – and does she know, can she imagine just yet, what *it* might be? – will wait for her.

Martin is dealing out the cards, in the bar on the Kochstrasse. Another friend of his, known slightly by Friedrich, has come along for the game. He is a lawyer, a man who still sees his old friend Martin, known from university, and whose slight gormlessness and comic Bavarian accent make him more popular than he quite deserves. Most people whose lives had diverged from Martin's in the way Christian's has would not be able to stick around; Martin is touchy in small ways, and in small ways he dislikes Christian. He notices, for instance, the number of times Christian has managed to pay for all the beers at the end of the evening. Christian doesn't mind, Martin knows that; it's Martin who watches out for the rich, getting above themselves, wanting to pay. But Christian sticks around and is tolerated; it's his divergent teeth and his thick glasses and his low-IQ accent which make you forget that he works sixty hours a week and lives in a long narrow flat, parqueted and smooth and empty as a bowling alley.

They contemplate the hands they have been dealt. Friedrich is looking at this friend of Martin; he hasn't the poker face, he will let them know with the millimetre movement of a cheekbone upwards what Martin has dealt him. But he is no good for reading; not because his face betrays no emotion, but because his constant facial twitchings, his continuous screwing up of the mouth and blinks and winks and bulging of tongue in cheek, do not change as the hand is dealt. His constant tics of excitement depend not at all, it seems, on the outside world; an ace is as exciting as a two of spades. He fidgets with every inch of his face, somehow unhappy, somehow pained, and pained from within, not from what comes to him over the table.

The bar is empty. The barman comes across from time to time, remarking as he does that it seems quiet. It is quiet, though not unusually so. There is a television over the bar; there is a match of some abstruse and possibly foreign sport going on, which nobody is watching, just taking in a general sense of furious hurling of something or other at something or other.

A man comes in. He does not sit down; he goes straight to the bar, almost frantic. He leans over the bar and talks to the barman. The barman shrugs, one eyebrow raised. The man spreads his hands, then, abruptly turns and goes. The barman calls after him.

Friedrich throws down his hand.

'Shit,' he says, and it is a shit hand, he is right. But Martin has lost interest, somehow; he is looking at the barman, who has hoisted himself on to the bar, and, one arm up, is flicking through the television channels, the squash or pelota or billiards abandoned.

'What is it?' Martin calls out.

'That guy –' the barman gestures with his head – 'just said that the Wall's come down. Have you heard that –'

'Nothing,' Martin said. 'I've heard nothing.'

The other two say nothing; the bucktoothed Bavarian lawyer looks almost scared, at the prospect, perhaps, of being asked to speak.

'He wanted a bottle of champagne,' the barman said. 'That's what he came in for. I can't find anything about it, We don't have champagne. I was saying to Martha, We ought to get some more champagne in. But she said, What's the bleeding hurry, we've been trying to get shot of the last case of champagne since 1984 and half of the case we've drunk on your birthday or mine, not that she even likes the stuff, Martha. So we haven't got any anymore. But I was going to go and get some before Christmas. And now someone walks in off the street on a Thursday night in November and asks for a bottle.'

'What else did he say?' Martin called, putting down his cards. 'Right, beat that.'

'Nothing, just that. I don't believe it. I can't find anything anywhere about it, about the Wall coming down. He must have been having me on.'

'A nutter.'

'A nutter,' the barman agrees. 'I'll believe it when I see it.'

'Mine,' the Bavarian lawyer, Christian, his name, Friedrich remembers, says, as he throws down a marvellous flight of cards, a crowned flurry of blunt vivid faces on the waxed paper, and into his own face came a marvellous sparkle of a grin, transforming the rich solicitor's guilty face into the charm and loppy easy pleasure of a child, against his planned disappointment, at, for once, winning a game, and transforming the whole world with a single lucky hand.

And here she comes, here she comes; lucky Sandra, her flat abandoned, East Berlin shedding itself behind her with every step, the hard glisten of her eyes fixed on what they reflect, the lights, so close, as if, for all her life, she has averted her gaze from what they could see and now, this one night, she will look at what is there for her to take, and walk into the unmapped white, the blank circled city, waiting for her, waiting for her to do whatever she wants with it, and, now, her long entranced walk almost at its unknowing goal, she steps, with what now surprises her, with a crowd, into the magic circle of light, never hurrying, allowing nothing to delay her, stepping into the magic radiant circle of television, and on, thinking something which will surprise her later when things work out so differently and nothing in her life, in the end, changes, thinking only that never in a thousand years will she turn round and retrace the steps she has now taken, never in the thousand years' history of an empire, the promised thousand years of German empires which last, at best, for a few decades. And behind her and in front of her and around her come dozens, then hundreds, then thousands of people, running towards the Wall; and on the other side of the Wall, there are the same numbers, all running towards her. Two great waves of people, all running as fast as they can to see this unthought of amazing thing, this banal demolition which resembles something which happens, somewhere, every day, and which will only happen once; two floods of different peoples, two floods of different crowds of Germans, running to meet each other this rainy November night, and not quite knowing what they are going to find. Each one of them with a different feeling; each one of them with different thoughts, about the Wall, about their own lives, about what they have lost and what they will never find again; and, for some reason none of them will ever be able, quite, to explain, in many of them, a feeling of dread and wrongness and of catastrophe about to happen. What is happening is what was always meant to happen, that is clear; but they cannot for the moment rid themselves of the sensation that such an overturning of what has always been, what, for many of them, was always going to be the same, cannot be right. And yet they run, and, like the blue clean wall of a wave, the crowd – the crowds, multiplying at every point, until there is no one in Berlin left inside, no one who can still walk who is not at the Wall, shouting and screaming at the Brandenburg Gate – the crowd batters up against this temporary barrier, and with unarguable innocent rightness, breaks through.

Not everyone knows, yet; not everyone would care if they knew. Peter Picker, for instance, is at home, doing his paperwork, plotting graphs of expenditure against income, making his plans, organizing his three hundred folders of contacts, of names, of figures he has met and learnt about. In the corner of the surprisingly handsome drawing room there is a grey metal filing cabinet; one drawer is open, and empty. The contents of the drawer are over the dining table, lit by an anglepoise lamp, clamped to the side of the table. His tie is loosened, and he is bent over the papers, trying to make sense of them, and failing. He does not think of Friedrich; right now, in his empty and silent flat, he is trying not to think of anything, ever again; he concentrates, or tries to, on what is in front of him.

He has been working all day, and can hardly produce any more rational thoughts about all this. He recognizes that when he starts to wonder what he is doing here, and what on earth he hopes to achieve by his files and his information and his strange investments of time and money, this is the moment to pack up and do something else. Dancers know that when they start to think of their legs, start to wonder what is holding them up, they should go and sit down; similarly, when Picker starts to consider whether there is any point to any of this, when his thoughts turn to what is never far from his thoughts, he has the sense to stop, and turn the television on.

He stands in the gloomy room, lit by the down-thrown spot of the anglepoise and the swimming blue of the television. He stands there; the news programme he often watches is just beginning. He stands, and watches, and follows exactly what he is being told by the excited announcer, without concentration or effort. The Wall is down. The world is changed. And soon he will start, against his will, against his expectations, to feel something of the joy everyone is saying they feel, all those flushed November faces, not far away. He carries on watching, and after a moment or two a thought slides into his mind, an insidious wrong thought: *What*, Picker thinks, *would Tom have thought of this?* He stands and lets himself think the thought he makes so much effort to keep from himself, and, for once, there is no pain in the thought, only consolation; the thought of what Tom would have thought of this changing world, changed from a world he had known almost nothing of, into a world he would have come to know, is like a kindness, offered him against his expectations, against his will. The thought of what Tom would have thought is like the presence of Tom himself; it is as if the thought, small, peaceful, kind, has gently shouldered its way into the room, and come to Picker, and quietly taken his hand without looking up. The thought is consolation, but not consolation enough. No thought will, ever again, be consolation enough. And Picker stands in his empty flat, alone, in the empty room, and lets himself have one thought, and looks at the television, and sees the beginnings of the world in which, from now, alone, he must now live.

THE INSTEAD-OF SONG

HE WENT INTO the theatre, leaving the thickly manned streets for a silent plush space. He wanted to be alone. He wanted to be within walls, and to sit, for a time, in the dark. Mario stood there, at the door to the foyer of the theatre, wild-eyed with the fury of the mob he was escaping from, and looked at the few in the bright-lit room. Freedom, divine spark of the gods, they were singing, Elysian daughter; and here, for a man who knows you, and knows your black sister, here you are.

'It was sold out,' the woman at the cash till said to Mario. He stood there, holding his money, and looking at her, without speaking. It was the best way to get results. 'But –' she gestured around her at the nearly empty foyer.

'What is it?' he said.

'What? The play?' Mario nodded. 'The Threepenny Opera. Do you still want a ticket?'

'Anything,' Mario said. Distantly, outside the theatre, no more than a mile or so away, there was some great roar; the roar of a natural force, the noise of a waterfall plummeting its weight fifty feet, endlessly, unstoppably; the noise of a forest fire, the noise of one wave after another, the noise, finally, of wind. It was the noise of a crowd, shouting, and shouting for what; and it was a noise impossible to hear, and not think of falling water, of fire, of wave, of wind. Of some natural force, impossible to contradict; unstoppable, unarguable, uncontainable, overwhelming. Everywhere, people were thinking that there was the inevitability of wind in these great changes; only Mario saw that there was no inevitability in this. He thought of it as a million people, all going wrong, all breaking with their discipline, all using their wills, and using them wrongly. These wilful unpredictable movements of people, acting for no good reason, simply because there was suddenly a course of action open to be taken, they were not natural movements, but a natural perversity.

How tempting it was to think that this was how things happened, by natural forces; how history was. How history took its calm course because that was how one element acted on another, and led, as it was always going to lead, to the same conclusion. There was no resisting, no arguing with the wind. For the moment, that was how the crowd outside seemed; a force, a will with which no government could argue, which no intelligence could contain. But it could, for one moment, be shut out.

He wanted walls around him; he wanted darkness, and silence, and solitude, and, for once, no deception and no secrecy and nothing, nothing, which might resemble thought. He took his ticket, and walked forward into the empty foyer.

He had been almost in hiding for months. Though he had kept up his studies, he had stopped working at the university, turning up only for classes, and working at home in his temporary flat, among his temporary and flimsy furniture. Everything else he had abandoned; he had stopped going to the direct action group, ignoring their phone calls, not reading a couple of letters beyond the first line or two.

He didn't quite understand it; maybe it was Daphne, who had, without explanation, just said that it wasn't working out for her, and said, see you around, no more. But he wouldn't see her around; not at the university, nor at the direct action group, to which, he found out by chance, she too had stopped going. He hadn't seen her for months. Sometimes in the street he saw a girl the right height, blonde hair cut short, dressed in black. He watched the girl go, and always there was something wrong, the walk, the nose, not snub enough, too snub, but always not Daphne, nothing like her, and he had not spoken to the woman he had written so much about, for, perhaps, weeks.

There were few people in the foyer. Mario was used to this kind of place. He often agreed to meet people in some public place, detecting in the crowds in a room some chance of anonymity. But this, unpredictably, emptied; he felt conspicuous as a loud organ in a morning cathedral, and he felt as if they were all looking around for something, letting their eyes fall on him. A few couples, a madman or two, and a fat girl, who, right now, was looking directly at him, and beginning to smile. Fat girls were easy; that was part of his lore, as it was part of Friedrich's, and he looked back with his studied irresistible indifference, almost bleakly. She came over.

'An odd night to come to the theatre,' she said.

'Very odd,' he agreed. 'I decided to come tonight, just on the spur of the moment.'

'I've had the ticket for weeks,' the girl said, seriously. He was struck by the way, even while talking to him, she managed to give the impression that she was rationing her glances at his face, her slightly shamed sneaky looks at him.

'I thought about not coming, when – well, you know, all this – and the girl, well, my sister really, I was supposed to be coming with, she decided she didn't want to come. I don't know what she thought she'd do instead, and, honestly, well, I thought, I don't want to waste the ticket, it's supposed to be good. But –' She gave a little laugh, for no particular reason. 'I do go on, don't I?'

Mario looked at her with his unblinking eyes. 'It's supposed to be very good,' he said, solemnly. 'Do you like the theatre?'

'Oh,' she said gratefully. 'Oh, a lot. Me and my sister, I mentioned, I was supposed to be coming with her tonight, we try to go to the theatre every week or so, there's always something worth seeing, even if it's only the opera, which can be good, too. We like – oh, we like all sorts of things, really. We never disagree. Only tonight, because I wanted to come to this, and she thought, well, I said.'

'What do you like best?' Mario said. The fat girl seemed on the point of hyperventilating; he continued to look directly into her eyes, six inches or so too close to her face. She started fingering her clothes; the velvet headband keeping her mid-brown hair back, the lace collar and cuffs which edged the floral dress, mapping out her sad contours and bulges.

'All sorts of things,' she said. 'I like musicals a lot. I went to see *West Side Story* last year seven times. Did you see that?'

'I can't remember,' Mario said. 'What's your name?'

'Petra,' the girl said. She seemed to be waiting for him to say something.

'I'm Egon,' Mario said.

'Egon?' she said. 'That's my grandfather's name. I never met anyone my age called Egon before.'

'No?' Mario said, mentally tossing up whether to walk away, or carry on with this girl. 'It's almost time to go in. Did you sell your sister's ticket?'

'I tried. They said they couldn't sell it, the theatre's so empty. Do you –'

'Can I sit with you?'

'Delighted,' the girl said, and, despite the unsuccessful attempt at flirtatious good manners, delighted is what she was, her eyes brimming with excitement as if with tears. 'No, please do, I was thinking that I was in for an evening without company. This is quite a pleasant treat.'

'A treat?' Mario said.

'A surprise,' the girl said, faltering as her half-practised polite manner flopped, and tried it again. 'A pleasant surprise.'

'Let's go in,' Mario said, taking her arm, and almost pulling her towards the doors to the auditorium. He felt as if he had seen somebody on the other side of the room he wanted to avoid; what he wanted to avoid was only the crowd, the distant roar outside. 'It's going to start soon.'

'I didn't hear the bell,' the girl said, but came with him. They were settling into their seats when she spoke again. 'So why did you decide to come tonight, if you didn't have a ticket?'

Mario bundled up his coat underneath the seat. 'I don't know,' he said eventually. 'I'd heard it was good, and I thought it might be the only chance to get to see it, tonight.' She nodded, as if she wanted something more. 'And,' he went on ruminatively, 'maybe I don't quite know whether I want to join in with all that, just yet. I think I probably want to think about it for a while first.'

'I see,' the girl said. 'Egon. Do you come from the East?'

He jerked his head; for the first time he could remember, someone had surprised him. 'Why do you say that?'

'A sense I had,' she said, smoothly. There was more here than he had quite anticipated or wanted, he could see that as the lights went down. 'You can tell, you always can tell someone – even if you don't remember them – you can always tell someone who comes from the same place you do. You see, I come from the East, as well. You can always tell. Did I mention?'

'No,' Mario said, with the beginnings of nerves, the nerves that any chance encounter always started off in him. And already it was too late to get up and go; the play was beginning, with a clattering chant, a chorale in the orchestra and the unconvincing milling, on stage, of fifteen actors who, attempting to impersonate a crowd, find no way of doing it but by circling, endlessly, the space behind the lights. It was an old play, and he could not concentrate on it; its world of crooks and official deceivers seemed hard for him to get a handle on. He could hardly understand who was meant to be good and who was meant to be bad; who was thought to be a criminal and who was thought to be a policeman, an official, a hero. There was no police here, and nothing but wrongdoing, nothing but betrayal on betrayal, and all of it presented to amuse, and no more. Only when it hit the songs did something stir in him, and he could not tell if it was familiarity, or recognition, or a simple acceptance of some simple truth. He sat, and watched two grubbied-up actors stand and, with the awkward clinking of the bitter little orchestra, begin on the 'Instead-Of Song'; a tune he almost knew, and almost understood. He reached his left hand and, in the dark, disconsolately, let it take one of the pursed hands of fat Petra, held its pudgy palm in her lap, listened to the barely altered tempo of her surprised breathing. How easy it was to give people pleasure; how easy to think that others would always come along in return, to give pleasure where pleasure was due. He sat, pressing at hand's flesh, and listened to the song.

Instead of, instead of; how many worlds, how many stories conjured up there in a word or two. His life was an instead-of song. Instead of sitting here, in this nearly empty theatre, watching the critically acclaimed go through their paces, he could, right now, be walking through the border checks, in the other direction. He could have finished the Tour de France; he would not have won, but he could have finished. He could have stayed in the DDR. Another instead-of song; a bigger one. He could have refrained from betrayal, from selling, from walking away from trust; he could, even now, be talking to his mother; he could be calling his tutor, Hans-Christian, and, still, asking for cycling advice; he could have refused when they had asked for what, in the event, he had so spontaneously offered. *Instead-of, instead-of*; he saw how much choice there was in all this, how he had always forced himself into action by pretending that there was no choice. But there always had been, and he had always been a fool for thinking otherwise. And all those betrayals, all that blank lying, for nothing; for nothing but money and the shivering feeling of your own treachery, the shivering feeling that someone who so innocently and frankly was talking to you, telling you everything, unguarded, in their mind, someone who without tension or thought or worry could embrace you, might, just once, look up into your eyes and see what was there. See that there was someone who was on the verge of going home, and writing down the conversation, and sending it to a man who none of them would ever meet, who only Mario had ever even heard of. He looked straight forward, not giving anything away by his posture, his gaze. In his mind was a single locked drawer in his kitchen, filled with copies of sent letters; filled with receipts of payments; filled with photographs; filled with objects no one but he would ever see. *Instead-of; instead-of*; and it was as if one of those easy alternative lives, an alternative fanciful history had risen up outside, in response to someone, somewhere, saying, *What would happen if there was no Wall*, and the fanciful was made real, and filled the street, and distantly roared for joy, or hunger, or rage. Even in the theatre you could hear it.

The interval came, and the lights went up. 'Enjoying it?' the girl said, extracting her hand from his. He had almost forgotten about her; he had long since stopped paying any attention to the play, or to the songs.

'Yes,' he said. 'It's really good, isn't it?'

'Oh, yes,' she said; his appreciation was like a personal compliment. 'Do you want to go and get a drink?'

'Sure,' he said, smiling kindly. 'I'm just going to go to the bathroom.'

'What can I get you, Egon?'

'Thanks, I'll have a beer,' Mario said, as they came out into the foyer. He stood, and watched her go to the small desk from which drinks were being dispensed, and then, as she struggled with her money, he turned and left the theatre sharply. He walked away quickly down the street, imagining her standing with a beer and an orange juice, looking at the few people in the foyer of the theatre, smiling brightly as she waited for this nice man to come back from the lavatory, and, after a minute or two, sipping at her orange juice; not accepting or understanding, quite, that he had gone without a word until the bell began to ring for the second half, and then putting down the full bottle of beer so as to draw the least attention possible, and going back into the theatre, not feeling angry or even, for the moment, sad, but just accepting that these things happen. He carried on walking, accepting that this was the sort of thing he was always going to do, and, all his life, always had done.

He did not know quite where he was walking to; knowing only that he was walking away from what seemed the source of the crowd's noise. He walked in the dark, allowing himself to think about the past, constraining himself only from thinking about the future. He had never seen, he understood, what was going to happen; he had always guessed wrong, and now he was only going to walk. Sometimes another man or a woman approached him on the streets, and once or twice he saw what the strange Petra had meant; you always know when you see a man from the same place as you. Once or twice, a lost face, looking round, with no idea of what was there; a DDR face, a DDR set of clothes, alarmed, bewildered or stunned, and he looked at them coolly. He had seen them, or people like them, before; it was only Berlin which had never seen them, and which seemed silently to observe that here were men like any other, men quite different and new and strange to fill the unwalled city.

The night went on, and as the dark thickened, and rain came and went and finally cleared into an empty clean black sky, an idea came to Mario. He was not tired, and did not become tired; and what he most wanted was to escape, and to exhaust himself, and disappear. And the night went on, and, in the end, Mario was at a familiar place as the heavy black began to lighten, like a jar of ink slowly thinned and made translucent by clean water. He sat on the wall by the garage he rented, and, mapless, thought of what he was going to do. The marvellous weightless bicycle, in the garage, hardly ridden for years; it had, now, what it deserved; it had a journey, a trajectory in front of it which was not a circle, not a dreadful trapped buzzing round in a solid trap. For the first time, there was a straight line – Mario could almost see it, like a two-hundred kilometre runway, stretching out to the blue horizon. And he would take it; shoot out like a bullet, across the old Wall, across the old DDR, and ride forwards, forgetting boundaries, just ride forwards until he could only fall off with exhaustion. And then; and then; and then there would be something else to consider.

He stood up, and went to the garage door to unlock it. In the quiet early morning light, the up-and-over mechanism made a deafening groan. It seemed to echo in the silent street. He stood there, his arms stretched out above him, as if holding the garage door up, and for a moment, just looked at the superb weightless machine. It would be the right thing. It was the right thing, and, barely running his finger over its dusty fork, Mario went to the back of the garage to change his clothes.

Many months went by after the Imperial Crystal Night before something odd occurred to Daphne, or somebody suggested something odd to her. She heard a good story, that a student activist in her class, someone who spent years organizing student strikes and noisily fighting for socialism, had gone to inspect his Stasi file. The secret service of the old DDR had had its files opened, and people started to make jokes about going to see who had had their eyes on them, and what they had managed to find out. The student activist had made quite a big deal about it, telling everyone when he was going to look, and taking a girl with him who he wanted to impress. Daphne had always thought the man a bit of an amateur, and was as amused and pleased as everyone she knew when the girl came back and reported that the Stasi had not had any kind of file on the man. When you read about the scale of the Stasi's files, there was something very gratifying about their ability to pass fastidiously over any really hopeless loser.

Daphne laughed, like everyone else, and only afterwards thought about it. After all, she had been pretty active in Class War, even if she'd completely dropped all that now. Three or four times she'd been involved in an action which had got into the newspapers, which might, she supposed, have been of some interest over the Wall. There was also the Caspar business, which she brought to mind unwillingly, and tried not to think too much about. She'd been involved, in some loose way, with that. She wouldn't get her hopes up of finding anything very interesting, but, all in all, there was a possibility that the Stasi had had something on her. She wouldn't mention it to anyone, but she'd wander over in the next week or so.

It was a hot day, and she decided to walk there. Berlin was always crowded now, with visitors, handling their maps, from West and East; people who could hardly speak German and people incapable of understanding the U-bahn. There was something about Daphne which suggested to strangers that she was approachable, and was a Berliner, and she was always being stopped and asked where Checkpoint Charlie was. It was a bore, but she put up with it; she almost liked the fact that she had so shed her identity that to everyone who did not know her she had become what she had, for years, tried to sculpt herself into. She wondered when it had happened.

She was in time for her appointment, and went through the narrow corridors with her temporary pass in her hand. She wondered whether the people working here were ex-DDR, if they were even ex-Stasi employees, or drafted in from the West. It had been easy to tell; now it was not always so simple. Like her, people had left their homes, and had gone to a place that suited them, where they had always wished to come from, to which they could only go. And, finding a place which had always been there for them, a place which was always like them, they had settled, and hardly noticed that the place was changing them, quietly.

The lightbulbs were low-watt, and gave the dim unwindowed corridors a brownish tinge. Only from time to time, a new lightbulb had been put in; one to Federal standards, shining brilliantly in the slightly grubby rooms. And this was the way it would go; each substandard component of the Democratic state allowed to wear out, and then quietly replaced with the glitter and brilliance of the Federal standards. The lightbulbs would go; the street signs unremarkably replaced; the institutions, the supermarkets, the bars, the schools, all changed without much comment, until one day people would wake up, look out of the window and see nothing they could remember from their childhood. Daphne walked on.

It was a large building, and she got mildly lost once or twice. When she reached the room to which she had been directed, there were a couple of clerks behind glass, and a shirtsleeved man with a file, sitting at a hastily acquired table, reading, his head in his hands, his elbows on the desk. Daphne filled in a form, and handed it to the girl clerk, who looked at it expressionlessly before going off into the archives. Daphne sat down, opened her paper and began to read.

It was only five minutes when the girl returned; Daphne fully expected her to come in with an apologetic expression and the news that there was no file, but she came into the room with two manila files. She came to Daphne's desk, put them down and gave Daphne the form to sign. She looked at the top file.

Egon Lenz, the label read.

'No,' Daphne said. 'This isn't right. I asked for a different one.'

'No,' the clerk said, her voice lowered, as if in a library. 'No mistake.'

'It isn't right,' Daphne said. 'I asked for my file.'

The girl looked round. There was no one near. 'I know. That's underneath. The second one. I'm just –'

'Why have you –'

'I'm giving you this,' the girl hissed, 'as a *favour*. I'd get sacked if they knew. I'm giving you this. You want to see it. Trust me. And don't ask for anything else.'

She was abruptly upright, and, secretary in a movie, walking away with her slip of paper to her desk, her face recomposed. So mysterious, why people did these things for each other, and all Daphne understood, as she opened the file, was that something had been done for her, and all she had to do was read.

Daphne was alone, with the beginnings of dust in the strip-lit gloom, the quiet, punctuated only by a man, six or so desks away, who from time to time coughed as he went on reading. The girl went away, leaving Daphne with the thick file of Egon Lenz before her. She opened it, and began to read.

Egon Lenz
Born 20.02.65

Birthplace Berlin
Father Klaus Lenz, born 17.11.31, died 15.7.85
  Birthplace Berlin
  Married Gisela Kreisch, 22.5.58
  Place of death Brandenburg Prison no C. 7
  Cause of death heart failure
  See file 67805.B. 3313
Mother Gisela Lenz, nee Kreisch, born 26.6.35
  Birthplace Berlin
  Married Klaus Lenz, 22.5.58
  See file 67115.B.7992
Sister Monika Schnitterling, nee Lenz, born 15.3.63
  Birthplace Berlin
  Married Marco Schnitterling, 18.6.85
  See file 67013.B.8741
Agent acquired 15.9.81
Exported 20.05.86

She turned the page.

Summary history of informal co-employee

Egon Lenz was identified 12.6.74 as suitable development material for the State Sports School (App.A, initial
reports). Began preliminary training 5.9.74 in the
Harzgebirge Academy under supervision of Hans-
Christian Schmidt, qv. Satisfactory development reported, 1974–1980 (App.B). Cyclist (racing history,
1976–1986, App.F).

In 1981 it became apparent that Lenz was no longer to
be considered as first-rate material as far as his sporting
development was concerned. He was, however, of first-
rate reliability in other respects (Schmidt's reports,
App.C; party history, App.E).

He was acquired by the Service in 1981, and assigned to work in West Berlin 1986, after demonstrating his reliability in the trial of Klaus Lenz. His father.

Lenz's transfer was effected through public defection which aroused no suspicion and subsequent to which the Western authorities extracted, by Lenz's account, nothing of any interest from him. The defection was staged on the fifth day of a French bicycle race. To all concerned, including Schmidt (attached letter, app.G, of Schmidt's concern and regret, of documentary evidence) the defection was genuine. Under instructions, Lenz declined all approaches from Western sporting bodies to compete on their behalf. He was suitably rewarded (App. K). The limits of his sporting ability were not established by the Western authorities and the nature of his defection not thereby suspected.

Subsequently Lenz took the name of Mario Ullstein. His cover aroused no suspicion that he was aware of, and (App.D.27, App.D.31, App.D.46) stated more than once that he believed he was accepted by all those he made contact with. Independent assessment by the Committee carried out two years after the staged defection would seem to confirm Lenz's opinion, and no reason for doubting his continuing good faith with the Department and the Committee (App.H) He made contact with small-scale leftist groups in West Berlin and submitted monthly reports on twenty-five associates, of whom, at most, four are to be considered of interest. Cross references to Lenz's reports, App.D. He was useful in two instances, effecting the transfer of West German anti-fascist activists pursued by the West German authorities into the DDR. In other respects his use became limited. The Committee conclude him to be reliable but not valuable.

Recommendation to replace or wind down agent, to be considered by the Committee, 15.1.90.

Attachments, App. A-H, K. App. I and J refiled under security status 7, 26.3.89.

She read it again. She could not understand it. But when things started to clarify for her, when Mario's deeds, his name, his tales, began to surface from the miasma of her wilful obfuscation, what struck her first was the question, not of what Mario had said about anyone she knew – that quarter-century of mild associates, that quartet of unspecified interest to these strange authorities, so nameless, so uncommitting – but the simple question of what had happened to Caspar. The man she met once, the murderer, his fate was somewhere here, in these dividing steel-and-card corridors, somewhere, encased in a wall of papers, recorded in careful unfeeling triplicate, his change of name, his becoming, for now, someone else. And he was hiding, now, in some town, knowing that the Wall behind which he sheltered was down, that his deeds were coming for him, that no name, no newness could wipe away his acts. She could see that. Mario – and that was not his name, but there was no more Mario for her, and no man still there to call anything else – had helped two murderers across the border. That was what it said. But where they were, and who they were, this file was not going to say.

Everything was clear to her. It was as if she were in a world where everything bore an incontrovertible label; a cartoon-world where the good and the bad wore their deeds on their face, what they stood for and what they had done on a card round their neck. The clerk at the desk; Mario; she herself. Yes, that was it; she was made clear to herself, in all her foolishness and gullibility, her willingness to be led and her willingness to do wrong for the sake of good.

'Excuse me,' she said to the clerk.

'Finished?'

'No,' Daphne said. 'No. It's just that there's a cross-reference here –'

'I don't know about that,' the clerk said. 'We can't always give you files just because there's a cross-reference to it, we have to respect people's privacy.'

'No,' Daphne said. 'You know –'

'Don't push it,' the girl said, lowering her voice. Behind her, there was a man in a dark blue blazer, his hair slicked down over his bald patch, rearranging a group of files. From time to time he tutted, at nothing in particular. 'I've broken the rules for you. Don't push it.'

'Sorry,' Daphne said. 'I didn't mean to say anything. Anything wrong. I was just going to say that there's a cross-reference here that's missing. I need some help to find it.'

'We can't always help,' the woman said. 'There are issues of privacy.'

'Can you look?'

The clerk took the file, and began to read. Daphne indicated the sentence about the two defectors into the DDR, unsignalled.

'That's an issue for the police, and the courts,' she said briskly. 'I'm sorry. That would not be cross-referenced under the systems obtaining here under the previous political regime, and if there were, it is important to respect the privacy of the people concerned.'

'They were murderers,' Daphne said. 'And this –' she indicated the two refiled appendices.

'The security category 7 applies,' the clerk read from the

file. 'Yes. That comes under the same category. Under the rules of access determined by the present government, those are inaccessible files at present. I'm sorry, I can't help you with that at the present moment, but it seems likely that things will continue to open up. It is the intention of all concerned that the files be made accessible over time, but it hasn't proved possible to release everything simultaneously.'

'I see,' Daphne said, and turned and went back to her seat. The clerk annoyed her, and yet the way her tired late-afternoon repetition of *the privacy of the individual, the issues of privacy* fell on her was the confirmation of what she had only known, never felt, the confirmation of the great unfeeling weight of all those individuals, betraying each other, a nation of betrayals, a nation of people lying to each other, selling their wives, their husbands, their children, their neighbours; selling strangers, selling teachers, selling people they had never even seen, for nothing, for no money, for the ungrateful State, for the sheer simple pleasure, at the present moment, of betrayal and loss. They wanted to lie, to show the nothingness of their lives, and they gave a few dull sentences about people who loved them; people who, perhaps, loved them, and went home and slept with the people they wrote about, and thought nothing of it.

She sat down. The thick file was before her. Here, if anywhere, was the life she had led, seen by a patient and scrupulous observer, whose name she had not known, to whom, for the sake of a few bones and a glowing skin, a knack of raising the eyebrow and crumpling the forehead, the dark shade of the unshaven chin, the narrow lovely hips and the heavy lolling cock, the delineations of muscle under the thin flesh, the lines of strength and power and what for some weeks had seemed like honesty, she had given, in whom she had invested *the thing about Daphne*. And here it was; on paper; under her hand; the thing about herself, set down.

She waited for a moment. All her life, Daphne had waited for insults, had let casual comments in conversation lodge beneath her skin, had stored things up to brood over, to plan revenge. And here was the biggest of all insults. A man she had thought she loved, who she thought she could remember saying he loved her, had written in a series of letters what, exactly, he thought about her. She almost relished the feeling, of having something which was going to lodge, like a splinter of steel, in her brain, there in front of her, and, just for the moment, not knowing what was in it. For a second she considered, laughably, not opening it; leaving it here; walking away; forgetting it. But that was a path she knew nobody – and not her – could ever take. If she did not read it now, she knew she would be back, and soon. She opened the file, and, sniffing from time to time at the outbursts of dust from the miles of manila files, the thousands and tens of thousands and millions perhaps of betrayals differing in no way from this one, she began to read. To read about a man she had never known; about Egon. To read about a woman she had never, until now, quite understood; to read about Daphne.

And off he went, off Mario went, like a bullet out of the unguarded open garage, boy on his machine, fast boy on his fast machine. It had been – how long – months maybe since he had even thought of getting on this bicycle. He had forgotten the superb legerdemain of its movements, its sense that all the cyclist's strength was spent not in driving it onwards, but, like a jockey, pulling back at it, holding its tensile ringing inner strength and speed back, restraining it. But if he had forgotten the bicycle, his legs had not. He was a sleepwalker, as the heavy riotous night turned towards dawn, and the bicycle, and his unconscious legs took him where they wanted to go.

The streets, at last, were almost empty, and he found he was riding westwards, his back to the sun as it rose. His surety of his movement, his direction, was such that from time to time he closed his eyes and just felt the pleasured sense of motion, his now sweating face against the still air creating the knowledge of wind. This was what he was always meant to do, he knew that now as he approached the western edge of West Berlin. Always meant to be strapped into a glittering machine, always meant to ride, not in circles, not buzz around fruitlessly, hopelessly, returning to the place he left, but to set off in a direction, to ride westwards, in a single line, until he couldn't go any further. His life had pulled him away from that single aim; it was what he was always supposed to do, his single purpose, but the daily imposed function of betrayal and reportage, the banalities of education and secrecy, they had kept him from this thing; riding westwards. It was what he was set on the earth to do. He set off. He did it.

He came to the crossing point; the guards barely troubled to look up as he showed his identity card, waving him through. And there he was; in the great flat river and lake landscape of East Germany; of Brandenburg; of Germany. On an earth, somehow, older than countries; a place conditioned not by politics, barely touched, even, by geography; riding, somehow, over geology. There was something right, as he sped onwards, out through the edges of the dawn-lit Potsdam, about riding not eastwards, into the new Lands, but westwards, his face set against the unlimited eastwards expansions just now beginning, cycling towards the western border of the DDR, cycling away from the great eastern plains, towards the old rich heartlands of the old Europe. He felt as if to look eastwards, to ride eastwards, would be to contemplate more than, just now, could be understood or felt; and he turned away from the great opening spaces of the earth, and, half-awed, rode away from it. The East, for him, was a Medusa, to be seen in mirrors, to be glimpsed, to be ridden away from; and it gave him such fear because among the worst things it contained, the worst things of all, were his own deeds, what he had seen and written and done. He turned his back on it, as if to receive the punishment, the beating he knew he deserved, in the feeblest hope of mercy.

The world was changing. Two worlds were changing, and, as he shot forward, unstoppably, returning to the place he had fled, completing his long journey between two worlds, he saw why they were changing; he saw what they wanted from each other, and he saw how mistaken they were. How little the West knew of the East; how little the East knew of the West. And how much they hoped for.

And he saw, for once in his life, what the West wanted from him, and from people like him. How much it hoped for innocence. The East would, like him, ride innocently westward; so full of gratitude that the bitter end of the bargain would not be tasted for long years. The bitter end of the deal was the gratitude of the West for what the East was offering them. Very quietly; no noise of gratitude, no wish to scare off the innocent East. But still, nothing but gratitude for what the East could, unknowingly, offer the West. They would give them cars, and money, and freedom; bright lights gawped at, for so long, over the Wall. And they, in return, would give the West the innocence they had lost. That was the deal.

The West wished for innocence; it wanted to think the East was innocent; it hoped for a cure for its taint in what had never been tainted. But the East must, in return, believe that what they were being offered was sheer generous goodness, offered out of the goodness, the self-belief, of the West; because the West so believed in its way of life that it simply wanted to share it. And the West believed it too, made every pretence of believing it; believed that the great westward ride was inspired by an idea, a love of some idea of freedom; and when the first step of every Easterner was into a sex shop, the West would, in its own innocence, look away, because it so wanted, so needed, the East to be better than the West, to be better than itself. The West thought the East was superior; the East thought the West was superior; and only Mario, just now, saw all the disappointment there, understood how wrong things were going.

They wanted too much; they all wanted too much. They wanted an unconditional love; and never understood that love is never unconditional, that always, a love depends on what one man can offer another. Never understood that experience needs innocence; never understood that experience never purifies itself in the presence of innocence, is only ever capable of corrupting. And Germany would never become better, kinder, purer by an influx of holy fools; they never existed, except in the *over-there* fantasy of the West. The hope that people over there are just like us. German; but pure. And only Mario, hurtling westwards, his back towards the East, understood and really felt and really heard the quiet voice, asking how long an innocent, leaving Frankfurt an der Oder and, like him, journeying westward, would preserve that innocence in Frankfurt am Main.

He was so soon out of the city, and into the flat river and water landscape which surrounded Berlin, which no Berliner had ever seen. It was so flat there was nothing to hold him back, and he seemed to himself to be going faster and faster, unhindered. From time to time a man or woman, thick-waisted, wrapped in their heavy mud-coloured clothes as if in bandages, flashed past him. A sudden glimpse of expression like the splash of sun in the still-standing waters which looped through the green landscape; and on he went, not thinking at all, not even trying not to think, but his whole mind bent on the ecstasy of speed, the bliss of unconscious unplanned velocity. He had no idea of time passing, just of a growing thrill, of a growing marvellous concentrating beauty of direction, of oblivion, of forgetting. It must have been hours before the constant flat emptiness of the land yielded, at the horizon, to the bright-lit uprising beginnings of mountains. And then, of course, he knew where he was; knew, and for the first time in hours, he found a thought deliriously, electrically coursing through the synapses of his brain.

It was the Harz mountains. He had been cycling for hours, shot out of Berlin in a line straight as a stone from a catapult, and he could almost see his old training ground. Some unaccountable muscle-memory had brought him here, brought him back, and now, after hundreds of kilometres, he was at the edge of the DDR. He was where he had started from. He was back. He was back. And with the beginning of the hill a million things, two thousand afternoons were in his brain, Hans-Christian's dry voice, describing *the onset of the incline*, and it was there. He felt as if he had not climbed a hill for years, as if he had been waiting only for this moment. The feeling of excitement and terror and the sheer hard beauty of it, the great steep climb of the Harz, and now, only now, the weight of a sleepless night, the burden of the hundreds of kilometres was in his legs, with an intensity of exhaustion and thrill and knowledge of what he had done, and what he could still do. He was up the hill, up the incline, and fighting him was not only the hill, but his memory; the phantom trainer – and who knew where he was, by now, five days after the Wall was down – beside him. Cycling beside him, not, like the real Hans-Christian, phlegmatically, pensively, but with the same loose relaxed feeling, as if descending, not climbing, he now found in himself. Look at the road, look at the road, he chanted, and, for once, heard his surprising voice in the empty road. He chanted his single simple belief, and then he disobeyed it; he looked upwards, at the summit, so near, a mere couple of hundred metres, so much *there*. And then, in the empty road, in the empty land, he lost his balance, as never before, and he fell. Fell on to soft good earth.

God the earth; the unbounded boundless earth, like the sky above it. He lay on his back. His eyes were shut. The only sound was the noise of the wind in the trees, a noise bringing back who knew what memories, memories only inside his head, a head full of thoughts he had not shared with anyone and would not. The nearby trickle of the wheel spinning on the fallen abandoned bicycle, like the noise of water falling quietly, and something further away, a pale distant piping. If he stretched out his arm, he would be able to feel, against the back of his hand, the damp new earth he could smell, the cool good smell his breath brought in. And there he was. Not knowing where he was going; where he had come from; just where he was. Across his face he felt his enormous unseen smile, in this solitary shade, this forest, like an ache, felt the cold November sunlight of the sky he shut his eyes against, felt it descend on his sweat-damp face like the weight of all those wrongs, all those blank wrong deeds. There he was. There he was. There he was.

TWO MEN, EACH BELIEVING THE OTHER OF A HIGHER STATION THAN HIMSELF, GREET EACH OTHER

AND THE WALL came down, and they all came out, and celebrated, for a while, but, after a while, they all went home. Or almost all; nothing more was ever heard of Mario, and he had no home to go to, even if he had wanted to. But Peter Picker went back to his empty flat, and took the memories of his son Tom with him, who had had so much growing up to do, so much to find out, so many new things. And Daphne went back to Charlottenburg, where she lived with her aunt; and the aunt, who had once given a nice young man called Friedrich a lift to Cologne through the Mitfahrzentrale and wondered from time to time quite what had happened to him, that nice young man, had, to her slight surprise, found herself on the streets celebrating something she wasn't quite clear about. And Martin went back to his flat on the fourth floor of a building on the Erkelenzdamm. And Sandra Bonheim, not understanding why at all, went back to her flat on the Kopenhagenerstrasse, off the Schön-hauserallee, in Prenzlauerberg, and waited for the world to carry on changing round her. And Hans-Christian Schmidt stayed in his slightly damp small cottage in the Harz mountains, where the bicycles and the bicycle tools had an irritating knack of migrating from the shed into the kitchen, the small living room, as he worked on a machine while watching the telly, and thought that, all in all, he was too near retirement to go anywhere else. And the Museums' Director of all Prussia walked through his Schinkel villa and looked through the huge windows, and wondered how long this would go on. And Juan Richter, the border policeman, still went back from time to time to his two-room flat in Köpenick, although it must be said that he spent a great deal more time than he used to with his trousers round his ankles, a regular adornment of the cellar in Tom's Bar just off the Fuggerstrasse. And Friedrich's mother went on much as before, and Martin's father went on very much as before. And Friedrich's father, who was – oh, come on now – who was still travelling, somewhere in Europe, no longer in Germany, but, like all of us, still somewhere in Europe, still alive, still moving on, still utterly scared, thought a strange thing, a thing he had never imagined ever again thinking; thought that now, perhaps, now everything had so changed, perhaps now this was a time to stop. To stop; to pause; to settle; to claim, once more, one small piece of Europe, some place for himself. Some land. And Helmut Meier rubbed his hands with glee, knowing he was going to get the flat back, was going to turn it into a pair of bathrooms and up the rent, right at the right moment, couldn't be bettered. And Herr Strich, in the hills not very far from Cologne, went into his immaculate kitchen and opened the cupboard door, and got out a cup, and poured himself a cup of coffee, and shut the door of the cupboard, let it fall shut with a perfect ease and smoothness he barely noticed. And fat Petra went back to the flat she shared with her sister in Wedding, and told her, perhaps rather too many times, a patently enhanced version of her meeting with an extraordinarily attractive man at *Dreigroschenoper*, till the sister was obliged to tell her that really, enough was enough. And Pierre Stifter went back to the exquisite pale ash and brilliant white spotlit minimal flat he lived in, and looked at his single incredibly expensive painting, a two metres square piece of blank *turquoise* in acrylic, and asked his neighbour's opinion, a nice but perhaps not very exciting buck-toothed Bavarian lawyer called Christian, on whether there were likely to be lots of bargains for hard cash in the way of furniture, jewellery, furs or the merest *bibelots* now that the Wall was down, and failed to pay full attention to the answer. And Caspar, who had changed his name several times in his life and grown, ineffectually, a beard, looked out from the unattractive and cramped house in the suburb of Dresden the fucking DDR government had assigned him to, and wondered whether he had envisaged this and whether he in any sense had ever wanted to be a member of the proletariat, the enlightened proletariat, among the grimly and irritatingly unenlightened *lumpenproletariat* who worked in the factory where he now worked, and, though he now shrank from the answer, he would not shrink from it in another few weeks. And Friedrich went out every morning, as he had no choice in the matter, and tried to find a flat to move to.

It was the worst time in the world, perhaps, to try to find somewhere to live in Berlin. He had thought it was going to be easy. The finding of a flat had always seemed to him a leisurely business, without problems or trauma; in the old Berlin, it resembled two people in a train, exchanging newspapers with hardly a word. Now – he hung about news-stands for the first editions, asked everybody he ever met, in the laundrette, customers in the bookshop, people he'd never spoken to in bars and people he hadn't spoken to for years, asked everyone if they had heard of a flat going cheap, or going at all – it much more resembled a frantic game of musical chairs, in which not one, but all but one chair had been removed, around which an unknowable and constantly growing crowd surged and fought.

He bought the Sunday newspaper as it appeared, and read the columns as he half-ran, tripping over his own feet, to the nearest telephone kiosk. Four numbers out of five were always already engaged. The fifth said, wearily, that the flat had already been taken. On average, Friedrich saw one flat a week, and always it was a flat which, by the time he saw it, had been rented out. He walked home, letting the sudden waves of panic run tingling up his sides like goose-pimples, feeling the grim set of his face.

To have nowhere to live; nowhere at all. To be in this full city, and as the dark set in, know that the street was the only place there was; to know that you were still in a bar at six o'clock in the morning not because you wanted to be, but because you had nowhere to sleep; to sleep, like Martin, in a bar because that was all there was.

He wondered how these efficient lodgers found their way so swiftly to the telephone, agreed so immediately to take the flat, whatever it was like, wherever it was, however much it cost. He traced the delivery route of the Sunday newspaper back, from the Oranienstrasse kiosk back into the centre, back to the Nollendorfplatz and beyond, back as far as the office of the newspaper itself, and stood, in the end, shivering, in the dark, with a small crowd of other shivering wrapped figures, like supplicants to some black god, their twitching votive gestures towards the string-wrapped bundles as they were tossed to the ground. It made almost no difference; perhaps, now, one in three numbers could be reached, to summon a patient or blunt voice, informing the gentleman that unfortunately the flat was now let.

He could have told Meier he had changed his mind, but would not; there was no doubt Meier would have shrugged his shoulders and said that unfortunately it was too late, and the builders had been informed of the date of the commencement of the work, and that they could not now be recalled, with great regret. He tried flirting with the girls who took the advertisements at the newspapers, without success; it was horribly clear they had all seen it tried before. And so he went out every morning, and travelled all over Berlin, and asked assistants in shops, postmen, strangers in the street, if they knew of any flat at all, or even a pleasant room, and every day returned, fruitlessly, to the space he had rented, which would be his for only four weeks longer, and sat, and stared at the blank walls, and wondered what on earth he was going to do. Be kind to your future, he said to himself, remembering what Picker's son had once seemed to say to him, and the more he said it the less he meant it.

He started in Kreuzberg, and travelled out, daily, to strange, outlying places; places he had only ever seen on maps, never heard of anyone living in. He went to grey lines of houses squatting at the end of the airport runway; he went to a place called Uncle Tom's Cabin; he went to leafy suburbs he could never have afforded, and just looked, and walked. He would have gone to the East, if there had been any point; he would have gone to skinhead quarters in Lichtenberg and the bleak pillared blocks of

Marzahn, the bullet-pocked grey palaces of Mitte, the serious quiet of Prenzlauerberg; he did go to these places, and found what he knew, that there was nothing to rent, that there was nothing to be found, nothing at all.

It was a Thursday morning, six weeks after the Wall came down. There was a clear stillness in the air; the sky was still blue, against all remembered Berlin winters, as if the weather, too, was eager to celebrate the destruction of the Wall. It was nearly Christmas. Friedrich had taken, by now, to getting up early and being out by ten. It was difficult to know what else to do. One more week, and he would have to go on bended knee to everybody he had ever met and ask to stay with them for an indefinite period of time. He was not tempted by the idea.

As he came down the stairs, he saw a figure, standing at the bottom, looking out into the courtyard. At first, he thought it was Meier, the landlord, and braced himself for the usual round of rudeness. He was almost at the foot of the stairs before he saw who it was.

'Your door was open,' Picker said. 'The door to the building. I came in. I heard you coming down.'

'Yes,' Friedrich said, not quite knowing what else to say. 'I was just going out.'

'Anywhere special?' Picker said. 'Are you in a hurry?'

'Not a hurry, exactly,' Friedrich said. 'Did you want to come up?'

Picker recoiled slightly. 'No,' he said. 'No, I thought we might talk. You seemed –'

'I seemed?'

'The last time we met – you seemed –' Picker paused. He could hardly look at Friedrich, who could hardly look, in turn, at Picker. There was a shivering sudden intimacy about the way they found themselves talking to each other;

after they had disappeared from each other's lives, a couple of months before, it was as if a barrier had been removed from them, as if they had now to discover the right way to speak to each other.

'Yes,' Friedrich said, at random.

'I wondered,' Picker went on, seeming to collect himself, 'if you would like to come for a drive, or something. I just felt like a talk.'

'Of course,' Friedrich said. 'Of course I would.'

They left the building. Picker indicated his car; another dark blue car, but a big German car rather than the British one which had suffered the puncture, almost a year before.

'You've changed your car,' Friedrich said, getting in.

'Yes,' Picker said. 'I'm impressed. You noticed. No, I change my car every year, about November. I like to have a new car every so often. It keeps you on the ball.'

'Nice car,' Friedrich said. 'Where are we going?'

'I thought,' Picker said as they set off, 'I thought we'd go East. The world has changed rather a lot, hasn't it, since we last saw each other.'

'It has,' Friedrich said. 'Where in the East do you want to go?'

'I thought Potsdam,' Picker said. 'I remember you saying once that you'd never been, and I've never been either, so –'

'I don't know where you're allowed to cross, now,' Friedrich said. 'It's all changing so fast. Soon there won't be a Wall to cross. They've started knocking it down already.'

'Perhaps they ought to keep a little stretch, just for old time's sake,' Picker said. 'Still, it was what we wanted, wasn't it, to bring down the DDR. I don't suppose either of us thought it was going to happen, and there you are.

Fancy that. And now what? I start to wonder if any of it means anything much, any more. Ein Land, ein Reich, ein Volk? Unification?'

'Re-unification, you're supposed to say,' Friedrich said. 'I've no idea. I suppose so, some time. Not in our lifetimes, I expect.'

Picker merely nodded, sceptically. 'I've heard enough of people saying *not in our lifetimes*. Anything can happen in our lifetimes. It's up to us.'

'You sound like a politician, saying "it's up to us".'

'No,' Picker said. 'I meant it seriously. I really mean, it's up to us to decide whether we want it or not. Maybe we don't want it. But we can decide, and it's not right to say, Oh, other people can deal with it, it's not going to happen to us. Here we are.'

'Don't you love this?' Friedrich said.

This was the border crossing; a couple of guards glanced at their identity cards, waved them through. As they passed the checkpoint, Friedrich caught the eye of one of them, and was struck by the angle of his cap; probably tipped no more than a centimetre to the left, but deflating the whole force of the grey uniform as efficiently and immediately as a tie half-done-up, a pair of sandals instead of boots, a smiley yellow badge. Things were changing. They were changing so fast.

'It's still a bit peculiar,' Friedrich said. 'I haven't really worked out how far you're allowed to go. I mean, if you're still supposed to stick within the boundaries of Berlin.'

'I think they've given up trying to stop that,' Picker said. 'It's not going to last much longer, any of that. None of them seem to be taking it very seriously any longer. I can just imagine the annual reporting system for the border police, for the GrePos, the entry for motivation and commitment. I wonder what they're all going to do when the whole thing finally collapses.'

'Sit around in bars moaning, I suppose,' Friedrich said. 'Or take up jobs as guides at the Checkpoint Charlie Museum. How is your son?'

Picker said nothing. He just seemed to concentrate on the road.

'I imagine,' Friedrich said, 'he must be in kindergarten today. Or have they broken up for Christmas already?'

'Friedrich,' Picker said eventually. 'He died.'

Friedrich said nothing. He could not understand, for a moment, what Picker had said.

'It was the day after you came round. I thought you might have heard.'

'No,' Friedrich said. 'I hadn't heard. I don't know what to say.'

'You don't have to say anything,' Picker said. 'There's nothing to say.'

'I'm sorry,' Friedrich said inadequately, to say something. 'I'm really shocked.'

'My vocabulary is improving,' Picker said in a measured way. 'I learnt a lot of medical vocabulary. I learnt the word *meningitis*. I learnt it a day too late. I even wrote it in my book, in case it was ever going to be useful again. It was too late. I'm never going to have to use the word again. Once was enough. I thought it was just a fever. He was really ill. It's contagious, you know, meningitis. I don't know how he got it. Since then – I don't know if you want to hear this – I just wish every day, no, every minute, that I'd caught meningitis off him, too. And I wouldn't let myself be cured, not any more.'

'I'm really sorry,' Friedrich said. 'I don't know what it must be like.'

'No,' Picker said. 'I don't think anyone can imagine what it's like. You know, it comes on so quickly. I couldn't have stopped it. There's a fever, and a headache, and a rash. All very ordinary things, and he never complained. Only once, he said, my head hurts. Only once, never complaining. He was so good. Everyone commented on how good he was, when he was a baby even, never crying more than absolutely necessary. And never complaining, even when he was dying. He said, once, my head hurts. And then he seemed to lose interest, and he said, You know, that man? – as if he was beginning a question. But then he seemed to forget what he was going to ask. I don't know what man he meant. He might even have meant you. You were the last man he saw, apart from me and the doctors. And all those symptoms, all so ordinary. A fever and a headache, and a rash. Only the rash; I learnt afterwards that to tell a meningitis rash, you press a glass against the skin. And ordinary rashes will disappear, turn white, under pressure. But meningitis rash stays red. I never knew the thing to do, I'd never heard it, or had been told it once and forgotten it. I've found out all these things since Tom died. You know, since then, I've become a world expert on meningitis. I know the progress of it, I know exactly when to call a doctor, I know how to tell it from anything else. And I'll never have to use the knowledge, ever again.'

'I don't know what to say,' Friedrich said again.

'You don't have to say anything,' Picker said. 'Have you ever – have you ever seen a dead body?'

'No,' Friedrich said. 'I never have.'

'It's not common, now,' Picker said. 'You don't see dead people, you never do. But I did. I saw Tom, and he was dead. I held him and he was dead. The weight of it, the weight of him. He was so small, and he was so heavy, with all that inside him. I never thought he was heavy when he was alive, but I picked him up and he couldn't feel me any more, and I couldn't feel him, and he was so heavy. So limp. His eyes were shut and he was gone and I was holding him. They let me be with him for a while. They were good to me. I want to go back there, so that someone will be good to me again, but that's it. No one again. Never again.'

'He was such a good child,' Friedrich said.

Picker was silent. He nodded, and then, not saying anything, he pulled the car over to the side of the road. 'I wasn't going to tell you,' he said. 'I don't like talking about it. I still don't.' And then he was crying; Friedrich saw how long, and how many hours he had spent alone, in his flat, doing just this.

After a time, Picker dried his face, and began to drive. There was nothing to say; Friedrich could not begin to talk; could not begin to console Picker's grief, which was, he unaccountably felt, the same as the grief just now beginning in him, and after a time, he started to notice the changing town around him. It was a town, a world Tom would never see; it would have been a world Tom would never have known the new strangeness of; and it was a world whose new strangeness was fast disappearing. He looked at the cars, which drove past, and now, for the first time, he saw that there were not just the small hardboard cars, in the three colours officially sanctioned by the German Democratic Republic, filling the sad grey streets. There were other cars. There were expensive cars, like theirs; there were cars with West German numberplates, and in the unaccustomed mix, the strange variety in this strange and no longer peaceful town, Friedrich saw the beginnings of what freedom might mean. He wondered about the cars;

he wondered how many of them were already being driven by East Germans, and how many, in a year's time, would be driven by East Germans; and how long before there would be no means of telling which was which; and how long before the arbitrary divisions of the earth disappeared, and there were no initialled temporary states, there was only Germany; there was only Europe; there was only, he thought with a terror of loss and bereavement, there was only earth, and air, and fire, and water.

The car drove on, peacefully, quietly; it was much more that grief had left them than that it had silenced them. And, as Friedrich settled into the drowsy thick upholstery, a memory came to him, a memory of being driven. He was seven or eight, perhaps slightly less. The family were on holiday, and had driven out of the North German seaside town for a day on an island. One of his sisters had felt sick, ten minutes into the journey, and his father had stopped the car. After she had stood outside for a while, they carried on, but his mother had swapped places with Friedrich, and he was allowed to sit in the front. The sensation of the leather of the front seat against your bare legs and the feeling of having only a window in front of you, not your mum and dad. He looked round at his father, who smiled and winked, a cigarette in his mouth, his face handsome and brown and drawn with nice deep lines, his eyes almost shockingly blue; and maybe Friedrich realized, even then, that the moment of his father, looking at him, and smiling, and winking in undiluted pleasure and fondness was a picture which was always going to be somewhere in his head, always for the rest of his life, and never brought to mind without a second of pain. It was his father between fits of rage; a father caught at a moment unlike Friedrich's usual memory of him, and a father who could, Friedrich thought, have recorded the message of love he had thrown away. For a moment, remembering the recorded voice of his vanished father, remembering the vanished sweet face of his Baltic-browned father, it occurred to Friedrich that his usual memory of his father was not a true one; that the terrifying ogre had blanked out other fathers, fathers he had never let himself know; epitomes of kindness and fondness and goodness; a father who would leave them, not out of selfishness, but out of care and concern.

It had been one of those silent lemonwashed blue days on the Baltic, when if you stand and look in any direction, you can see forever; you can hear nothing, nothing but the quiet rustle of grass, the suck of clean water on sand. They got out of the car, and began to walk along the beach. He fell behind his family; his mother, awkwardly adjusting her sunglasses as she carried the picnic basket; the sisters traipsing along; the father, the blanket over his shoulder, saying nothing, walking next to them amicably. He watched them go ahead along the empty white beach, walking, at first, more slowly than them, and then, when they were a hundred or two hundred metres in front, he stopped altogether, and turned round, and he was looking; looking at nothing, and thinking nothing; looking at the flat white sand and the flat blue sea and the infinity of blue in the sky, a single radiant white zip, a jet-stream, marking the journey of some aeroplane, dissolving, leaving nothing behind, passing through the unknowable hugeness of sky. He stood and looked and waited until he had the good clean sense of being alone. One moment. How easily consolation came. How wrongly.

'We're here,' Picker said. Friedrich hadn't realized that he'd fallen asleep. 'Come on. It's time to get out and go for a walk.'

They were at the end of a quiet old street, lined and made dark with thick trees. They got out and followed, without saying anything, a footpath between allotments. After fifty metres or so, they came to an iron gate, which Picker pushed open.

'Where are we?' Friedrich said. 'Is this the imperial park?'

'Friedrich's park,' Picker said. 'Friedrich the Great. Sans Souci. I've never been, I've only ever seen photographs.'

'Me too,' Friedrich said. No one knew, any more, exactly where you could go in this country, this fast dissolving country, and he felt like an urchin raiding some orchard of fabulous and unobtainable fruit; an orchard glowing with precious lychees, a hot sudden orchard which might be broken into, but which would not be robbed; which protected its treasures with the surprising gift of awe. They walked into the empty park, following a scruffy path; above the trees, somewhere to the right, a few hundred metres away, a brilliant splash of gold, the roof of some jewel-bright pavilion.

'The world has changed,' Picker said suddenly. 'Hasn't it?'

Friedrich shook his head; it seemed to him that the world was, now, as it had always been.

'You know,' Picker went on, 'it doesn't matter any more. What you did to me. That's it. That's all I wanted to say.'

'Thanks,' Friedrich said. 'Thanks for saying that. I sort of guessed it.'

They walked on. The pavilion, a long low summer palace, had come into view at the top of a cascade of glass-backed terraces. It was as if a palace had been built above a deep-stepped country vineyard, and the unruly vines, to match the formality of the summer palace, had been boxed in, contained by the decaying glass houses with their smashed panes, divided by the falling folding stair. Each turn of the stairs was marked by a statue; what it was, what each statue meant, hidden, now, as winter set in, each one coffinned in against the fierce and stone-snapping Brandenburg frost. At the top, the palace; glittering, still, though in disrepair, the huge letters of its name, announcing its curious and outplaced devotion, *SANS SOUCI*, from the top of a hill to this careworn, this exhausted city.

'Last week,' Picker said. 'In the street. A man came up to me, someone I'd never seen before. An Easterner, I suppose. And he said, without saying hello, or anything, just suddenly said, *What does it all mean?* I didn't know what to say.'

'It's the sort of thing fifteen-year-olds say,' Friedrich said. 'What's the meaning of it all. And there is no meaning.'

'No,' Picker said. 'No, there isn't. But they want to ask something, I suppose. You grow up saying, *What's the meaning of life*, and you grow out of asking it, because you see how ridiculous it is, how pointless a question it is. But what would happen if you suddenly were given a new, a different sort of life, so that you wanted to ask, all over again, *What's the meaning of life?* So this stranger came up to me. He just wanted to talk. People are upset, you know, as well as thrilled about all this. There aren't enough people to listen to what they have to say. I just listened, and then, after a bit, he got annoyed. I don't know why. Maybe I was listening too much. And then he went away, to find someone else to ask. And maybe I felt like asking the same question, but I didn't know, and I still don't know, who I should ask.'

'I thought,' Friedrich said. 'I thought once about coming here. To the East. Of moving here, for good.'

Picker nodded.

'I know it sounds strange. I just felt like it, suddenly, once, when I was in the East.'

'What's the point?'

'There's no point now,' Friedrich said. 'It's gone. There used to be a solution there. It was like a solution, a solution there when everything else failed, and now it's gone. Now everywhere's exactly like everywhere else, or it soon will be. And you might as well stay where you are, because there's no solution, no complete solution, anywhere apart from the place where you are.'

'I know,' Picker said.

'I thought about moving here, and having an ordinary life,' Friedrich said. 'Moving here, and getting a quiet little flat, and a quiet little life, and letting other people organize my life for me. But it didn't work. Everything changed, so quickly. It was gone, so quickly. It was like something I needed, and it was never there, and now it's gone, anyway. The East. The idea of the East.'

'I see that,' Picker said. 'A solution.'

'It's not even the idea of a happy ending,' Friedrich said. 'Just some sort of an ending. So tempting, the sense of an ending; if your life ends up in a small flat in the East, or if you throw yourself in a river, or anything. I wanted an ending, and I couldn't have it. Something went, some kind of solution.'

Picker nodded, looking at him as if Friedrich had divined something he was never expected to see, as if at the surpassing achievement of a nervous but clever pupil. 'Come on,' he said. 'Let's sit down.'

He sat down on a bench, a little damp from last night's

rains. But Friedrich would not; there was something he had to do, and, as he stood and looked at Picker, it came to him what it was. He reached into his pocket and got out the envelope he carried round, full of money. The one thing he could tell Picker was that he could really use this money. If he had ever needed fifty thousand marks, he needed it now; and if ever Picker was in a state of complete indifference to a sum of money, it was now. But somehow he did not want to dignify or dramatize his sacrifice. He just wanted to give it back to Picker, selfishly, for the sake of what he thought about himself, for the sake of his own good opinion.

Picker opened the envelope, and looked at Friedrich, one eyebrow raised.

'I haven't touched it,' Friedrich said. 'Or not much. The drugs were just paracetamol. I told you. I was never going to run off with the money. Please take it. I wanted you to take it, and you wouldn't. Please take it back. It's almost all there. I haven't touched it. I don't want it – and – I'll tell you one thing –'

'Thank you,' Picker said, in his slow way. 'I don't mind, not any more. I don't mind if you keep it, or if you throw it away, or if you give it back to me, I really don't. It doesn't change what I think of you. Or anything else.'

'So, nothing has changed,' Friedrich said.

'No,' Picker said. He stopped, and there, under a black yew tree, he looked up at Friedrich. 'No, you still have my good opinion.'

'What good opinion I have, or deserve, anyway,' Friedrich said.

'No,' Picker said. 'You still have it all. You always did.'

Friedrich turned, not quite understanding why, and faced away from Picker.

'You're right,' he said, going on, and as he talked,

Friedrich began to hear the long days, the weeks of silence, the weeks of loneliness; he felt how much Picker needed and wanted to talk; to talk not about Tom, but about Germany, about which he had always cared so much. 'You're right about the East. A solution has gone now. The idea of the East, it was always a solution, wasn't it? And now it's gone. But it will be back, because we need a solution so much, we need the opposite of what we want, so that we can live our lives. So that we can say, well, our lives may not be what we want, but at least we don't have to live – over there.

'You watch. In ten, fifteen, twenty years' time, the West will be shouting, *Give us our Wall back!* They're saying it now as a joke. But in ten, fifteen, twenty years, they'll see they always needed it. They didn't need to go there; they just needed the idea of it. Some *over there* to imagine, some place worse than here, some place you could, if everything else fell apart, go to, and hide. They always needed to believe in the innocent way of life they had over the Wall. They always wanted to believe that there was some place where you could thrive if you were innocent. And in twenty years' time, they'll be building a Wall again. Not where it was, but around some place. Maybe around Karl-Marx-Stadt – excuse me, Chemnitz – or maybe that would be too neat, somewhere else, or just around a district, just around Friedrichshain. And inside, there'll be informers, and the Stasi, and no freedom and no private enterprise, and one shop every half a mile labelled *Means of Living*. And they'll shoot everyone trying to get over the Wall, just like before.'

'With one difference,' Friedrich murmured, gazing into the empty middle distance.

'What's that?'

'This time,' Friedrich said, turning round, 'they'll be shooting people trying to get in.'

Picker stared at him, breathing heavily, as if exhausted, as if he had said everything he ever wanted or needed to say; as if no one had responded to his monologues for many long weeks. Then, hugely, he started to laugh, as if a joke he had been told years before and always remembered, always been able, word for word, without faltering or understanding the punchline, to recite, had suddenly dawned on him in all its massive hilarity, obliterating all the blank yesterday recitings in the blank blessed hilarity. It went on, Picker's laugh, as if there was no end to it, no end to the cause of laughter, as if beyond the end of laughter there was something which could not be laughed at; as if, by not stopping, he could himself put it off, delay the moment when laughter would come to an end, for good.

'Yes,' he said, finally. 'Yes, they'll be shooting people trying to get in. Because we need innocence so much. We all do. We saw the law-abiding pleasures of innocence in them; they saw the innocent pleasures of indulgence in us. And we always let the idea of other people's innocence pleasure us; we lie back and let it all happen, without our doing anything at all.'

'The thing is –' Friedrich said. He wanted, he wanted so much to make a statement about the future, say what was true about what was to come. But he did not know how; he had never known what was about to come, that had always been the case. But now he had no idea how, even, to say anything about the future. His; Picker's; the city's; Europe's. He stopped on the brink of saying something, not knowing what, something true and big, stopped, perhaps, by his certain knowledge that now, after all this, there was no future, no radiant future, nothing.

'The thing is, people will always want some kind of solution,' Picker said. 'They always will. Everybody wants a happy end for themselves. Everybody wants other people to suffer, and that'll be their own happy end. And maybe, in Germany, people ought to know better.'

'In Germany,' Friedrich said, with great deliberation, 'Happy End is a brand of toilet paper.'

'Is that right?' Picker said, and again started laughing; and this time Friedrich joined in. The gardens were empty, and it was true that everyone had somewhere better to celebrate whatever there was to celebrate. They were alone in front of the terraces; distantly above, one man, perhaps a gardener, was slowly making his way down the folds of the vine-cased staircase, like the voluptuous folds of a ball-gown, hiding what it knew, not showing what it had seen, not responding to what it heard.

'You still have my good opinion,' Picker said again. 'You always did.'

Friedrich turned, not knowing what else to do, and looked away. There was nobody in the park, nobody at all, but him and Peter Picker. The noises of the city were still there, but distant; just the two of them. He began to walk, not knowing why, not saying anything to Picker, walked away from him. He could not see what was in his own eyes, what was stopping him from seeing; he did not know why he should walk, or stay, or go, but he knew his own limits. Picker did not call after him, and in a minute or two he came to a small building, a pavilion; brilliant with gold and blue, surrounded with life-size statues of Chinese musicians, Chinese women, smiling with the innocent uncontradictable pleasures of gilded stone. There was a pile of nailed-together planks by the pavilion; these golden summer statues, too, would soon be boxed up to protect them from their hard winters. He started to walk round it, enumerating the instruments the statues were playing. Some were recognizable, some exotic, some, quite possibly, invented. He walked round the pavilion twice, and stood, and looked, and it was as if a sharp bright music was starting, the sourceless music of no orchestra ever assembled on stage, an orchestra of golden Chinese smiling unmoving statues. The sky and the park were empty. He turned, to walk back.

Picker smiled at Friedrich, and patted the bench by the side of him. Friedrich shook his head, thinking how little he knew, really; how little, in the end, he needed or wanted to know, and, just as Friedrich had wanted him to, Picker stood up and they began to walk, towards the elaborate empty vined staircase, towards the palace, towards Friedrich's palace.

'I thought you'd gone,' Picker said.

'Of course not,' Friedrich said. 'I'd have said if I had to go.'

'I thought you'd gone,' Picker said again.

'You know,' Friedrich said, and then he stopped; he had little, he felt, to say. 'You know something. You know once, that time, when we went to that friend of mine in Kreuzberg, and I told you he was a drug dealer?'

'There's no need to talk about it,' Picker said. 'There really isn't.'

'No,' Friedrich said. 'This is something you ought to know. He said, he actually said, well, here you are, a thousand painkillers. And you said, painkillers? and I thought the game was up. But what you thought was that painkillers was the word for Ecstasy. But it isn't, and we just watched you writing the word down in your notebook. Do you still have the notebook?'

'Of course,' Picker said, and, out of nothing, he smiled, almost shyly.

'It isn't the word. It's just the word for painkillers.'

'That's right,' Picker said.

'And that was Tom's joke, wasn't it?' Friedrich said. 'The joke about the parrots. Did he ever get it right? Did he ever manage to tell it properly?' Picker looked away from him in the direction of the flash of gilded plaster, the Chinese tea-pavilion. 'And, my god, if we had your stranger here, your man, saying to us, *What does it all mean*, my god, I would know what to say to him. I would. I really would.

'There are all sorts of painkillers. And none of them work. There are other people, and they can be painkillers. And drink and money and drugs, all that, and the best thing of all, there's the best painkiller ever, there's the belief that somewhere, somewhere over a Wall, somewhere in another country, somewhere after you die, somewhere you might, one day, get to, there's a place where there's no pain.'

He seized Picker, with both hands, felt the juddering breath in him, gripped him with all his new excitement, an excitement of being, for once, absolutely right, of seeing so far, seeing so clearly, as if mountains and atmosphere and earth had reshaped to allow, only, his unrestrained joy, unconstrained ability to see, to the unbounded end of the earth. 'And all of them fall down in the end. All of them, in the end, don't kill the pain. There's an English joke – stop me if you've heard it before – not a very funny English joke, but still, a joke about painkillers. Why are there no aspirin in the jungle? Have you heard it? Do you get it? There are no painkillers in the jungle because the parrots always want to eat them. Do you get it? There are no painkillers. You know that. There never were. The parrots always get them. They always get there first.'

'Yes,' Picker said finally. 'Yes, I know that.' And, as Friedrich turned him round and looked at all his long silence, all his knowledge, at his face, he understood that; understood how much Picker knew that there were, in the end, no painkillers. How much Picker understood that, in the end, there was only pain. They were there; they were silent; they did not move.

'Do you want to come home?' Picker said, in the end.

He had said what he could. 'Home?'

'There's no one here,' Peter said. 'They've all gone. All the strangers. I told them to go. They've gone.'

'What do you mean?' Friedrich said.

'I told them to go,' Peter said. 'And they went. It's just us, now.'

'Is that right,' Friedrich said, summoning his reserves, but now it was as if he could no longer do casualness, as if disaffection were no longer an option for him, and he stood and looked at Peter's bulky figure, nervously standing, through what seemed the beginnings of tears. 'Please,' he said, closing his eyes, as if in modesty, but it was, it seemed, an eternity before he felt the dear damp grieving hand take his own, the hand of this man, standing before him, almost trembling, felt the breath on his face, for what might, indeed, prove an eternity of patience and goodness. Be kind to your future, he said to himself, thanking the proffering tentative universe, be kind.